The Wildlife of the Bristol Region: **2**

# *The Butterflies of the Bristol Region*

## *Ray Barnett, Rupert Higgins, Tony Moulin, Chris Wiltshire et al*

## *Illustrations by Andrew Daw and Brin Edwards*

## With a foreword by Bill Oddie

"*Of BUTTERFLIES, those familiar lovely images of the soul, raised from its first crawling, greedy, imperfect state, to soar above the earth, feed on ambrosial sweets, drink nectar from floral cups, and enter the wedded state, our hills and vales rejoice in most of the English kinds.*"

Theodore Compton (1888) *Winscombe sketches of rural life and scenery amongst the Mendip Hills*. Elliot Stock, London.

First published 2003 by the Bristol Regional Environmental Records Centre (BRERC).

British Library-in-Publication Data.
A catalogue record for this book is available from the British Library.

ISBN 0-9545235-0-4

Printed by H Charlesworth & Co Ltd, Huddersfield

# CONTENTS

Foreword                                                    v

Acknowledgements                                            vi

Introduction                                               vii

Chapter 1

*The Character of the Bristol Region*
• Habitat accounts                                          1
• Weather and climate                                      10

Chapter 2

*Watching and studying butterflies*
• Recording area                                           13
• Case studies
  1 – Wetmoor – Lower Woods                                15
  2 – Dolebury Warren                                      21
• Site Summaries
  1. Avon Gorge                                            26
  2. Leigh Woods                                           27
  3. Walton Common                                         29
  4. Weston Big Wood                                       29
  5. Sand Point and Middle Hope                            30
  6. Uphill Cliff Area                                     30
  7. Hellenge Hill                                         30
  8. Brockley Combe, Cleeve Toot,
     Goblin Combe & Kings Wood
     Complex                                               30
  9. Cadbury Hill, near Yatton                             32
  10. Cheddar Valley Railway Walk                          32
  11. Folly Farm                                           32
  12. Brown's Folly                                        33
  13. Bannerdown                                           33
  14. Cleaves Wood                                         34
  15. Tucking Mill                                         34

Chapter 3

*Conservation*
• Butterflies and biodiversity                             35
• National and regional trends –
  changing fortunes                                        36
• Biodiversity action plans/conservation                  37

Chapter 4

*Recording butterflies: the history and use of
butterfly data*
• History of Bristol region collectors and
  recorders                                                41

• History of the Avon Butterfly Project                    46
• Using the Avon Butterfly Project data                    49

Chapter 5

*The Butterflies of the Bristol Region*
• Species accounts                                         53
  Chequered Skipper                                        55
  Small Skipper                                            56
  Essex Skipper                                            58
  Silver-spotted Skipper                                   61
  Large Skipper                                            62
  Dingy Skipper                                            64
  Grizzled Skipper                                         66
  Apollo                                                   68
  Swallowtail                                              69
  Wood White                                               71
  Pale Clouded Yellow                                      72
  Berger's Clouded Yellow                                  73
  Clouded Yellow                                           74
  The Brimstone                                            77
  Black-veined White                                       80
  Large White                                              81
  Small White                                              83
  Green-veined White                                       85
  Bath White                                               87
  Orange-tip                                               89
  Green Hairstreak                                         92
  Brown Hairstreak                                         94
  Purple Hairstreak                                        97
  White-letter Hairstreak                                 100
  Small Copper                                            102
  Large Copper                                            104
  Long-tailed Blue                                        105
  Small Blue                                              106
  Silver-studded Blue                                     109
  Brown Argus                                             111
  Common Blue                                             113
  Chalkhill Blue                                          115
  Adonis Blue                                             118
  Mazarine Blue                                           120
  Holly Blue                                              121
  Large Blue                                              123
  Duke of Burgundy                                        125
  White Admiral                                           128
  Purple Emperor                                          131
  Red Admiral                                             134
  Painted Lady                                            136
  Small Tortoiseshell                                     138
  Large Tortoiseshell                                     141

Camberwell Beauty 143
Peacock 145
Comma 147
Small Pearl-bordered Fritillary 150
Pearl-bordered Fritillary 153
Queen of Spain Fritillary 156
High Brown Fritillary 158
Dark Green Fritillary 160
Silver-washed Fritillary 163
Marsh Fritillary 166
Glanville Fritillary 170
Speckled Wood 173
Wall 175
Marbled White 177
Grayling 180

Gatekeeper or Hedge Brown 182
Meadow Brown 184
Small Heath 186
Ringlet 189
Monarch 191

References 195

Other sources not mentioned in the text 197

Contributors 199

Butterfly organisations 201

Index 203

# Foreword

Picture the scene. An area of chalk downland, overlooking the Channel Tunnel. It's not a pretty sight – or should I say site? – but it is home to some very pretty wildlife. A bearded bloke in dark green waterproofs is crawling through the long and slightly damp grass. He is looking for Adonis Blue butterflies. On a day like this, it's not going to be easy. It's showery and very windy and – considering it is mid June – it's pretty chilly. This is certainly not butterfly weather. Nevertheless, the bearded man suddenly leaps forward. He has obviously found something. We move closer to see what it is. There, on his finger, is a male Adonis Blue. Or at least we assume that's what it is. The underwing pattern looks right; but it's not the underwings that have earned the Adonis its name. The man whispers soothingly – and what he hopes is persuasively – to the insect. 'Come on, open 'em.' And it does. There on his finger, is what for all the world looks like the most exquisite cobalt blue ring anyone has ever worn. The kind of thing that Richard Burton used to buy Liz Taylor! Except that this jewel is alive. In fact, the butterfly appears to be licking the man's finger. 'Probably taking salt from my perspiration' he surmises. He gets out a magnifying glass, and literally gasps at the close up. With a satisfied sigh, he speaks again. 'You know, I have seen lions in Africa and elephants in India … all sorts of wildlife, all over the world … but I can honestly say that nothing was any more exciting than seeing this little insect this close.'

Oh come on! Surely the typical hyperbole of the wildlife presenter!? No, actually, I meant every word.

Ok, I may be best known as a 'bird man' but – especially during the last few years filming 'Bill Oddie Goes Wild' – I have discovered – or maybe confirmed – that just about any wild things can be equally thrilling and absorbing. I have become fascinated by dragonflies, batty about bats, and beetles, and badgers, and … oh, anything and everything really. And I absolutely love butterflies.

Of course, they have quite a bit in common with birds. They fly. Males and females are often different. Identification involves noting the exact position of spots, bars and other markings, whilst – just like with birds – 'jizz' is often totally distinctive. Moreover, some are resident whilst some migrate, and a few even hibernate (as far as I know, there is only one bird that does that: the Oilbird of South and Central America). In fact – as I have discovered for myself – in at least two respects, getting to know butterflies is easier than birds. Firstly – in Britain anyway- there aren't so many of them (different species I mean). And secondly – if you really get lucky – they might perch on your finger! (Any bird that does that has probably come out of a cage.)

Butterflies – brilliant. It's as simple as that. Enjoy the book.

Bill Oddie. March 2003

# ACKNOWLEDGEMENTS

## *Ray Barnett*

The authors and the Committee of the Avon Butterfly Project thank all those who have submitted records and sightings to the recording schemes, supported by the Bristol Regional Environmental Records Centre (BRERC), over the last twenty or more years. Particular thanks go to Ralph Stabb and others who have carried out the onerous task of entering thousands of records onto computer as part of the Avon Butterfly Project. Sarah Myles and Philippa Burrell, previous managers of BRERC respectively, played a very important part, as has the current BRERC Manager, Tim Corner. Other staff at BRERC, especially Rachel Corlett, Martin Evans, Roger Edmondson and Jennifer Le Blanc have made an enormous contribution.

Special thanks to the Bristol Magpies (Friends of the Bristol Museums & Art Gallery Service), the Bristol Naturalists' Society and the British Entomological & Natural History Society for their support in the production of this book which has included substantial financial assistance. Also thanks to those who have contributed sections but are not acknowledged on the front cover and to those who have commented on various parts of the text e.g. John Burton and John Muggleton.

As always with these projects, the number of people involved is just too great to thank everybody individually. However the results summarised here, act as testament to the concern and interest shown by so many, with regard to their local environment and to the local butterfly fauna in particular. If this publication stimulates more protection for butterflies, more recorders and more champions for these beautiful insects, then the job will have been well done.

**Crown Copyright.**
Each map is reproduced using the Ordnance Survey Mapping with the kind permission of the Controller of Her Majesty's Stationery Office. South Gloucestershire Council Licence No LA 09065L, 2003

**The Maps**
The distribution maps in this book have been produced using the MapInfo Professional geographical information system. This is a powerful computerised mapping programme the Bristol Regional Environmental Records Centre uses to digitally map its data holdings, carry out routine enquiry searches and perform sophisticated research and analysis. Further information on MapInfo and their products can be found by contacting them direct by email: europe@mapinfo.com or by visiting their website: www.mipro.com

# INTRODUCTION

*Ray Barnett*

It could be seen as a luxury to launch another book on the market about butterflies. There are countless guides to identification of British and European butterflies. There are books about ecology, life-cycles and the national distribution of the small number of species we have in the British Isles. There are published plans as to how to protect and conserve the rarest butterflies and there are beautifully illustrated photographic volumes. This particular publication is an addition to the considerable number of county, or local, butterfly books that have been produced across England, at least in the last twenty or so years. These have collectively done much to raise local concerns about the state of butterfly populations and have helped guide and direct the conservation movement as to where to put emphasis into protecting certain species. The aim of this book is to enable that process to take place for this particular region, a region that separates two counties famous for their wildlife and yet contains two major cities, Bristol and Bath. The Butterflies of the Bristol Region attempts to highlight the past history of butterflies in the region, to summarise the current position and to draw attention to the need to protect the butterfly fauna we have left. For that we make no apologies.

The Avon Butterfly Project began in the early 1990s as a group of concerned enthusiasts came together under the aegis of the Bristol Regional Environmental Records Centre (BRERC). The main aim was to stimu-late as many people as possible to record the butterflies in that former county and so to build up a more accurate picture of how butterflies were fairing in what had become an increasingly urbanised and built on environment. The Project had the experience of the Common Butterfly Survey of the 1980s and the organisation of the Avon Flora Project to draw upon. Both these previous schemes had involved large numbers of interested volunteers who had carried out the hard task of capturing the raw data, observing and recording butterflies in the field. The success of the Butterfly Project is evident in the distribution maps that accompany most of the species reports in this book.

The production of a book to summarise the results of the survey during the 1990s was just one aim of the Project. In the end, as can be seen it was felt that rather than just presenting a snap shot of butterfly populations in that decade, that the known history of the different butterflies should also be included so as to show more longer term changes and to provide greater contextual information. Consequently there are species discussed here which were last seen in the region over one hundred years ago. However rather than being irrelevant these species accounts are interesting in their own right and may provide salutary lessons for us today.

The most obvious conclusion to draw from the survey work and the more recent history of butterflies in and around Bristol and Bath is that many are in dire trouble. At first glance the fact that 40 species are either resident or very regular immigrants would seem very respectable and reassuring. This is bolstered by the very occasional appearance of a further six immigrants plus an introduced, although non-endemic species to our region, namely the Glanville Fritillary which has survived for about 20 years (although it may have very recently become extinct). However five species have been lost in the latter half of the 20th century, the Silver-studded Blue and Adonis Blue by the 1980s, the High Brown Fritillary during that decade and the Pearl-bordered and Marsh Fritillaries during the 1990s. Worse still, of those 40 species the Duke of Burgundy may have become extinct in the last couple of years and the Small Blue may be about to follow it. Other species are now so restricted to a very small number of remaining sites where their particular requirements are met that they are in an extremely vulnerable position. These include the Small Pearl-bordered Fritillary, Grayling and the Chalkhill Blue. Numbers of even those species considered common give further reason for concern. The Dingy and Grizzled Skippers and Small Heath can be included in this category.

The causes for this tale of woe would seem to be a combination of continued and dramatic loss of suitable habitats along with a general degradation in the quality of the "countryside" environment. The effects of intensive agriculture are all too evident particularly in the north of the region where it is very hard to identify species rich areas except for one or two notable exceptions. Species reliant upon "natural" habitats such as undisturbed grassland are now only surviving in tiny pockets and often in relatively small numbers and the species more able to adapt such as the Small Tortoiseshell and Peacock are not as numerous as they once were. Grassland in particular has been lost due to agriculture, building, change of land use or by scrubbing up as grazing has ceased. Occasionally it has even been lost by the misguided planting of trees.

To compound this situation further is the potential impact of global climate change. Generally accepted as a reality now, the question remains as to how exactly this might change our weather patterns and so affect wildlife. Will butterflies such as the Chalkhill Blue, now only present on a very few sites in our region, be lost if climatic changes occur as they exist in such small isolated colonies that they cannot disperse to new sites?

On the positive side there are some species which are apparently increasing. Essex Skipper, Brown Argus and Holly Blue all appear to be more numerous than say in the 1980s. There also appears to be an increase in the numbers of Clouded Yellow migrating to our region each year. The reasons for this are probably complex but may include an element of benefiting from the recent climatic conditions we have seen, i.e. milder winters and warm summers although tempered by more extremes in terms of rainfall which have resulted in very wet autumns and springs in recent years. Also good news has been the development of Species Recovery Programmes across the country for the most endangered species and the local authorities and Wildlife Trusts being committed to producing Biodiversity Action Plans. The latter identify species at risk and attempt to put in place strategies that will enable them to recover or at least not decline further. In the Bristol region this process has been directly informed by the results of the Avon Butterfly Project supplied through the Bristol Regional Environmental Records Centre (BRERC). Consequently this book is just one aspect that draws the plight of our butterfly fauna to an even larger audience.

The final conclusion to draw from the results published here is one of the most important. A book containing distribution maps must not be seen as the end point of the butterfly recording process but more as the start. Now there is a base line that has defined the status of each species it is essential that monitoring continues in order to ensure that the situation does not get worse and which will help guide and inform as to the successful steps that are required to keep butterflies flying in the region.

Butterflies are aerial ambassadors that enrich the lives of us all but act as very visible gauges as to the health of our own environment. If butterflies are not doing well then it is likely that other groups of less well known creatures are also fairing badly. It is in our own interests to ensure that we live within an environment that supports a rich diversity of plants and animals, our own future may depend upon it. The results shown in this book suggest that we need to do much more in this region to improve the environment as a whole.

# CHAPTER 1
# The Character of the Bristol Region

## HABITAT ACCOUNTS

*Rupert Higgins*

### Introduction

One of the over-riding factors influencing the distribution and numbers of butterflies within the region is the availability of suitable habitat. For a particular butterfly species to survive the habitat on a site has to provide the appropriate larval food plant, adult food in the form of nectar, honeydew or fruit, the necessary microclimates for each stage of the insect and niches for pupation and over-wintering. The extent of suitable habitat needed varies greatly from species to species and some butterflies require a network of linked habitats. The distribution of different habitat types in our area is the result of several factors, the most important being underlying soil type and the history of land-use, which themselves are influenced by other factors including topography and underlying solid geology. Habitat type is generally defined in terms of the combination of plant species which grow together, but the physical structure of the habitat often has an

equal influence over populations of invertebrates, including butterflies. The following accounts cover those habitats which are of importance for butterflies, rather than the full range present in the region. Those habitat types not described here, such as saltmarshes, arable fields, rivers and lakes, are described in the *Flora of the Bristol Region*.

### Woodland

Before human activity began to influence the landscape, woodland covered lowland England, apart from small areas along rivers and coasts and on steep cliffs. Clearance of woodland, largely in order to create agricultural land, has left woodland concentrated on areas of heavy soils and on steep slopes, both of which are difficult to farm. Elsewhere, secondary woodland has grown up from abandoned farmland and the planting of trees, either onto farmland or into existing woodland, has created plantations. "Tumbling down" of farmland to secondary woodland is perhaps becoming increasingly commonplace as agriculture is beset by a series of financial crises, which also makes woodland planting a more commercially attractive option for landowners.

No wood within our region is wholly untouched by human influence and the wildlife of each is a result of the combination of past and present management and of natural influences. Up until 150 years ago, the production of both firewood and timber were the predominant driving forces behind woodland management. Since then management for landscape and sporting reasons has been increasingly important, whilst nature conservation has become a significant aim of management over the past three decades.

Ash is the most frequent canopy tree in our region. It thrives on the limestone rubbles and limestone-derived soils which occur on and around the Mendips, Cotswolds and most of the other hills in the region and which underlie most of our woodlands. Extensive ash-dominated woodlands occur along the northern slope of the Mendips, around the Gordano Valley and in the Goblin Combe area. Oaks would have been relatively uncommon as canopy trees in natural woodland in our area, but Pedunculate Oak has been either planted, or heavily favoured, by woodland management in many woods. Fine examples of Pedunculate Oak dominated woodland can be seen at Lower Woods and at Barrow Gurney Woods, on areas of heavy clay soils. Sessile Oak is much less common with us and is only an important canopy constituent in ancient woodlands on sandstones, such as those along the River Avon between Bristol and Keynsham. These woodlands also contain a large proportion of Wild Cherry, Silver Birch and Rowan. Less frequently other tree species dominate the canopy, for example Small-leaved Lime or Wych Elm on heavy calcareous soils or Alder and willow species in very wet places. Other canopy species, such as Field Maple, Beech and Aspen, are widespread but rarely if ever dominant. Introduced tree species are becoming increasingly important in many woods. Sycamore, a very long-standing introduction, is co-dominant in many ash woodlands and can dominate following opening up of the canopy. Other frequent species include Holm Oak and Turkey Oak, and many other species are widely planted but rarely spread. We have fewer conifer plantations than many other parts of the country but there are some large

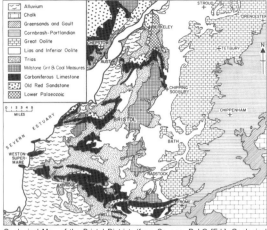

Geological Map of the Bristol District, (from Savage, R.J.G [Ed.], Geological Excursions in the Bristol District; copyright University of Bristol)

woods of pine, spruce and larch species, especially in the south-western part of our area. Most of these have been planted over formerly broad-leaved woods as at Lords Wood and parts of Leigh Woods. At Goblin Combe large areas of previously important downland and heath were planted with conifers. In many of these woods, such as Lords Wood, vestiges of formerly more widespread entomological interest survive along rides.

The structure and species composition of the woodland shrub layer or understorey is highly influenced by management. Historically almost all woodland in our region was managed as coppice with standards. Other systems used elsewhere in the country, such as wood pasture and high forest, do not seem to have been common here. Under the coppice regime small areas within the wood, known as coupes, were managed on a rotation. Widely scattered mature trees were retained for timber production and a large number of shrubs, almost always Hazel, were coppiced by cutting them at the base. This leads to a rapid regrowth of very straight stems which can be used for hurdles or fence-posts or as firewood. The shrubs are re-coppiced on a cycle of approximately fifteen years, with different coupes being cut in different years. This highly artificial management regime allows more light and warmth to reach the woodland floor and promotes a huge flush of spring-flowering plants such as Bluebell, Primrose and violet species. In their very early stages, coppice coupes may support grassland butterflies such as Common Blue and Meadow Brown, but the distinctive coppice species are those that appear as the coupe begins to mature. These include Orange-tip, White Admiral and Silver-washed Fritillary. As the coupes mature bramble becomes dominant until, under mature coppice, the ground flora is much more sparse and butterfly numbers drop. Coppicing is highly labour intensive and as labour costs rose, especially during the two World Wars, and as alternative fuel and construction materials gained importance it gradually ceased. Abandoned coppice woodlands are very dense and dark with large overgrown coppice stools and most ground flora species are either absent or much smaller and flower less freely. Butterflies, unlike some other invertebrates, do not favour abandoned coppice although some species, notably Ringlet, may still be present. Many of the invertebrates associated with coppice woodland became rare in the second half of the twentieth century, most notably the fritillary species. From the mid 1970s onwards there has been a slight renaissance in woodland coppicing as nature conservation organisations revived the practice, most notably at Lower Woods, but the area under coppice management remains much smaller than it was previously and of the fritillaries only Silver-washed has survived in large enough numbers to take advantage.

Rides and glades in woodlands exert a disproportionate influence over woodland invertebrate fauna compared to the ground area which they occupy. This is as a result of their hot, sunny and sheltered micro-climate and of the flora which takes advantage of these conditions. Butterflies such as Speckled Wood, whose males characteristically hold territories along ride edges, and Gatekeeper can be particularly reliant on such features. With changes in woodland management many rides became overgrown but they are now often created or restored as part of nature conservation management. Along the edges of clearings and rides there is usually a much denser growth of shrub species than in the woodland interior. On limestone soils the shrub assemblage can be very rich and often includes Wild Privet, Wayfaring Tree, Purging Buckthorn and wild rose species. The dense growth of these species along rides provides far more attractive larval food plants for butterflies such as Holly Blue and Brimstone than do small and spindly plants under a shady woodland canopy. Brambles may form extensive patches which flower and fruit far more profusely than do plants growing under tree cover. The flowers provide a nectar-source for species such as White Admiral and Silver-washed Fritillary, whilst over-ripe blackberries are particularly attractive to Comma and Red Admiral. The presence of nectar-rich plants such as Hemp Agrimony, Common Ragwort, Marsh Thistle and Cow Parsley is also very important, especially in high summer when few true woodland plants are in flower. Such plants along rides may offer the only opportunity to obtain close views of both Purple and White-letter Hairstreaks. Finally, rides provide a habitat for grassland and wetland species and due to frequent trampling there are often patches of bare soil which provide basking habitat. Brown Argus, Small Skipper and Small Heath are amongst the butterflies which take advantage of these conditions. Particularly fine rides can be seen in Weston Big Wood, Lower Woods and Kings Wood.

*Sites of Interest:*

*Browns Folly*
*Kings Wood*
*Leigh Woods*
*Lords Wood*
*Warleigh Wood*
*Weston Big Wood*
*Wetmoor and Lower Woods*

*Characteristic Species:*

*Purple Hairstreak*
*Holly Blue*
*White Admiral*
*Comma*
*Silver-washed Fritillary*
*Speckled Wood*

**Scrub**

Scrub generally occurs as a transitional habitat in the succession between open habitats and woodland, but it also occurs on cliffs and steep slopes where the thin soil does not allow the development of woodland. Species composition of scrub varies greatly. On heavy nutrient-rich soils scrub is usually dominated by Hawthorn and Blackthorn, with saplings of Ash, Sycamore and Pedunculate Oak and some Bramble at the edges. The ground flora beneath this dense scrub is often very sparse but Ivy can form a continuous carpet. Butterflies are generally scarce but woodland edge species such as Speckled Wood can be common. Where there are also patches of tall-herb vegetation Small Tortoiseshell and Peacock can be common. Purple Hairstreak can occur on quite young oak saplings in scrub, but despite the abundance of extensive Blackthorn thickets Brown Hairstreak remains extremely rare in our area. Scrub on thinner limestone soils and rocks can include a wide range of trees and shrubs such as Dogwood, Wayfaring Tree, Purging Buckthorn, Hazel, Yew, Ash and whitebeams. Non-native species are frequently introduced by wind or birds and can include Buddleia, Laurustinus and cotoneaster species. These limestone scrub communities can be quite open, with sheltered grassland pockets surviving on very thin soils and a ground flora under the scrub which includes such species as Dog's Mercury, Dog Violet, Ivy and Stinking Iris. The butterfly fauna of such open scrub can be more diverse, with widespread species including Brimstone, Orange-tip and Holly Blue. Less common species include Green Hairstreak and Duke of Burgundy.

*Sites of Interest:*

*Browns Folly*
*Burrington Combe*
*Clifton Downs*
*Dolebury Warren*
*Inglestone Common*
*Walton Common*

*Characteristic Species:*

*Brimstone*
*Brown Hairstreak*
*Gatekeeper*
*Green Hairstreak*
*Holly Blue*
*White-letter Hairstreak*

## Grassland, Heath and Tall Herb Vegetation

These habitats exists in our region almost entirely as a result of clearance of woodland for farming and most requires some form of management in order to prevent reversion to scrub and woodland. Almost all of the grasslands in our area are intensively farmed to the detriment of their wildlife interest. They have been sown with agricultural grass mixes and regular applications of fertiliser are commonplace. This treatment, coupled with regular grazing or mowing, leaves a sward which is dominated by rye-grass species and White Clover, with very few other species of plant. Such grassland is usually completely devoid of butterflies, unless a few patches of thistle attract nectaring Red Admirals or provide a larval foodplant for transient populations of Painted Lady. Neglect of intensively farmed grassland can lead to slight diversification as grasses such as Cock's Foot and False Oat-grass and herbs such as Creeping Thistle and Hogweed invade. Some butterflies, including Meadow Brown, Large Skipper and Small Skipper, can be quick to take advantage of this tall grassland.

Those very few areas of grassland which have escaped agricultural intensification support a much higher diversity of plant and animal species.

## Limestone Grassland

The limestones of the Cotswolds, Mendips and associated hills weather to produce soils which are freely draining and have a high pH. These grasslands are traditionally grazed by sheep, cattle or rabbits and where this grazing is withdrawn the grassland can rapidly be lost to scrub. Under heavy grazing pressure on thin soils the sward is very diverse with often a low frequency only of grass species including various fescues, bents and oat-grasses. Herbs can make up a very high proportion of the sward and widespread species include Common Bird's-foot Trefoil, Rock-rose, Salad Burnet and Wild Thyme. Kidney Vetch is slightly less common but is found on several Mendip sites and Horseshoe Vetch is less common still. A huge diversity of other species, including several rarities, also occurs. Rock outcrops and patches of bare soil can be frequent and are important as basking and egg-laying habitat. Limestone grassland is one of our best butterfly habitats and Dingy Skipper, Grizzled Skipper, Small Blue and Green Hairstreak are amongst species which

Tony Moulin July 2002

Tony Moulin 2002

**Dolebury Warren, North Somerset**. Calcareous, herb-rich grassland. Grayling flies here and elsewhere on the Mendip ridge. In the 1990s the Small Blue was subject of study but is now thought to have become extinct at the site.

**Dolebury Warren, North Somerset**. Limestone heath. One of the two localities at the Warren where the Small Pearl-bordered Fritillary still occurs.

Andrew Daw 27ᵗʰ May 1999

Andrew Daw May 2001

**Sand Point, North Somerset**. The introduced Glanville Fritillary colony flourished here from 1983 until its disappearance around 2001. The butterfly used to be found on the southerly facing slope to the extreme left in the photograph.

**Sand Point, North Somerset**.
Floristically rich hedgerows and green lanes are typical haunts of the Orange-tip in spring and other 'whites' and 'browns' during the year.

Tony Moulin Winter 1994/95

Tony Moulin 2002

**Folly Farm, Bath & NE Somerset**. Old meadow in winter, revealing ancient ant-hills. Green Hairstreak occurs in spring. Dark Green Fritillary has been seen in summer but with no evidence of breeding.

**Folly Farm, Bath & NE Somerset**. Old meadow in summer, the last known naturally occurring site for the Marsh Fritillary in the region, last seen in 1993. An unsuccessful attempt to reintroduce the species followed.

Chris Wiltshire  May 1998

**Entrance to the old Wetmoor Reserve, South Gloucestershire**. Once an important site for fritillaries. The Pearl-bordered was lost in the early 1980s, Small Pearl-bordered towards the end of that decade and Marsh in the early 1990s.

Chris Wiltshire  May 1998

**'Tip of India', Horton Great Trench, Lower Woods, South Gloucestershire**. This ancient and large woodland supports one of the few colonies of White Admiral in the region, established here since the 1960s.

Tony Moulin  Summer 2000

**Uphill, North Somerset**. Unimproved calcareous grassland, home to Chalkhill and Small Blues. These specialised butterfly species are now confined to a handful of sites in the region, leaving them at great risk of local extinction.

Tony Moulin  26th June 1994

**Folly Farm, Bath & NE Somerset**.
Tony Moulin and a young lepidopterist at the Folly Farm, Butterfly Family Day.

Tony Moulin  26th May 1991

**Folly Farm, Bath & NE Somerset**. Kurt Vickery photographing the first Marsh Fritillary discovered at this reserve. Kurt's photograph accompanies the detailed account of the history of the butterfly in the region in Chapter 5.

favour short grassland on such sites. Where grazing pressure is less heavy taller grasses, especially Upright Brome, become dominant and floristic diversity declines slightly, although tall herbs such as Greater Knapweed, Ox-eye Daisy and Common Knapweed can become more common. Meadow Brown and Marbled White are amongst the most widespread butterflies of tall limestone grassland, whilst Essex Skipper is becoming more frequent in this habitat.

*Sites of Interest:*

*Avon Gorge*
*Browns Folly*
*Burrington Combe*
*Dolebury Warren*
*Goblin Combe*
*Hellenge Hill*
*Narrowways Junction*
*Uphill*
*Walton Common*

*Characteristic Species:*

*Dingy Skipper*
*Grizzled Skipper*
*Green Hairstreak*
*Small Copper*
*Small Blue*
*Brown Argus*
*Common Blue*
*Chalkhill Blue*
*Wall Brown*
*Marbled White*
*Grayling*
*Ringlet*

## Coastal Grasslands

A distinctive variant of limestone grassland occurs at coastal sites along the Severn Estuary at Sand Point, Middle Hope, between Portishead and Clevedon and on the island of Steepholm. The general habitat structure is similar to that of inland limestone grassland but as maritime influence increases plants such as Sea Campion, Thrift and Rock Sea-lavender become frequent. Wall Brown and Grayling are closely tied in our area to this habitat type and coastal sites can attract large numbers of migrant species. Other coastal habitats in our area are not of importance for butterflies; only

very small remnants of sand dune remain and the extensive saltmarshes which fringe most of the estuary do not support butterflies.

*Sites of Interest*

*Sand Point and Middle Hope*

*Characteristic Species*

*Grayling*
*Wall Brown*

## Neutral Grassland

Clay soils are very widely distributed in our area, especially around the Mendips and Cotswolds, the lower lying hills of the Chew Valley area and in the northern part of Avon, and alluvial soils occur along river valleys and in the Severn Vale. Both support neutral grassland, with subtle variations in sward composition depending on both the exact chemistry of the soil and on management history. Grasses are generally more important in a taller and lusher sward than in limestone grasslands, with frequent species including Crested Dog's-tail, Yorkshire Fog, Red Fescue and Sweet Vernal Grass. Characteristic and widespread herbs include Common Sorrel, Common Knapweed, Ox-eye Daisy and Meadow Vetchling. Other herbs are restricted to a smaller number of richer sites; these species include Dyer's Greenweed, Betony and Devil's-bit Scabious. Elements of either calcareous or acidic grassland, or of wetland vegetation, are often present depending on the nature of the under-lying soil. Neutral grasslands are generally either grazed or mown, as pastures or meadows respectively, and withdrawal of management leads quickly to dominance by tall grasses and then by scrub. Scrub reduces the area of grassland but it adds some diversity and provides shelter from both the weather and from grazing stock. Brown butterfly species are particularly characteristic of neutral grassland and Meadow Brown, Small Heath and Marbled White may all be abundant. Large Skipper, Small Skipper and Small Copper are also very widespread but generally less numerous than the browns.

A distinctive variant of neutral grassland grows on marshy and water-logged soils. Most of the grasslands on the low-lying areas of the region in North Somerset and South Gloucestershire are intensively farmed and have little to offer the naturalist, but more interesting marshy grassland covers a large area of the Gordano Valley, with smaller examples elsewhere. In such areas rush and sedge species can be more frequent in the sward than grasses. Widespread plants include Common Fleabane, Greater Bird's-foot Trefoil, Cuckoo Flower and Meadow-sweet. Butterflies which thrive in this habitat type include Common Blue, Green-veined White, Small Copper and Meadow Brown.

*Sites of Interest*

*Blagdon Lake*
*Chew Valley Lake*
*Folly Farm*
*Hawkfield Meadows*
*Lawrence Weston Moor*
*St Catherine's Valley*
*Weston Moor*
*Wetmoor*

*Characteristic Species*

*Small Skipper*
*Essex Skipper*
*Large Skipper*
*Green-veined White*
*Orange-tip*
*Small Copper*
*Common Blue*
*Marbled White*
*Meadow Brown*
*Small Heath*
*Ringlet*

**Acidic Grassland and Heath**

Acidic grassland is uncommon in the Bristol region and largely restricted to the old coalfields area to the east of Bristol where the underlying rock is sandstone. The most extensive surviving examples are at Troopers Hill and Siston Common. Acidic grasslands tend to be less herb-rich than either calcareous or neutral grasslands and are usually dominated by grasses including Wavy Hair-grass and fescue and bent species. Frequent herbs include Heath Bedstraw, Sheep's Sorrel and Mouse-ear Hawkweed. Dingy Skipper, Small Copper, Common Blue and Green Hairstreak are

amongst the butterflies which should be looked for.

Typical heathland occurs on acidic soils and in our region only small areas are present, for example at Troopers Hill and Siston Common. Slightly more extensive areas of heathland are present locally on Carboniferous limestone, as at Dolebury Warren and Goblin Combe, as a result of an unusual mixture of soils. Both Ling and Bell Heather grow at these sites along with Western Gorse and, at Dolebury, Bilberry. Herbaceous species growing amongst the heather plants include Common Dog-violet, Common Golden-rod and Wood Sage. This habitat type is rich in butterflies, probably due to its mixture of micro-climates. At Dolebury, heathland supports healthy populations of Small Pearl-bordered and Dark Green Fritillary along with more relatively widespread species.

*Sites of Interest*

*Dolebury Warren*
*Goblin Combe*
*Siston Common*
*Troopers Hill*

*Characteristic Species*

*Dingy Skipper*
*Green Hairstreak*
*Small Copper*
*Brown Argus*
*Common Blue*
*Small Pearl-bordered Fritillary*
*Dark Green Fritillary*
*Grayling*
*Small Heath*
*Ringlet*

**Tall Herb Vegetation**

Tall herb vegetation occurs along the edges of wetlands, in open woodland and on neglected land. The most widespread type occurs on nutrient-enriched soils, including those along many rivers and streams, and is dominated by Stinging Nettle with other plants including Hogweed, Hemp Agrimony and Burdock. Along rivers this vegetation seems particularly prone to invasion by non-native species and Japanese Knotweed, Himalayan Balsam and comfrey species all favour such habitats. In wetter places by lakes and rivers or in field corners where drainage is impeded, a more diverse tall herb vegetation develops. Meadowsweet is often dominant, with other plants such as Water Mint, Angelica and Soft Rush. The lush growth of Stinging Nettle in tall herb vegetation provides abundant larval food for Peacock, Small Tortoiseshell and Red Admiral, and on wetter soils Green-veined Whites and Orange-tips can be frequent. Butterflies which breed in adjacent woodland or grassland habitats often rely as adults on the nectar sources which tall herb vegetation provides. On wet soils Common Fleabane and Water Mint can be especially important as a nectar source for species such as Gatekeeper, Common Blue, Small Copper and Small Tortoiseshell in late summer when plants in other habitats dry up.

In upland areas Bracken can spread and become dominant on mis-managed grassland or cleared woodland. Although dense bracken can form a monoculture, a more diverse flora can develop under open bracken. Frequent plants under Bracken include dog violet species, Bluebell, Primrose and Soft Grass. Dense stands of Bracken have a bad name amongst land managers and naturalists, but more open stands are often important to butterflies, notably Dark Green Fritillary and High Brown Fritillary (the latter species though, absent from the region).

*Sites of Interest*

*Burrington Combe*
*Chew Valley Lake*
*Dolebury Warren*
*Narrowways Junction*
*River Avon*
*Weston Moor*

*Characteristic Species*

*Green-veined White*
*Orange-tip*
*Red Admiral*
*Small Tortoiseshell*
*Peacock*
*Small Pearl-bordered Fritillary*
*Dark Green Fritillary*

## Hedgerows

Hedges are artificial features of the countryside, created and retained as stock-proof bar-riers or as boundary markers. In parts of our area many hedges are several centuries old and some show signs of having been carved out of the original wildwood. Hedges often incorporate significant elements of woodland and grassland flora and fauna. They can be the only significant reserves of biodiversity in intensively farmed landscapes. Woodland edge species find hedgerows especially attractive.

Ancient hedges are often characterised by the dominance of Hazel rather than of either Hawthorn or Blackthorn. The diversity of shrub species can be very high, especially on slightly more calcareous soils, and Holly, Field Maple, Purging Buckthorn, Wych Elm, Dogwood, Wayfaring Tree and Wild Privet are all widespread. Mature trees are present more often than not, with Pedunculate Oak and Ash being the most common species. The ground flora of these hedges is also rich and often includes Bluebell, Yellow Archangel and violet species. Where there is a hedge bank or verge, a variety of grassland species can survive. The butterfly fauna of hedges can be rich, with a combination of woodland edge and grassland species depending on the structure and species composition of the hedge. Gatekeeper is widespread, often living up to its name as it frequents gaps and openings in hedges, as are Comma and Brimstone. Purple Hairstreak often occurs around oak trees and Ringlet is common in larger hedges. Meadow Brown and Small Heath can be abundant along hedges with wide grassy verges. Mapleridge Lane, south of Lower Woods, is lined with excellent hedges.

In some parts of our region there are probably now more hedges than there were one hundred years ago. These are in areas where other features were used to divide fields: rhynes in the Levels and dry-stone walls on the Mendip and Cotswold uplands. Hedges have become established in these areas as changes in land management have led to the neglect of the more traditional habitats, in the levels to the great detriment of wetland flora and fauna. These recent hedges are often rather species poor, with Hawthorn or Blackthorn being dominant, but Ash, Sycamore or Pedunculate Oak trees are often present and wild roses may be prominent. In the Levels old pollards of willow may have become incorporated into hedges. The ground flora of these hedges is also often rather poor but, especially in upland areas, there can be Primrose and Dogs Mercury along with a good variety of ferns. Green-veined White, Small White and Speckled Wood are the most widespread butterflies of such hedges. In the lowlands, Stinging Nettle, Cow Parsley and Hogweed are more common, often with remnant wetland species such as Cuckoo Flower and Common Reed. Orange-tip almost always finds a food plant – either Cuckoo Flower in wet hedges or Hedge Garlic elsewhere.

English Elm was traditionally a distinctive hedgerow tree; it has only ever been very rare in woodlands. Dutch Elm Disease has deprived us of almost all mature English Elm trees in our region over the last thirty years, with only a small number of hybrids such as Huntingdon Elms surviving. As the disease swept through lowland Britain there was considerable concern that several insects dependent on elm, including White-letter Hairstreak, would be very badly affected. Wych Elm, however, is the preferred larval foodplant of this butterfly and Wych Elm has not suffered as badly from Dutch Elm Disease as has English Elm. Even English Elm plants are not killed entirely, however, and suckers form a dense growth around the base of the former tree, growing until they reach a size where they are attacked by the beetle vector of the disease and the cycle starts again. Sap runs on diseased elm trees can be attractive to feeding adult butterflies such as Peacocks and Commas. Rows of dead elm saplings interspersed with younger scrubby growth are now a permanent feature of many of our hedgerows. Fortunately these are sufficient to sustain populations of White-letter Hairstreak and also provide a favoured foodplant for Comma larvae.

*Sites of Interest*

Folly Farm
Inglestone Common
Mapleridge Lane

*Characteristic Species*

Brimstone
Green-veined White
Orange-tip
Purple Hairstreak
White-letter Hairstreak

Holly Blue
Comma
Speckled Wood
Gatekeeper

## Artificial Habitats

All of the habitats described above are influenced to a greater or lesser extent by human activity but some habitats have developed on sites which are entirely the result of such activity. The wildlife interest of artificial habitats can be surprisingly high, and is often much greater than that of intensively farmed land.

## Road and Railway Cuttings

Excavation of soil has in many places created a substrate for colonisation by plants and animals, especially along road and railway cuttings but also in quarries. These often cut through nutrient-poor subsoil and are consequently colonised by a range of grassland types. They differ from more natural grasslands in that some species are unable to colonise new sites and are therefore absent and also in the greater variation of micro-habitats which exists in a small area. Because cuttings expose a variety of soil types they often support an intimate mixture of tall and short grassland and scrub, with patches of bare soil. Marbled White, Meadow Brown, Small Skipper and Large Skipper can be found in large numbers on some road cuttings. Essex Skipper seems set to become more widespread along road cuttings. Railway cuttings support similar species and a very few have colonies of Small Blue.

*Sites of Interest*

A37 Hursley Hill
B3114 Chew Stoke to West Harptree
Long Ashton By-pass
M5 Berwick Lodge Cutting
(most others are inaccessible)

*Characteristic Species*

Small Skipper
Essex Skipper
Large Skipper
Small Blue
Marbled White
Meadow Brown
Small Heath

## Post-Industrial Sites

Stony substrates such as railway ballast, rubble, building aggregates or mining spoil provide distinctive habitats. Soils are often highly variable over a small area. Rubble and limestone ballast form soils which may be calcareous and freely draining. These are colonised by short limestone grassland rich in species such as Common Bird's-foot Trefoil, both wild and cultivated strawberry and various cranesbill and toadflax species. Common Blue, Brown Argus and Grizzled Skipper are amongst the butterfly species which can be numerous on these sites. On spoil from coal mines the grassland is more often acidic, with a particular abundance of sorrel and hawkweed species. Characteristic butterflies here include Small Copper and Dingy Skipper.

Deeper soils support a taller community with many nectar-rich plants including garden escapes such as Canadian Golden-rod and Michaelmas Daisy species. Where soils are enriched tall herb vegetation with abundant Stinging Nettle may develop. Sometimes this vegetation supports Marbled White or Small Skipper and Small Tortoiseshell, Peacock and Meadow Brown are very widespread. Scattered scrub is often also present; a particular feature of our area is the abundance of Buddleia, but other shrubs often present include Goat Willow and Silver Birch. Scrub may have populations of Brimstone, Ringlet, Holly Blue and other woodland edge species. Unfortunately, these sites are generally promoted as development land despite their high wildlife interest and many fine examples, especially in and around Bristol, have been lost in recent years.

*Sites of Interest*

*Cheddar Valley Railway*
*Lamplighters Marsh*
*Norton Radstock Coal Batches*
*Pensford Coal Tip*
*Radstock Railway Sidings*
*St Philip's Marsh (small remnants)*
*Weston Big Wood Quarry*

*Characteristic Species*
*Dingy Skipper*
*Grizzled Skipper*
*Brimstone*
*Small Copper*
*Brown Argus*

*Common Blue*
*Marbled White*
*Small Heath*

## Gardens

Large areas in parts of the region are occupied by gardens, collectively forming a significant wildlife resource, and it is in gardens that many peoples' interest in wildlife is first awakened. Gardens are becoming less hostile places for insects as interest in organic and wildlife-friendly gardening grows and the battery of chemicals available to gardeners is restricted. The habitat provided by gardens differs enormously but collectively they often resemble a series of small woodland glades, with strips of open habitat divided by trees and shrubs. As such, they may be particularly attractive to woodland edge species such as Speckled Wood, Brimstone and Holly Blue. Nectar-rich plants are generally an abundant feature of gardens and Buddleia, Michaelmas Daisies and Ice Plant are amongst those often planted specifically for their ability to attract large numbers of vanessid butterflies. Ivy often provides an important nectar source for late-flying species such as Comma and Red Admiral. Larval food plants are usually in much shorter supply. Cabbages and related species are planted in abundance in some gardens, attracting large populations of Large and Small Whites and providing one of the few reasons for direct conflict between

Suburban garden, North Somerset.
Collectively, gardens cover an enormous area within the region. They supply important nectar sources for familiar species such as the Small Tortoiseshell, but often do not support the larval stages of butterflies.

Kurt Vickery  July 2001

humans and butterflies. Many gardens include decorative crucifers such as Honesty which may be used by Orange-tip and Holly Blues will lay their eggs on a wide range of ornamental shrubs. Neglected corners are often colonised by Stinging Nettle, Hedge Garlic or tall grasses, with butterflies such as Peacock, Orange-tip and Large Skipper surviving even in very small pockets of suitable habitat.

*Characteristic Species*

*Large White*
*Small White*
*Green-veined White*
*Orange-tip*
*Holly Blue*
*Red Admiral*
*Small Tortoiseshell*
*Peacock*
*Comma*
*Speckled Wood*
*Gatekeeper*

# WEATHER AND CLIMATE IN THE BRISTOL REGION

*Richard Bland*

The region's climate is a consequence of its geographical position, and can be described as basically mild, damp, and dull compared with other areas of Britain. The Severn Estuary acts as a funnel for south-westerly winds, which predominate, and such warm damp air prevents temperature extremes, and usually ensures more than adequate rainfall. Snow is exceptional, falling on an average of only 12 days a year, and it rarely lies for long. Many plants that are tender further north and east are hardy here, including Bay, and Loquat. All the statistics used in this account are derived from the records of the Long Ashton Research Station that has maintained a record since 1920.

## Temperature

The average mean maximum temperature since 1920, is 13.8°C. The coldest month, January, has an average of 7.5°C, and the warmest, July, 20.8°C. Temperature extremes are very rare. Even the coldest January, in 1963 had an average just above freezing, and the hottest July, in 1983, only reached an average of 26.2°C. The coldest year, 1963, averaged 12.3°C and the hottest, 1943, 15.5°C. To identify trends a ten year rolling average applied to the figures shows the annual average rising from 13.8°C in 1930 to 14.3°C in 1950, and then falling to 13.4°C in 1970, before rising irregularly to 13.8°C again in 2000.

This basic long-term cycle, which also occurs nationally, has had effects on all natural history. Both bird migration and tree bud-burst have been shown to respond by between five and ten days to each one degree change in average temperature. There has been much recent discussion of global warming, largely based on the fact that in the past twenty-five years we have switched from a period of progressive cooling to one of progressive warming. It is clear that there have been considerable climate alterations in the past 2000 years, quite apart from the much broader consequences of living in what is, geologically speaking, an interglacial period that began some 15,000 years ago. The underlying causes of these changes are very complex and not well understood, and human activity may well be altering some of the factors at work in ways we cannot predict. However it is worth emphasising that there is no local evidence of any long-term trend towards warmer weather, although anecdotal evidence may suggest an increase in storms and rapid fluctuations in weather type.

The pattern of individual months has been broadly similar to the annual trend, but no two months show the same pattern. The **January** trend figures fell by 2°C from 1930 to 1968, but had recovered by a degree by 2000. **February** fell by 2°C but took until 1987 to do so, since when it has increased by 1.5°C in 13 years, and this, perhaps more than any other recent change, has encouraged early springs. **March** was steady at 10.5°C until 1950, then fell by 1.5°C to 1970, before rising back to 10.5°C by 2000. **April** had a sharp peak in the 1950s, fell by 2°C to 1970, and has not recovered. **May** warmed by 1°C 1930–50, then fell by 1.5°C to 1975, before warming by 0.5°C by 2000, thus getting back to the 1930 figure. In contrast **June** peaked in 1942 at 20.5°C, and since then has fallen almost continuously to 18.5°C by 2000. **July** has fluctuated without trend, though was at its coldest in 1970, and its warmest in 1984, but by 2000 was back at an average level. **August** reached an average of 21.5°C in 1940, fell to 19.5°C by 1970, but was back at 21.5°C in 1984, before returning to an average level by 2000, a pattern similar to July. **September** reached a maximum in 1940 at 19°C, and fell to a minimum of just over 17°C in 1995. **October** peaked at 15°C between 1950 and 1960, then fell to a nadir of 13.7°C in 1994. **November** rose by 1°C from 1930 to 1950, fell by the same amount to 1970 then rose 0.5°C by 2000. **December** fluctuated between 7.5°C and 8.5°C for most of the century, but fell by 2°C from 9.0°C in 1960 to just over 7.0°C in 1970, before recovering almost completely by 1988, since when it has again fallen by a degree.

Thus most months, except June, reached a nadir around 1970 from a peak between 1940 and 1960, and most have recovered some or all of what they lost, so that the situation today is much as it was in 1930. All have tended to fluctuate within two degrees, and none have shown a trend that is other than cyclic.

## Rainfall

Rainfall potentially affects butterflies in a number of different ways. The growth, or otherwise, of larval foodplants may be determined by rainfall. High rainfall may encourage fungi and bacterial or viral attack of larvae and pupae. Sunshine hours are reduced by rainfall which may influence the ability of larvae to feed effectively or reduce the activity of the adult stage. The average annual total rainfall for the whole period is 910mm. The wettest year, 2000, had 1250mm, just beating 1924 with 1247mm. The two driest years were 1921 and 1964 with 634mm, well below the most famous recent dry year, 1976 at 765mm, which was actually wetter than 1975 at 735mm. It was the combination of two exceptionally dry years in succession that made 1976 so notable. Rainfall thus varies a great deal more than temperature, but applying a ten year rolling average reveals that there has been a trend. In 1930 the ten year trend was just under 1000mm a year, and that fell to just

over 850mm by 1950, and fluctuated around that level until 1980. Since then it has climbed back to 1000mm by 2000. This pattern is largely a consequence of the rain in winter. Spring (Feb to May) and summer (June to September) trends show a fluctuation of around 10mm either side of the monthly average of 60mm in spring months and 75mm in summer months. The winter figures (October to January) follow the annual ones very closely, varying from a maximum of 110mm a month in 1930 and 2000 to a minimum of 80mm a month between 1950 and 1980.

One theoretical consequence of global warming that has been predicted is an increase in rainfall, consequent upon more vigorous depressions, and the remarkable rainfall in the autumn of 2000 and the early months of 2002 may possibly be an indication of this. On the other hand they are just as likely to be examples of the sort of weather extremes that have occurred from time to time throughout the past century.

## Sunshine.

The annual average number of sunshine hours a day is 4.2 hours, and has altered very little in the course of the century because it is controlled primarily by the unaltering number of daylight hours a year, and secondarily by the amount of cloud. The sunniest year prior to 1950 had an average of 5.2 hours a day, and the dullest 3.6 hours. The monthly variation is considerable. December has the lowest figure, at an average of 1.5 hours per day, and June the highest at 7.1 hours. The sun actually shines on average for only some 34% of the time that it is above the horizon.

## Summary

Rainfall and temperature patterns are dissimilar, though the coldest and driest periods during the century coincided in the 1970s. The long term impact of climate change upon butterfly populations is likely to be considerable, though it is only one of the many variables affecting habitat, and its impact will vary from species to species.

# CHAPTER 2

# Watching and Studying Butterflies

## RECORDING AREA

*Ray Barnett*

The major cities of Bristol and Bath are not situated centrally at the heart of traditional counties. Before the creation of the modern county of Avon in 1974, Bristol was a city and county in its own right straddling the River Avon, and Bath part of the county of Somerset. The subsequent abolition of Avon in 1996 saw the city and county status re-instated for Bristol. The creation of three other unitary authorities, Bath & North East Somerset, North Somerset and South Gloucestershire to administer local government for the former Avon county has meant that a true re-unification of these areas with the historic counties of Somerset and Gloucestershire has not really happened, they are not administered from the county towns of Taunton and Gloucester respectively. Hence the county sign for Somerset, for example, is still situated on the M5 south, just after Weston-super-Mare rather than just past Bristol.

Bristol, is the largest conurbation in the region, and therefore home to the greatest number of lepidopterists locally. Butterfly collectors and recorders have always travelled both to the north and south from the city and therefore into different 'traditional' counties. Hudd, in the 19th century, recognised this by publishing his first list based upon the lepidoptera that could be found in the region loosely defined by the map of William Sanders of 1862 'The Bristol Coal Fields and Country Adjacent'. (Originally Hudd and his colleague Harding had intended a list based upon a radius of nine miles from the centre of Bristol but recognised quickly the limitations that represented.) The coalfield region is actually somewhat larger than that later defined as Avon, in the north reaching to Berkeley and in the south to Wells and Shepton Mallet. After producing this list, Hudd compiled the Victoria County lists for the whole of Somerset excluding the northern part of the coalfield region. Subsequent liaison of Bristol's entomologists with compatriots both in Gloucestershire and Somerset has been a feature ever since, for example the Bristol Naturalists' worked with the Somerset Natural History & Archaeological Society over attempts to introduce the Swallowtail butterfly into the Somerset Levels in the 19th century. Also, individuals such as Stephen Blathwayt of Weston-super-Mare visited sites like Wetmoor in Gloucestershire in the 20th century. Interestingly there has been much less interaction between the Bristol region and Wiltshire which also abuts it.

It was in 1852 that Watson introduced his concept of national 'vice-counties'. The aim was to create areas that were much more comparable in size than the widely varying counties and to that end Gloucestershire and Somerset were both divided in two, vice-counties 33 and 34 being East and West Gloucestershire, vice-counties 5 and 6 being South and North Somerset respectively. Consequently, the Bristol region, as defined by the old Avon boundary, is an area within vice-counties 6 and 34. As vice-county boundaries have remained static over time, unlike county boundaries, the former have been adopted by some national recording schemes as a convenient sized and defined recording unit for poorly recorded groups of organisms including many insects.

This current book could be criticised for not adopting either the vice-county or full county boundaries as its recording unit. The justification is on a number of grounds. Primarily it is because most users of the book are expected not to be professional lepidopterists and ecologists but members of the general public who are interested in the butterflies of their local area. Furthermore, there is an historical basis for adopting the Bristol region in that the Victorian naturalists did likewise, for example, Alfred Hudd. Also, a large percentage of contributors to recording schemes based in Bristol record both to the south and north of the two major cities. Although traditionally most recorders visit the classic sites south and south west of Bristol, such as Goblin and Brockley Combes in vice-county 6, very many of those same recorders submit their garden records from their homes in north Bristol which is in vice-county 34. Finally, despite the abolition of Avon, many structures set up when it did exist, still persist. This includes four local authorities that are totally separate from Gloucestershire and Somerset County Councils and which regularly cooperate over joint initiatives amongst themselves. It also includes the Avon Wildlife Trust and the Bristol

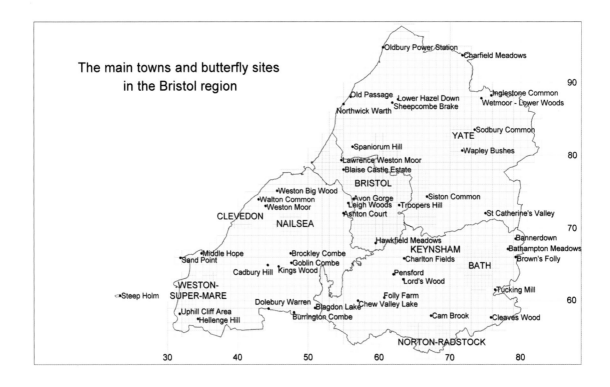

Regional Environmental Records Centre (BRERC). It is the latter organisation which acts as a central point for collating and managing data on the environment for the region, and which has enabled the current survey to take place. As computing power is continuing to develop at a great pace, the professional entomologist or ecologist can now request data from record centres and national recording schemes and receive exact grid references rather than summaries of occurrence by crude estimates such as presence or absence in a vice-county.

## CASE STUDIES:

### 1. WETMOOR – LOWER WOODS ST7488
### South Gloucestershire

*Chris Wiltshire*

There are several ways in which butterflies can be monitored. Mark-recapture is one of the more obvious methods, this gives a fairly accurate measure of the population and over time can give measures of emergence and death rates. This is all very well but it is time consuming, covers one location and usually one species at a time so this would become a full time job to cover all species over representative habitats around Lower Woods.

Flight interception traps, bait traps and suction traps are a few of many other possibilities but most of them have been ruled out for a variety of reasons. There is no perfect method. What is required is some method that is relatively simple, fairly quick, will give a reasonable measure of the population for all species that occur on the site and is repeatable year after year to be able to detect changes. The practical solution, the transect method, is a bit of a compromise, it does not give an absolute measure of the population but gives an index of abundance, it is not very quick but is easily repeatable and is simple to carry out.

The butterfly transect is also known as the Pollard walk after Ernest Pollard who perfected the method at Monks Wood (Pollard *et al*, 1975). While he was not the first to use the method he and his team did refine it and lay down a set of rules for operating a transect which meant that it was possible to have a standard method that would allow results to be compared between different sites. The method adopted for Lower Woods at Wetmoor is described as follows.

At the time the route was chosen in 1988, Lower Woods reserve did not exist in its present form. It was then Wetmoor reserve, a Gloucestershire Trust for Nature Conservation reserve (even though in the county of Avon), within the Lower Woods Site of Special Scientific Interest (SSSI). As a result the route ran through the reserve and around part of the immediate surrounding SSSI forming a triangular course. The route was divided into sections, each of which ended where there was a major change of habitat type, direction of the route or some significant landmark. Ten sections were chosen and then described, the total length of 2,506.7 metres (1.56 miles) was measured using an odometer. No change of route is allowed because it is important that the route is followed precisely in order to monitor any changes that occur, to the habitat and to the butterfly population.

This defined route is then walked at 'normal walking pace' and butterflies observed are counted in an area extending five metres either side, and five metres in front of the recorder. (It should be noted that some long-standing transects around the country are only recorded in a maximum width of five metres.) Any butterfly seen in this imaginary box is identified and counted, if it is known that a particular specimen has already been counted then it is not counted again but if in doubt it is included. This is repeated for each section. This answers the 'where?' and 'what?' questions but 'when?' is a little more complicated.

The recording season is basically a period of twenty-six weeks with week one commencing 1 April and week twenty-six ending on 29 September. The transect is walked once each week. It is not sufficient to walk it any time, it must be between 10.45am and 3.45pm BST, and then only when certain meteorological conditions are met. The reason for this is that butterflies will not fly unless they reach a high enough temperature. The temperature threshold is considered to be 13°C although this is a bit of a compromise because it does vary slightly between species.

Recording can proceed if the shade temperature is between 13 and 17°C and there is 60%

sunshine for the duration of the count (i.e. it is mostly sunny when 60% of the sections are walked). If however the temperature is above 17°C when the transect is walked then the count can be made even if there is no sunshine but providing that it is not actually raining.

One other factor to take in to account is wind speed. The recommendation is that transects are not walked if the wind speed exceeds force 5 on the Beaufort scale (force 5 is defined as 'Fresh breeze – Small trees in leaf begin to sway – 19–24 miles per hour or 8.0–10.7 metres per second). This is not a hard and fast rule because at force 5 in a woodland site there may be many sheltered places but on an exposed downland site the butterflies would probably cease flying and find shelter.

The author carries the following equipment when carrying out a transect:

A digital thermometer. The shade temperature is recorded before starting and at the end of the count with occasional checks along the route.

A vane type anemometer. The wind speed is checked before starting the count and then checked and recorded at the end of the count.

A low powered close focus monocular. This is useful to check the identification of any difficult or doubtful specimens without having to disturb them.

A butterfly net. While this is recommended to catch and confirm identification of doubtful specimens, the author has used it only once in fifteen years of monitoring!

A clipboard with optional bank of hand tally counters. Essential for the recording form. The counters are only carried during peak season recording when it is necessary to count up to ten or twelve species at once.

When the previously described method is carried out, the end result is a transect record sheet with data indicating how many of each species were recorded and in which sections. The rows of data are added up to give a species count for that particular week while the columns of data are added up to give a section count of all species for that particular week. At the end of the season the weekly species counts are added up to give an index of abundance for each species, this figure can be compared with other years and with known

changes to the habitat, for example coppicing, ride clearing etc. Similarly the section count for each week can be added up to give an index of abundance by section. This is a rather crude method but an effective one.

*Species resident or regularly visiting Lower Woods.*

### Small Skipper

The counts range from 203 in 1994 to just three in 2000, the lowest level since monitoring began. It prefers a turf height between 15 and 30 centimetres and this may be the reason for its decline because the vegetation in the meadows is becoming more rank and overgrown.

### Large Skipper

Like the Small Skipper a resident of the open areas but preferring even shorter turf height of 10 to 20 centimetres. The highest count was 64.5 in 1988 and the lowest count was zero in 1998. Numbers have remained low since but there are good populations in the fields outside the woods that could repopulate the site should a local extinction occur.

### Dingy Skipper

This species has not been confirmed as a breeding species in the reserve although it has been recorded on the transect in a number of years; 1989, 1991, 1992 and 2000. It has only been found in the meadows and on Horton Great Trench. It requires Bird's-foot Trefoil *Lotus corniculatus* growing in turf up to five centimetres tall and there is not much suitable for it within the reserve. It is interesting to note that the highest count was in 2000 when five were recorded in the recently cleared area at the top of the slope at the east end of Horton Great Trench where there was some *L. corniculatus* growing in relatively short grass. There are colonies of Dingy Skipper breeding in parts of the adjacent Horwood Farm which may restock the reserve as and when areas become suitable for it again.

### Grizzled Skipper

This species has only been recorded on the transect in 1988 and 1991 with a maximum count of just two. Until the early 1990s it was said to be found in the rides just to the north of the Little Avon river but as they became over-grown and much reduced in width it disap-peared from the woods altogether. The Grizzled Skipper has not been found in the surrounding area recently but it is small and inconspicuous and could just have escaped attention.

Clouded Yellow
The greatest number of this migrant to have been seen on the transect was three in 1994. In years when they have occurred, none has been seen before early August and the latest record is 23 September 2000.

Brimstone
The highest index of abundance for this regu-lar resident was 34.5 in 1990 and the lowest was 11 in 1997. The highest weekly counts are usually in week one and the spring emer-gence from hibernation is usually more numerous than the late summer emergence of the new brood. This curious situation is proba-bly explained by the newly hatched adults feeding up quickly on nectar and then seeking out hibernation sites. At this time they are less active than they are in emerging in the spring. At that time finding nectar sources to replenish food reserves must be a driving force along with males searching out females and females looking for Buckthorn on which to lay their eggs. The current population seems to be fair-ly healthy and under no threat.

Large White
Most Large Whites seen on the reserve are passing through looking for more suitable habitat. The highest index was 55.5 recorded in 1989 but the lowest was in 1993 when only three spring generation adults were seen and none of the summer generation. The earliest specimen that has been seen was in the last week of April while the latest were five individ-uals in the third week of September and prob-ably represents a third emergence in the warm year of 1989.

Small White
Another common species but like the above individuals are usually just moving through the study area. Smaller numbers than the Large White and Green-veined White are seen in general and very few individuals of the spring brood are seen at all. A double peak of sight-ings in the summer probably represents not a second and third generation of the year but firstly the offspring of the resident populations followed by immigrants moving across. The highest index was recorded in 1994 whilst the lowest was zero in 1998.

Green-veined White
The favourite breeding sites are the meadows where the preferred foodplant *Cardamine pratensis* grows. They also utilise some of the rides where they seem to seek out *Cardamine flexuosa* or at the edges where they will use *Alliaria petiolata*. It is usual for the summer emergence to be much more numerous than that of the spring. After hot years the popula-tion may crash as in 1993, however it soon recovers. The highest index was in 2000, a very wet year which was to its liking.

Orange-tip
A delightful species of the spring. The females lay their eggs on the flower stalks of *Cardamine pratensis* in the meadows or *Alliaria petiolata*, as does the Green-veined White. The pupae survive nine months proba-bly hidden in tall vegetation. The highest index of 42.5 occurred in 1990 and the lowest was a modest 3.5 in 1993.

Purple Hairstreak
It would appear from the transect monitoring that this is a scarce species. This is not the case but an artefact caused by the fact that it spends most of its time in or on the trees. It is actually very common throughout the woods as revealed by winter time searching for the tiny white eggs on the oak tip buds. Numbers do not mean very much using the standard transect method. Where hairstreak colonies need to be monitored then special evening transects are carried out as they are late fly-ers, becoming quite active in the early evening and the recorder has to look up into the trees.

White-letter Hairstreak
Like the previous species a mainly arboreal butterfly and so easily missed. The author was unaware of the presence of this species in Lower Woods until a single battered specimen was found in 1990. This presented a further puzzle as the larval foodplant Wych Elm *Ulmus glabra* was not known from the site. Repeated searches in 1990 failed to find the

plant but in the following year a single seed blowing in the wind gave the location away. At that time three trees were found two of which were supporting the butterfly but now the colony is surviving on only one tree. Although a few other Wych Elms have been found since, they do not appear to be used by the White-letter Hairstreak. It has been noted on the transect in 1990, 1996 and 1998–2000 with a maximum index of two.

## Small Copper

There are usually two generations per year of the Small Copper in Lower Woods. They lay their eggs on *Rumex acetosa* or *R. acetosella* in warm sunny positions in the meadows or sometimes the wider rides. The spring emergence is usually the smaller and has been seen in only five of the thirteen years of monitoring. A histogram (not illustrated) of all sightings over the survey period shows two peaks in the late summer: this is misleading because the September peak was caused by a high number of, what is believed to be, a late second generation in 1989 – a year when no spring adults were seen. This particular generation gave rise to the highest index of 42 but the lowest index was zero.

## Brown Argus

The Brown Argus is found occasionally in the meadows but has only been seen in four years during the course of the transect surveys, including 2000. In the meadows and abandoned fields of Horwood Farm to the west of the woods, the author has observed oviposition on *Geranium dissectum* which also grows in the meadows within Lower Woods and so it is just possible that this species breeds there. It is interesting to note that the *G. dissectum* plants chosen for egg laying were in tall grasses and the eggs were laid about 30 to 40 centimetres above ground level.

## Common Blue

The first generation has seldom been seen but the second used to be more common, appearing in the meadows and some of the broader rides. Vegetation of five to fifteen centimetres high is preferred, any higher and breeding will cease. Consequently the meadows have become less to its liking. The highest index recorded was 41.5 in 1996 after which only one was seen in 1997 and none have been

seen since. This may not be a total disaster because the species is still plentiful in the fields of Horwood Farm and so it may be able to move back into the meadows within the woods if and when they become more suitable.

## Holly Blue

In the 19th century this species was known as the 'Wood Blue' which still seems an appropriate name especially since it is the only 'blue' confirmed as breeding in Lower Woods. The author has watched oviposition on flower buds of *Cornus sanguinea* in the rides rather than the usual Holly *Ilex aquifolium* in the spring. Unlike most species with two generations during the year, the second generation of Holly Blues at Lower Woods is often smaller than the first. The seven-year gap between highest counts is typical of this species.

## White Admiral

Undoubtedly the most majestic resident butterfly in the woods. Spindly, wispy examples of Honeysuckle *Lonicera periclymenum* are sought out in the darker parts of the woods for egg laying. The period of time in the pupa, most of June, is when the species is most vulnerable and cool, wet weather then will inevitably result in low numbers of adults in July. The last few years have not been good for the White Admiral and the population is at a low level.

## Red Admiral

The earliest date for Lower Woods is 6 January, possibly evidence of overwintering rather than immigration. The lowest index number was zero in 1991 and the highest was 19 recorded in 1989, 1995 and 1996.

## Painted Lady

The larvae feed on a variety of thistles but those most likely to be used in the meadows at Lower Woods are *Cirsium vulgare* and *C. palustre*. The adults have been found here from mid-June to late September but usually only as the occasional individual. In five years none was recorded but in others between one and four were seen. 1996 was an exceptional year nationally and at Lower Woods the index of abundance was 134. The count for the first week of August that year was 71; that is nearly 18 times the previous highest total for Lower Woods.

## Small Tortoiseshell

Larvae have been found on nettles around the edges of the meadows. In the spring the highest numbers of post-hibernation adults has been seen in the second week of April. The numbers have declined to an index of zero in 2000 but are prone to variation as the adults are not colonial, fly great distances and so can easily occupy any suitable area.

## Peacock

Again the larvae feed on nettles bordering the meadows. Adults emerging in summer feed up quickly and enter hibernation so that the numbers seen flying have fallen sharply by mid-August, which is earlier than at most sites. The lowest index of 34 was recorded in the first year of monitoring, 1988, and the highest index of 219.5 was recorded in 1996 and was mainly due to the large numbers of the summer flight (180.5).

## Comma

Following hibernation, the spring flight peaks in mid-April and is usually over by the end of that month. The next peak is in mid-July when the lighter golden coloured *hutchinsoni* form appears before gradually tailing off. The final peak occurs in late September with adults which will overwinter. The larval foodplant used here is usually Stinging Nettle, the larvae resembling bird droppings are sometimes seen on the upper surface of the leaves. The alternative foodplants are *Ulmus* species and while there is some present around the woods the larvae have not been found to use this.

## Silver-washed Fritillary

Fine weather in early summer is conducive to higher numbers that year or the following as is thinning of the woodland to allow vigorous violet growth, the larval foodplant. The highest index of 126 was for 1996 but it is currently in decline with the lowest index of five during 2000.

## Speckled Wood

The transect data shows butterflies on the wing from early April to the end of September and into October with two 'out of phase' generations co-existing. Hibernating pupae produce spring adults, hibernating larvae produce adults peaking in early June.

## Marbled White

As a grass feeding larva the Marbled White occurs in the meadows and possibly the broader rides. The adult peak is in the second week of July. The highest index of 312.5 was recorded in 1992 while the lowest was in 1999. It is able to tolerate a range of turf heights from five to 20 centimetres.

## Gatekeeper/Hedge Brown

Found in the meadows and sunny rides where nectar rich flowers occur. The annual index follows the same trend as for the Marbled White but the number of individuals is often much higher, both species do well after drier years. The highest index of 871.5 was recorded in 1996 while the lowest was 51.5 in 1988.

## Meadow Brown

Without doubt the most numerous butterfly in Lower Woods. It prefers the open areas but will happily fly along the woodland rides. It requires a medium height to the turf. Adults appear from early June to mid-August and can be present in considerable numbers, peaking in early July. The highest index was from 1992 when it reached 1,229 but the lowest was 216 in 1997.

## Small Heath

Short turf, two to five centimetres high is favoured by this butterfly, habitat that is very scarce in Lower Woods. Consequently, it is doubtful if it breeds there regularly. It has been seen in four of the 13 years of the transect work and the highest index was a modest 5.5 in 1990.

## Ringlet

At home with grass height between 15 and 30 centimetres, the Ringlet is common in clearings and rides in the woods. It flies in dull conditions when many other species will not fly. In the first half of July they can occur in very large numbers, the highest index being 1,196 in 1991 and the lowest of 302 in 1998. In the horrible wet year of 2000 the numbers were more than double that of 1998.

*Species of doubtful occurrence or extinct in Lower Woods*

## Essex Skipper

A single record is known, reported by

C.W.V.Gane as part of a survey by the Bristol Naturalists' Society thought to date from the late 1970s.

Swallowtail
A local resident claims that Swallowtails bred here when he was a boy but have not been seen since. It was thought that this was in the 1930s. No evidence has been found to support this claim. Other, less exotic species have been recorded from this time with no mention of Swallowtails and it is felt that their occurrence here is extremely unlikely.

Wood White
There have been reports of the Wood White from one particular area on the edge of the reserve but repeated attempts to verify this have failed to find it. It is more likely to have been misidentification of small specimens of the Green-veined White.

Green Hairstreak
This species undoubtedly occurred within Lower Woods but had been lost by 1983. The site is no longer suitable for it although it may survive on Inglestone Common where there is abundant scrub and sheltered open areas.

Brown Hairstreak
There are supposedly records of larvae being found on *Prunus spinosa* in Lower Woods but I cannot find records of adult butterflies being seen. Despite concerted efforts by members of Butterfly Conservation and myself no trace of this species has been found since searching began in 1983. It would be possible to make the site suitable again with appropriate management of the Blackthorn to promote the new growth that the species prefers.

Silver-studded Blue
In late August, it is believed in 1979, C.W.V. Gane found three male Silver-studded Blue in Horton Great Trench. He stated that they were 'some thirty to fifty yards from the reserve boundary.' The reserve boundary he referred to would have been Wetmoor as it was then, not the present Lower Woods boundary. One of these specimens was sent to the British Museum (Natural History) for confirmation, after which it was given to his brother (J.V. Gane) who put it in his collection. One of the foodplants of this species is *Lotus cornicula-*

*tus*, this is found in the reserve and is generally common in the surrounding area. It is interesting to note that the Silver-studded Blue was recorded from Hawkesbury Upton in the 1950s and from Horton Common in the 1960s. If these records were correct then it is likely that the specimens from 1979 were some of the last for Gloucestershire as a whole.

Chalkhill Blue
There is a record of Chalkhill Blue from 'Inglestone Common' on 5 August 1967 by Alan Kennard. The next record for the area is of one or possibly two males towards the west end of Horton Great Trench on 30 July 1992 recorded by the author. The most recent record is of one female at the east end of Horton Great Trench on 12 August 2000, recorded on the transect by the author. The only known foodplant for this species is *Hippocrepis comosa* which does not, and is unlikely to have grown in the reserve. However, *H. comosa* does grow on Hawkesbury Hill some two kilometres away and John Muggleton stated that the Chalkhill Blue was present there in 1970.

Duke of Burgundy
There are two records of the Duke of Burgundy from 'Wetmoor', one from C.W.V.Gane in April 1980 and another from Dr Hartill on 10 May 1980. The foodplant for this species is *Primula veris* or sometimes *P. vulgaris*, both of which occur in the reserve but not in suitable quantities or situations today.

Purple Emperor
Barry Harper of the Bristol Naturalists' Society noted 'one reported in 1976 but not confirmed' whereas the author positively identified a female in Horton Great Trench during 1989. The woods seem suitable for this majestic butterfly and as it is a species of the tree tops it could quite easily be overlooked.

Small Pearl-bordered Fritillary
As a butterfly of more open woods and coppiced areas it was once considered common at the site where it probably fed on *Viola riviniana* as a larva. With the cessation of commercial management and the gradual reduction in open areas that ensued at Lower Woods it is not surprising that the last specimen was seen in 1989.

Pearl-bordered Fritillary
Once commoner than the very similar Small Pearl-bordered Fritillary, it vanished from the woods even quicker than that species, the last record is for 1983.

Dark Green Fritillary
As a fritillary of open areas rather than woodlands the larva would have fed *on Viola hirta*. The butterfly used to be reported regularly in small numbers up to about 1980. The last record is from Horton Great Trench in 1989. The reserve is now unsuitable for this species, the meadows are too rank and the rides too narrow for its liking.

Marsh Fritillary
In the past, this species has been described as common at Lower Woods – if only that was the case today! The main breeding area for it was to the east of Horton Great Trench in the Grubbings, which was more open until the 1970s when it finally closed over. It is now young Oak woodland. The Marsh Fritillaries then continued to breed in the meadows further to the west for some time.

The larval foodplant *Succisa pratensis* is still common in many of the rides today but much of it in narrower shaded rides which are unsuitable for the butterfly. Eventually even the meadows became too rank for the plant, leaving only a few weedy examples in the tall sward. The last adult Marsh Fritillary were seen in 1990.

Whilst it was present, the butterflies emerged in the first week of May and the last were seen as late as the second week of June. During the first three years of monitoring the species was present on the transect and the last four years of records are as follows.

1988 index of 4.5.
1989 index of 28.
18 February 1990 an estimated 2,050 larvae were seen in 41 larval webs. 1990 index of 50.
31 March 1991 only 11 larvae were found, none has been seen since.

The suggestion is that the large number of larvae in 1990 may have eaten out the available food supply.

Wall
Although never described as common at Lower Woods, it was certainly present up until 1978 and possibly as late as 1983 but has not been seen since. It is not a typical breeding site for the butterfly and it is possible that they were always strays from Inglestone Common or Hawkesbury Hill.

[This is an abridged version of the article published in Martin & Rowlatt (2001).]

## 2. DOLEBURY WARREN ST4458
## North Somerset

*Jean Webb*

Dolebury Warren is a limestone outcrop, roughly one mile long by half a mile wide, near the western end of the Mendip Hills above the village of Churchill. It is very rich botanically with calcareous grassland on the plateau and steep southern slopes, a small area of limestone heath, and a damp wooded valley, Dolebury Bottom, to the south. Since 1983 it has been leased by Avon Wildlife Trust from the National Trust.

The varied flora includes many species important for butterfly larvae – such as Garlic Mustard (Orange-tip), Wild Strawberry (Grizzled Skipper), Rock-rose (Brown Argus), Kidney Vetch (Small Blue), violets (fritillaries), Wych Elm (White-letter Hairstreak), oak (Purple Hairstreak) and Buckthorn (Brimstone). In addition there is a scattering of nectar plants throughout the year including Bluebell, Dame's Violet, various yellow composites, Hemp Agrimony, bramble and thistles which attract butterflies.

34 species of butterfly have been seen here in recent years. In spring Brimstone, Peacock, Small Tortoiseshell and Comma emerge from hibernation followed by the first brood of Speckled Wood and the three common whites plus Orange-tip. A small quarry provides shelter for Grizzled and Dingy Skippers and, in cycles, Holly Blue is present. As the season progresses, in a good year, the southern slopes become alive with Common Blue and its relation the Brown Argus. There has been a small, but important colony of Small Blue, but it may now be extinct. Both Large and Small Skippers are present in sunny spots. The limestone heath supports Small Heath and Small Copper.

With the advent of summer, Marbled Whites fly on the open slopes together with the browns – Meadow Brown and Gatekeeper, and Ringlet in the valley. Wall Brown and Grayling just survive on the rocky slopes in small numbers.

Two species of fritillary occur on the plateau and grassy slopes, Small Pearl-bordered and Dark Green Fritillary. The larger Silver-washed Fritillary flies nearer the woodland edge. There is only one recent sighting of the Pearl-bordered Fritillary and the last record of the High Brown Fritillary was in 1983 so both must be regarded as extinct here.

There are three species of hairstreak on the reserve. Green Hairstreak, (our only green butterfly) plus Purple Hairstreak and White-letter Hairstreak. The latter two both fly at tree-top height but Purple Hairstreak is easy to find as eggs and White-letter Hairstreaks sometimes descend to nectar in late summer. The migrant butterflies, Clouded Yellow and Painted Lady may be seen in small numbers in some seasons and Red Admiral in small numbers.

Dolebury is a rich butterfly reserve though the numbers seen fluctuate widely from year to year depending on rain or drought and migration, and some species seem only to be just hanging on.

There are footpaths and a bridleway across the reserve and it is open access.

## Transect Results

The dictionary defines a transect as "a line along which counts are made." Thus in its simplest form a butterfly transect is a fixed route along which butterflies seen are counted. In a small garden it may be possible to note every butterfly but over a large reserve this becomes an impossible task so a transect is used to provide a "snap-shot" of the population.

At Dolebury Warren the transect was set up in 1991 and care was taken to include several different habitats. The route goes through part of the wooded Dolebury Bottom, the sheltered quarry, the calcareous southern slopes and plateau and the small patch of limestone heath. It has been walked on a regular basis, in sunny weather, in the middle part of the day, and recorded on a standard form. Species numbers have been counted in eight sections. Since 1991 transect walking has become more sophisticated and the Butterfly Conservation Society has laid down certain rules to be followed. Ideally the transect

should be walked on a weekly basis, between 10am and 4pm, on a warm day with temperatures 13 degrees C or more, with minimum cloud cover and light winds, and counting only those butterflies seen in front or within a fixed distance either side. Even this ideal on a large site such as Dolebury may only give a limited picture.

Transect walking can be a very frustrating business. It is time consuming and becomes difficult when one's free days coincide with cloudy, cool or wet weather. Nevertheless it is an absorbing occupation and the observer learns a lot.

With regular counts, flight dates of many species can be plotted to within a day or so and compared with other years (phenology). On Dolebury for example, the first sightings of Marbled White for 1997–9 varied only between 16th and 18th June but in 1996 they did not appear until 7th July. Orange-tips have appeared consistently over the years between 21st and 27th April but in 1997 they were flying on 8th April. Numbers can often be correlated with weather conditions. In the drought year of 1996 when the upper grasslands turned yellow very early and most activity was round bramble, the only nectar available, Meadow Brown numbers were much reduced. As in other places Holly Blues have appeared in cycles with maximum numbers in 1997–8.

Regular observations soon give local information – the number of Speckled Wood territories along a length of hedgerow, the usual flight paths of Silver-washed Fritillary between shrubs and the honey-pot nectar producing plant species such as Hemp Agrimony or Dame's Violet. Recording a Red Admiral near an ivy clump in October one year and a Red Admiral in the same spot the following April, gives circumstantial evidence of over-wintering.

The most important aspect of transect work is that it gives an objective rather than subjective view of populations. It is better to quote the actual numbers seen rather than just saying that there are changes. This can be a depressing aspect, as on Dolebury where the Small Blue population has been in decline and now possibly extinct. It can also be rewarding as the sighting of a White-letter Hairstreak at the same spot as one was seen in 1994 suggesting a surviving population in the tree-tops.

On Dolebury it is a benefit to be able to compare the species recorded by John Weeks in the 1980s with present species. It is hoped that the more quantitative method of a transect, with details recorded at the Bristol Regional Environmental Records Centre (BRERC) will be a similar useful benchmark for the future.

## The Small Blue (*Cupido minimus*) at Dolebury Warren

*Jerry Board*

As keen butterfly recorders many of us make records of our butterfly sightings, both from our gardens and visits to the wider countryside, and send them into our local environmental records centre or butterfly group. I have done this myself for a number of years now; but have you ever wondered what contribution these records make to butterfly conservation? I certainly did, until I used local butterfly records as part of a study of the Small Blue at Dolebury Warren, North Somerset, for the Avon Wildlife Trust in partnership with the Bristol Regional Environmental Records Centre (BRERC) and Bath College of Higher Education. The following article is a summary of how, from an initial realisation that the Small Blue may be threatened at Dolebury Warren, a more detailed study of the species status at the site was undertaken, resulting in the development of a management plan for its survival.

### Serious decline of the Small Blue

It was in 1993 that I became familiar with butterfly recording and its importance to butterfly conservation. As a student I was looking for a study which focused on a local nature conservation issue, for my degree dissertation at Bath College of Higher Education (now Bath Spa University College). This led me to contacting John Martin then the Conservation Manager at the Wildlife Trust. John was a member of the Avon Butterfly Project (ABP) Committee and had recently discussed how local butterfly recorders were worried that there had been few records of the Small Blue at Dolebury Warren for a number of years; he suggested this might make a good study. I was first prompted by the ABP Committee to search the butterfly database at BRERC and

this is where my work began. Figure 1 shows the results of this database search, conducted in 1993.

As can be seen in Figure 1, the records sent into BRERC from recorders showed a dramatic decline in the observed abundance of the Small Blue at Dolebury Warren in the years from 1990 to 1993 – from 80 records in 1989 to 5 in 1993.

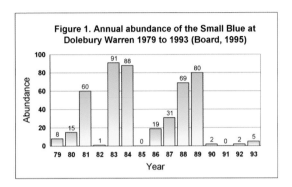

Figure 1. Annual abundance of the Small Blue at Dolebury Warren 1979 to 1993 (Board, 1995)

Three other useful results came from the database search. Firstly, the records showed that only six potential colonies of the Small Blue had been recorded since 1990 within the county of Avon, a decline from over twenty sites recorded pre-1990. This decline has been reflected across the UK in records collected for the Millennium Atlas of Butterflies in Britain and Ireland (Asher *et al*, 2001) of which ABP records were a major contribution locally. Thus, the Small Blue's UK BAP (Biodiversity Action Plan) status is as a Butterfly of Conservation Concern (Asher *et al*, 2001), and is a locally notable species (Avon Butterfly Project, 1995). Secondly, the data showed that the Small Blue emerged at Dolebury Warren between May 20 and August 25. However the species was most likely to be observed in two distinctive emergence periods (a bivoltine species), between May 27th and June 23rd, or between July 22nd and August 11th. Lastly, from the grid references given by recorders and the survey records, the Small Blue was usually observed on the southern slopes of the reserve, possibly in two distinct colonies. These findings helped set the parameters of the study to determine the status of the Small Blue at Dolebury Warren and recommend suitable management at the site to maintain or improve conditions for the butterfly.

*Methodology*

A field study was set up consisting of a butterfly transect, a behavioural study and an egg/caterpillar survey. Whilst each of these surveys are more specialist than collecting simple records i.e. recording the 'what, where, when and who' on paper, they all contained the basic criteria of recording.

Firstly, a butterfly transect was established at Dolebury Warren during the summer of 1994, beginning in April and continuing up to September. This transect was walked once each week to record the number of different butterfly species and their abundance at the reserve in accordance with the National Butterfly Monitoring Scheme (Anon, 1986; Pollard, 1977 & 1982). The transect was divided into four sections to ascertain the distribution of the Small Blue at the reserve.

Once a distinct Small Blue colony was located using the butterfly transect the behavioural study began, in order to determine particular behavioural attributes of individuals within this colony, and study the habitats in which they were observed. In particular the study aimed to identify colony sub-sites where distinct activity occurred, such as male perch sites, feeding sites and egg-laying sites. The description of these sub-site habitats would provide conservation managers with the specific requirements of the butterfly at different locations. This would aid the accurate application of different conservation measures beneficial to the butterfly at different locations.

During the behavioural study Small Blue individuals were observed for 15 minutes, unless lost from sight, and the time spent undertaking various behavioural activities was recorded to the nearest second. Besides abiotic information, records of six behavioural modes were timed and recorded. These were: basking (B), resting (R), feeding (N), flying (F), interacting with conspecifics (own species) (C), and interacting with other species (O). If feeding occurred, the nectar sources were noted. If interactions occurred, the species and behaviour were noted. Perch site heights and descriptions were also described and measured. If the individual was lost from sight, the direction of travel was noted. A spatial representation of the observations was drawn; which included perch locations, measurements and descriptions of the site. From the observations, tables were constructed from which results were derived. During compilation of results, the conspecific interactions were split into two types: (i) mating, and (ii) territorial interactions, to emphasise differences between the two types of behaviour.

To provide further understanding of the butterfly's requirements for survival the early life stages of the Small Blue were surveyed. The egg/caterpillar survey was conducted once females had been observed laying eggs on the caterpillar foodplant, Kidney Vetch. The survey consisted of searching specific patches of Kidney Vetch within the egg-laying sub-site of the behavioural study colony, and recording any eggs or caterpillars found within the flower heads of plants.

*The results of the study*

The 108 Small Blue adults observed in the 1994 study exceeded all previous records. The butterfly first emerged on 29th May and made its last appearance on 2nd July, during the first emergence. During the week beginning 5th August a second emergence occurred, when two adults were observed at the site. The Small Blue was observed within all transect sections. However, the majority of observations, 90 in all, were made in just one of the four sections the transect was divided into. Other observations occurred in sections 3 (13), with some individuals at section 2 (3) and section 4 (2).

Figure 2 shows the distribution of Small Blue individuals observed within the environs of the behavioural study site. The diagram shows how restricted individuals movements were – the majority of individuals (103 of 108 records) were not observed more than 100 metres from the core of this colony. The behavioural study identified three areas where distinctive behaviour occurred within the study colony: the perch site, feeding site, and egg-laying site. The distinctive features of each are described in Figure 2.

The egg/caterpillar survey was conducted in mid June, when a third of all Kidney Vetch plants within the behavioural study colony were found to have an egg present within their flower heads. However, at only one other section on the southern slopes were Small Blue eggs found, and in very small numbers. No other plant species contained Small Blue eggs.

## Site management issues

The record number of observations of the Small Blue during the 1994 study suggests an element of under-recording at the site in previous years. The result also suggests that the Small Blue population appears to be cyclic in nature, with peaks in individuals observed occurring at 3–5 year cycles. The first point suggests that you can never visit a site too often, and that increased butterfly recording provides a greater indication of trends in localised populations. On the other hand, the second point suggests that even though a butterfly species may be only recorded in low numbers for a number of years it may not necessarily be close to extinction. However, low

abundance figures for a notable butterfly species at a site should always ring alarm bells for those actively conserving butterflies, even if this may be due to under-recording.

The butterfly transect also proved its worth in identifying the location of potential breeding colonies and species flight periods – both important pieces of information for site managers when monitoring and managing particular butterfly species. The high percentage of observations of individuals at a particular site enabled further behavioural and egg/caterpillar studies to be conducted with greater precision, reducing the cost and time spent on this more detailed analysis. The egg/caterpillar survey confirmed the findings of the transect by identifying eggs/caterpillars in only two separate areas on the southern slopes of Dolebury Warren, suggesting two separate colonies exist there.

The behavioural study provided much greater insight to the life strategies of

**Figure 2:** The results of the behavioural study showing the perch, feeding and egg-laying sites identified within the Small Blue (*Cupido minimus*) butterfly colony (Board, 1995).
**Key:** The continuous brown line on the diagram shows the suggested limits of the butterfly colony, the shading shows the distinct behavioural sub-sites identified within the colony, green dotted lines represent the scrub and woodland present; and the lines at the top of the diagram show the edge of the Iron-age hillfort.

**Egg-laying site**
Situated at the top of the southern hillslope of Dolebury Warren SSSI
The site has abundant Kidney Vetch within a calcareous sward.
*Females predominated     *Basking and egg-laying frequent
*Duration of behavioural activities was short    *Perches were short
*Site dominated by use of Kidney Vetch as a perch, foodplant, nectar source, and egg-laying
*No interactions with other species or individuals

**Feeding Site**
A calcareous grassland in a depression on the slopes of Dolebury Warren SSSI. Feeding was the dominant activity, but not exclusive as many interactions and other behavioural activities occured here.
*Feeding of long duration on a variety of plant species
*Much flight occurred     *Individuals spent 35% of time basking
*Both sexes present in equal proportions  *Perches used frequently
*Perch heights short (50 to 100mm), mainly on Birds-foot Trefoil
No egg-laying was observed

**Perch Site**
A mesotrophic grassland situated within a valley, outside the boundary of the Dolebury Warren SSSI, adjacent to a bridleway.
*Males predominated     *High ratio of basking activity
*Mating occurred frequently  *Other interactions were infrequent
*Perches were predominantly tall grasses (300 to 500mm tall)
*Neither feeding or egg-laying occurred here

individual butterflies within a Small Blue colony. It identified distinct behavioural sub-sites within the colony; perch sites where males waited for females to mate with; feeding sites where many interactions occurred; and egg-laying sites where females predominated, laying eggs on only Kidney Vetch. The habitats in which these sub-sites occurred were also distinct. For instance, perch sites need shelter and tall grasses for males to perch on and do not require the foodplant Kidney Vetch; whilst egg-laying sites had much shorter sward with high densities of Kidney Vetch for females to lay eggs on. These observations have profound repercussions for site management. A mesotrophic grassland with longer sward and shelter should not be cut to encourage Kidney Vetch, rather it should be maintained by low-density grazing for instance, in order for male Small Blues to perch and mate with females. On the other hand it is important that grazing on the calcareous grassland should be timed to remove emergent scrub and reduce sward length whilst not removing Kidney Vetch flower heads, if egg-laying is to be encouraged. Thus, grazing, and scrub clearance should occur in the winter months to avoid damage to the foodplant. Furthermore, movement corridors between the colony's sub-sites were observed to be narrowing due to the encroachment of scrub. This observation suggests that butterfly mobility could be enhanced if some scrub was cleared at the nature reserve. A further advantage of widening movement corridors especially between the perch site and feeding site would be that it might aid the establishment of a longer mesotrophic sward within the boundary of the nature reserve. This would allow greater control over management of the resultant perch site habitat on land managed by the Wildlife Trust.

In 1995 the Wildlife Trust along with ABP members acted on the recommendations of this study by implementing a scrub clearance programme within the reserve. An area between the perch and feeding sites was cleared of trees and saplings to improve the movement corridor at this point and encourage the grassland to re-establish there. The Wildlife Trust also introduced a grazing regime, where grazing was avoided between the end of April and beginning of September to minimise damage to Kidney Vetch flower heads.

*Conclusion*

This study has proved how beneficial butterfly recording can be to wildlife site management. With the application of both a butterfly transect and a behavioural study the Wildlife Trust found that declines in the Small Blue at Dolebury Warren during the early 1990s were likely to be part of a cyclic trend. Moreover, these recording methods identified the location, status and behaviour of individuals within the main colony of the butterfly at the reserve. The various habitats associated with the colony were also determined. The research also identified threats to the colony, such as narrow movement corridors, and grazing constraints that were subsequently mitigated for as part of site management activities.

Furthermore, it has shown how the ABP project and the hard work of dedicated recorders have made a contribution to butterfly conservation in the Bristol region. Even though in this case the management changes introduced after the study have apparently failed to prevent the colony from disappearing, the experience gained can be utilised as a method of surveying the needs of butterflies at other sites. With the continued decline of many butterfly species both locally and nationally it is important that ABP recorders note when they observe declines and increases in locally notable butterfly species populations, in order that these trends can be identified by the nature conservation bodies and hopefully acted upon in time to prevent any possibility of local extinction. It is such inputs, made by local butterfly recorders, which greatly enhance the survival of our rarest butterflies.

## SITE SUMMARIES

### 1. AVON GORGE ST564740
### Bristol / North Somerset

*Roger Edmondson, BRERC*

On the edge of Bristol lies the Avon Gorge. Over 400 feet deep in places, with steep cliffs and gentler lower slopes as the gorge drops down to the sea. The busy A4 Portway road runs down to Avonmouth on the eastern side of the tidal river and the newly renovated railway on the other. The gorge consists of unimproved calcareous grassland, ancient woodland and semi-natural broad-leaved woodland.

Both sides of the river are heavily wooded with exposed cliffs supporting calcareous grassland. These woods extend on to the plateau on the west or Leigh Woods side whereas they finish at the top of the cliffs on the eastern Clifton side. Sycamore is rampant, competing with Oak, Beech, Ash, Small-leaved Lime and other broad-leaved trees. Many species of Whitebeam, some of which are endemic to the gorge, can be found throughout. The Downs, and cliffs on the eastern side have only become wooded since the second half of the 19th century.

The area has been inhabited and modified for millennia and the remains of a Roman building still exists at the bottom of Roman Way road and there are three Iron-age hill forts at various points. Old quarries abound on both sides of the river and a lot of the calcareous grassland can be found in these. The steep cliffs on the Bristol side support many rare plants including Bristol Rock-cress and the Bristol Onion. Both Fly Orchid and Bee Orchid can be found on the Leigh Woods' side as can the rare form of Bee Orchid known as the "Wasp Orchid".

Over 25 species of butterfly have been recorded in the gorge. The exposed grassland areas support Dingy Skipper, Common Blue, Brown Argus, Marbled Whites, Wall and Ringlet.

The scrub and woodland edge have White-letter Hairstreak, Holly Blue and Brimstone.

Historic records exist of Adonis Blue, Chalk-hill Blue, Small Blue, Brown Hairstreak, Dark Green Fritillary, Marsh Fritillary and Grayling, partly reflecting its once, more open and unimproved grassland status.

The Bristol side of the Avon Gorge is a SSSI and is maintained by Bristol City Council. One or two tracks do exist down the cliffs but access is difficult, and can be dangerous. There are a few quarries off the Portway (A4) where it is possible to park and look up at the cliffs, but viewing is unsatisfactory and possibly dangerous from falling rocks. From the top of the cliffs you have a spectacular view over the Gorge, at the viewing point, by the road at ST560748.

On the North Somerset side of the gorge the 'Avon Way' towpath gives access to the river edge and some of the wooded quarries and calcareous grassland. The towpath starts at grid reference ST565723, but parking is limited.

## 2. LEIGH WOODS ST555745
## North Somerset

*Roger Edmondson, BRERC*

Leigh Woods lie to the west of the River Avon and the Avon Gorge, Bristol. The woods are on an ancient woodland site, although much of the woodland on the plateau was felled for the war effort of 1939 to 1945.

Where the wood slopes down into the gorge, less felling was carried out due to the difficult terrain. Much of the northern area around Paradise Bottom has been replanted with conifers.

Due to its ancient history the woods contain many unusual trees and plants including endemics and areas of Small-leaved Lime. The ground flora includes species such as Narrow-leaved Bitter-cress, Saw-wort, Yellow Pimpernel and Adder's Tongue Fern. The southern part of the woods is owned and now managed by the National Trust, but was until the late 1990s managed by English Nature.

Whilst under the management of English Nature, the pollarded trees were surveyed mapped and re-pollarded, which allowed much more light to reach the woodland floor. This resulted in the return of the Silver-washed Fritillary, which had been lost to the woodland in the 1980s. Other species which have been lost from the woodland over time include Marsh Fritillary, Pearl-bordered Fritillary, Dark Green Fritillary, High Brown Fritillary, Small Blue, Brown Hairstreak and more recently, the White Admiral. The latter had suffered badly since the 1950s, but hung on in low numbers until the last recorded specimen in 1988.

The White-letter Hairstreak gave concern for its future from the 1970s onwards, given the impact of Dutch Elm Disease on its foodplant, but it has survived on Wych Elm and suckers of English Elm.

The southern part of Leigh Woods National Nature Reserve is owned and managed by the National Trust. It can be accessed from North

Road at ST555730. A series of footpaths cross the area. There is also access to the wood from the towpath at the bottom of the gorge via the Nightingale Valley footpath, starting at ST563732.


Transect Results

*Rupert Higgins*

The Forestry Commission property at Leigh Woods is an ancient woodland site that was felled and planted with broad-leaves and conifers in the years following the Second World War. By the mid-1980s it was clear that the plantings were not commercially viable and management priorities changed to nature conservation and public amenity. Early works which were carried out to this end included widening rides, clear-felling areas of beech and conifers and re-instating coppice coupes. Between 1989 and 1991 a butterfly transect was surveyed through part of the wood. Although the three year period of monitoring was too short to reach any but the most tentative conclusions regarding long term trends it was possible to compare managed and unmanaged parts of the wood during the walks.

The walk through the then unmanaged sections of wood passed along narrow, densely shaded rides between blocks of closely planted trees over remnant ancient woodland ground flora. The only butterfly species seen in any numbers in this habitat was Speckled Wood; Ringlets were also present in very low numbers. Even these two species were more abundant in the managed sections of the transect. Where mature oaks had survived in the wood a few minutes pause at the right time of year would invariably produce sightings of Purple Hairstreak.

Where rides had been widened there was a dramatic increase in botanical diversity and in the quantities of nectar-rich plants. Within a year of the widening butterfly numbers were far higher along these sections than along unmanaged rides: at some times of the year more than ten times as many individuals were seen along widened rides than along comparable stretches of the same ride which had not been widened. The most significant species which favoured these widened rides was Silver-washed Fritillary, which was seen in

small numbers each year; over the same period the English Nature warden reported that this species was not being seen in the adjacent National Nature Reserve. Other species which particularly favoured the widened rides included Orange-tip, Brimstone, Holly Blue and Gatekeeper. One ride was widened between the first and second year of monitoring, producing prolific Hemp Agrimony and Bramble flowers. In the second year these attracted butterflies, especially Peacock, Comma and Red Admiral, in large numbers. In the third year flowers were already less abundant and butterfly numbers declined slightly; this effect was not seen along the other rides.

The small coppice coupes also provided a much greater growth of the ground flora and of small shrub species such as bramble and wild privet. These attracted similar species to those recorded along the widened rides, but the surprising feature was the rapidity with which grassland butterflies appeared in the coppiced coupes. Brown Argus, Common Blue, Small Copper, Marbled White, Meadow Brown, Large Skipper and Small Skipper were all seen. All of these species breed in the Avon Gorge, only 500 metres from the coupes they colonised, but to reach them they must have traversed woodland. Another feature of the coppice coupes was that Purple Hairstreaks were attracted to flowering plants in good numbers, along with smaller numbers of White-letter Hairstreaks.

The monitoring, albeit for a short period only, suggests that the management works were successful in nature conservation terms. Both numbers and species diversity of butterflies increased markedly. Those butterflies which benefited included uncommon species such as Silver-washed Fritillary and White-letter Hairstreak. On the other hand, several of the species which appeared were grassland species and it is arguable whether their conservation should be a priority in an important woodland site. Perhaps equally importantly, given the Forestry Commission's aims for the site, the management was successful in public amenity terms. The numbers and variety of butterflies which even casual visitors to the site were able to see increased markedly and for those with an interest in butterflies there were exceptional opportunities to see Purple and White-letter Hairstreaks at close quarters.

## 3. WALTON COMMON ST428738
## North Somerset

*Keith Giles, Voluntary Warden.*

Walton Common is situated on the limestone ridge along the western side of the Gordano Valley above Walton-in-Gordano. The 25.5 hectare common is leased by Avon Wildlife Trust from Sir William Miles and has been managed as a nature reserve for about 10 years. It is designated as a Site of Special Scientific Interest (S.S.S.I.) and is of high botanical and entomological value. The reserve is essentially a plateau with warm, steep slopes to the south and west. It is managed to conserve a mosaic of grassland and scrub with woodland around the perimeter. The resulting range of habitats provides a wide variety of plant species that are foodplants for both the larval and adult stages of many insects. The scrub and woodland also provide important shelter.

Over 30 species of butterfly have been recorded on the Common in recent years; some being present in large numbers.

Dingy and Grizzled Skippers are present in May followed later in the summer by Large and Small Skippers. Brimstones are seen over many months with peak numbers in May and late summer. The cruciferous foodplants of Green-veined White and Orange-tip are found along some of the woodland edges and these butterflies are seen in relatively low numbers. Green Hairstreaks can be found over most of the Common while Purple Hairstreaks are mainly seen around the oak trees at the woodland edges. Eggs of the Brown Hairstreak were found on blackthorn bushes in 1995 but no adults have been reported.

A small number of Small Coppers are seen each year. Rock-rose and Bird's-foot Trefoil are widespread on the Common. Brown Argus and Common Blue are similarly widespread. A few Holly Blue are seen most years as are Red Admirals and Painted Ladies. Peacocks and Small Tortoiseshells are often witnessed feeding on the abundant marjoram flowers in the more sheltered areas. July is the time for Dark Green Fritillaries, usually flying rapidly but sometimes nectaring on thistles at either end of the day. Perhaps a week later, Silver-washed Fritillaries can be seen patrolling the woodland edges or feeding on bramble flow-

ers. *Valezina* forms of the female have been seen in 2000 and 2001.

Speckled Woods are present all round the woodland edges but particularly on the western side of the Common. A small colony of Wall Browns is confined to an area near the disused quarry. Marbled Whites, Gatekeepers, Meadow Browns and Ringlets are all abundant across all of the grassy areas. Small Heaths are also numerous over a long period with peaks in late June and late August. It is interesting that this species seems to be virtually absent from apparently similar habitats across the Gordano Valley.

Two public footpaths join on the Common and access to the grassland areas is open.

## 4. WESTON BIG WOOD ST456750
## North Somerset

*Martin Evans, BRERC*

Weston Big Wood is a large, ancient woodland (37.5 hectares) situated to the south-west of Portishead, North Somerset. It is on a south-facing hillside overlooking the Gordano Valley.

The wood is thought to date back to the last ice-age and therefore supports a diversity of ancient woodland species. It is largely dominated by Ash, with Field Maple, except for discrete areas on the top of the hill, where there is Pedunculate Oak with an understorey of Hazel. On the slopes this gives way to large areas of Small-leaved Lime, while dotted about the wood are some of the rarer Whitebeams.

The wood is managed by the Avon Wildlife Trust who have coppiced some of the Hazel and opened up a large ride. The increase in light levels within the wood has meant an increase in the diversity of the ground flora, which includes rarities such as Purple Gromwell and Herb Paris. In the spring, carpets of Wood Anemone and Bluebells and large quantities of violets are in flower. This in turn has provided a suitable habitat for birds and butterflies. Regular cutting and coppicing of the ride maintains this diverse habitat.

The woodland and clearings are home to at least twenty-five species of butterfly including Orange-tip, Brimstone, Holly Blue, Small Copper, Brown Argus, Common Blue, White-letter Hairstreak, Purple Hairstreak, Silver-washed Fritillary, Speckled Wood, Small Heath and Marbled White.

This wood is managed by the Avon Wildlife Trust. The wood can be accessed by a stile on Valley Road, which leads up a steep track into the woodland at grid reference ST452751. Parking is limited, at the side of the road.

## 5. SAND POINT AND MIDDLE HOPE ST318659 to ST348665
**North Somerset**

*Martin Evans, BRERC*

This is an area of calcareous downland and cliffs on the coast of North Somerset, just north of Sand Bay, near Weston-super-Mare. It consists of a westward pointing peninsula (Sand Point), stretching east through Middle Hope to another outcrop of land known as St. Thomas' Head, a distance of 3 kilometres.

Sand Point is adjacent to a large area of saltmarsh in Sand Bay and the most easterly area of Middle Hope also overlooks saltmarsh in the mouth of the River Banwell.

The more diverse areas of downland are mainly unimproved limestone grassland and scrub, but the central area contains some semi-improved grassland. Sand Point and Middle Hope are owned and managed by the National Trust with the exception of the eastern area around St.Thomas' Head, which is privately owned. Although many butterfly species are found along the length of the downland, the richest area is the Sand Point peninsula which is just over a kilometre in length. This area consists of short-turfed limestone grassland amongst the south-facing scrub and on the exposed ridge, with coarser grassland elsewhere. There are also warm south facing rock faces which are clothed in maritime species such as Sea Campion and Thrift.

The grassland and scrub supports 27 native species including the Glanville Fritillary which was unofficially introduced in 1983, but which may now have died out. The other native species include Essex Skipper, Dingy Skipper, Grizzled Skipper, Brown Argus, Common Blue, Holly Blue, Dark Green Fritillary, Wall, Marbled White, Grayling and Small Heath.

Sand Point is owned and managed by the National Trust. There is a car park at the end of Beach Road at ST330659. A number of footpaths lead up onto the down from this point.

## 6. UPHILL CLIFF AREA ST317582
**North Somerset**

*Martin Evans, BRERC*

Uphill Cliffs are situated on the coast of North Somerset just south of Weston-super-Mare. The area is of considerable ecological importance and contains two SSSI's and two nature reserves. The cliffs themselves consists of carboniferous limestone. Adjacent to them is a small sloping area of short-turfed downland, which is a very fragile habitat and is for that reason fenced off from the public.

At the top of the cliffs the downland continues for half a kilometre to the east and for the same to the south, where it meets Walborough Hill, which is another area of carboniferous limestone grassland.

The downland in this area supports species such as Wild Clary, Green-winged Orchid, Honewort, Somerset Hairgrass and many other rare species. Common Rock-rose, Kidney Vetch and other typical limestone grassland species are present, while Cowslips are abundant.

To the south-west of Uphill Cliffs is a marina, which is surrounded by an extensive area of coastal grassland and saltmarsh.

It is the species-rich grassland which is so important to the butterflies in the area. Chalkhill Blue are resident in the area of the cliffs and have been recorded on Walborough Hill. Small Blue also breed on the downland in the area to the east of the quarry.

A total of 28 species of butterfly have been recorded in the area of Uphill Cliffs. Other species found here that are typical of local downland are Dingy Skipper, Grizzled, Brown Argus, Common Blue, Dark Green Fritillary, Marbled White, Ringlet, Small Heath and Grayling.

This area is partly managed by the Avon Wildlife Trust. Access is from the junction of Links Road and Uphill Way, which is also the start of the 'West Mendip Way' public footpath (ST314584).

## 7. HELLENGE HILL ST343575
**North Somerset**

*Martin Evans, BRERC*

This site is a steep south-facing slope situated about four miles to the south-east of Weston-super-Mare. The habitat consists of calcareous grassland with scattered bramble and gorse scrub. An area of over twenty hectares of the slope is under management of the Avon Wildlife Trust.

Much of the grassland is dominated by Sheep's Fescue, with a wide variety of limestone grassland species including Spring Cinquefoil, Hone-wort, Dwarf Mouse-ear, Somerset Hair-grass, Rough Clover, Soft Clover and a number of other scarce species.

The butterfly population is typical of scrub over calcareous grassland with Small Skipper, Large Skipper, Brown Argus, Common Blue, Holly Blue, Dark Green Fritillary, Speckled Wood, Wall, Marbled White, Small Heath and Ringlet.

This site is managed by the Avon Wildlife Trust. There are public footpaths running across the site from the Roman Road, which runs along the top of the hill.

## 8. BROCKLEY COMBE ST475665, CLEEVE TOOT ST464653, GOBLIN COMBE ST476652 & KINGS WOOD ST458647 COMPLEX
## North Somerset

*Martin Evans, BRERC*

Brockley Combe is a steep and wooded valley bisected by a B-road. It is situated to the east of Brockley village and about two kilometres south-west of Backwell. The area consists of mixed woodland with grassy clearings and rides stretching for over a kilometre south-west to Cleeve Toot and Goblin Combe. Wrington Warren to the south and south-east is now mainly conifer plantation.

Butterflies found in this part of the woodland include Purple Hairstreak and White-letter Hairstreak.

Records for the Purple Emperor from Brockley Combe date from 1870, 1918, 1945 and 1969. There are no records since this time, but it may still be present in this large tract of woodland.

There is also a single report of the Large Blue from Brockley Combe in 1945 by the famous lepidopterists Ian Heslop and Baron de Worms. No other sightings are known from this site.

Cleeve Toot and Goblin Combe are to the west of Bristol International Airport and nearly four kilometres south of Backwell. The habitat consists of Yew woodland and scrub with areas of limestone grassland and heath. These are situated along a steep-sided valley with limestone outcrops and scree.

Only a small remnant remains of the grassland and heath as most of the area has been planted with conifers. The site is unusual in its mixture of limestone and heathland plants. The heath contains Bell Heather, Ling and Wood Sage, while the less acid areas contain species such as Yellow-wort, Ploughman's-spikenard and Common Rock-rose. These open areas support several species of butterflies including Dingy Skipper, Grizzled Skipper, Green Hairstreak, Brown Argus, Common Blue, Dark Green Fritillary, Wall and Grayling.

Small Pearl-bordered Fritillary and Pearl-bordered Fritillary were still present in Goblin Combe in the 1970's, but both seemed to have disappeared by the early 1980s. This was perhaps due to the very large area of conifers that was planted in the early 1960s and had shaded out much of the limestone heathland by about 1980. Similarly, High Brown Fritillary was present until at least the early 1970s.

The Silver-washed Fritillary is still present in the Goblin Combe area and the woodland still supports a population of White Admiral. These were recorded in reasonable numbers during the late 1990's.

Kings Wood is southwest of Goblin Combe and Cleeve Toot and is the most northerly of another complex of woods which includes Urchin Wood, Ball Wood and Corporation Woods. These woods are again mixed woodland. The more southerly of them are on a south-facing slope. The clearings in this area support two of the larger fritillaries; Dark Green Fritillary and Silver-washed Fritillary. One part of these woods is owned by a conservation body, so some of the woodland could be managed to assist these species.

Other species found in the Brockley to Kingswood complex are Small, Large Skipper, Brimstone, Large White, Small White, Green-veined White, Orange-tip, Small Copper, Holly Blue, Red Admiral, Painted Lady, Small Tortoiseshell, Peacock, Comma, Speckled Wood, Wall, Marbled White, Gatekeeper, Meadow Brown, Small Heath and Ringlet.

Some of these woodlands are privately owned but public footpaths are available in places. There are several paths running from the A370 Weston-super-Mare to Bristol road.

Goblin Combe Avon Wildlife Trust Reserve can be accessed by turning into Cleeve Hill Road, off the A370 Weston-super-Mare to Bristol road. Park in the quarry on the left side near the school and follow the footpath through the combe to the reserve.

## 9. CADBURY HILL, NEAR YATTON
## ST443649
## North Somerset

*Tony Moulin*

This Iron Age Hill Fort in a Site of Nature Conservation Importance (SNCI) and Local Nature Reserve (LNR) managed jointly by the parish councils of Yatton and Congresbury. During the early 1980s A.H. (John) Weeks recorded a total of 26 species on the site including Silver-washed Fritillary with single records for Purple Hairstreak and White Admiral in 1984. The latter two have not been recorded since. Today on the lowland calcareous grassland butterfly species can be seen in good numbers, particularly on part of the reserve which is a reclaimed land-filled quarry. Regular surveying by Pat and Malcolm Oliver started in 1993 and led to the rediscovery of Silver-washed Fritillary (1995) and Brown Argus (1997). White-letter Hairstreak was added to the site species total in 1996. Notably there is a well established colony of Wall Brown on the hillfort top. There is open access at all times.

## 10. CHEDDAR VALLEY RAILWAY WALK,
## YATTON-CONGRESBURY ST424659-
## ST431641
## North Somerset

*Tony Moulin*

The northernmost section of the disused Cheddar Valley Railway branch between Yatton and Congresbury forms the eastern boundary of the Biddle Street SSSI and is managed by Yatton and Congresbury Wildlife Action Group (YACWAG). The railway path is

a Local Nature Reserve and provides a variety of scrub and rough grassland habitats above the surrounding low lying floodplain grazing marsh. An adjoining SNCI at the old Yatton Junction was acquired in 1998 and now forms a gateway to the reserve. The more sheltered parts of the walk provide a haven for a total of 24 species including Brown Argus (1996) and Wall Brown (1998). There is evidence that the Grizzled Skipper, first recorded in 1998, has become an established colony. There is open access at all times.

## 11. FOLLY FARM ST 607604
## Bath & North East Somerset

*Tony Moulin*

Folly Farm, situated in the north Mendips, was acquired by the Avon Wildlife Trust in 1987 and is often described as the "jewel in the crown" of its reserves. There are a variety of habitats within the 250 acre site including ancient woodland, but notably it is the nationally important unimproved neutral grassland which resulted in part of the site being designated as a SSSI in 1987. This species rich grassland supports good populations of grassland butterflies: Marbled White, Ringlet, Meadow Brown and Small Skipper can be seen in profusion. The Marsh Fritillary was first noted here in 1987 and is included in the SSSI citation as being "uncommon in the county". Its foodplant, Devil's-bit Scabious, occurs in abundance within the grassland.

Remarkably little butterfly recording had taken place before 1990 when a transect was established. The first evidence of recording was in 1982 when a total of nine species had been noted. At the end of the 1989 season the site total had crept up to 19 species but the reserve's true worth still remained to be discovered.

Regular surveying of the site added a further eleven species including White-letter Hairstreak (1991), Green Hairstreak (1992) and Duke of Burgundy (1991). Sadly, whilst both White-letter and Green Hairstreak continued to be recorded in subsequent years the Duke of Burgundy remains as a single record for the site and indeed an extremely rare record for the ABP region. An elusive butterfly at the best of times the Duke of Burgundy is in serious decline and if present only in small numbers highlights the difficulty of monitoring populations for conservation purposes.

Similarly the Marsh Fritillary at Folly Farm remains an enigma, being only rediscovered in small numbers in 1991 and 1993 after its original sighting in 1987. A re-introduction in 1996 resulted in a few records for 1997 but no observations since, despite the habitat appearing conducive to the butterfly's requirements and specific management being carried out. Climate change has been suggested as a possible causal factor in creating poor conditions in the short critical flight period when breeding takes place. The original presence of Marsh Fritillary at Folly Farm may be due to an explosion of a Mendips meta-population during the peak butterfly years of the mid 1980s when climatic conditions were more favourable and coincidental with a period when the butterfly slopes at Folly Farm were unfarmed. By the time conservation needs had been considered for a small, dwindling population it was "too much, too late" as witnessed by the only larval web seen in 1991 being poached out by cattle grazing during winter 1991/1992.

Transect work at Folly Farm covered the five year period 1990–1994 and generated over 10,700 records. The reserve still continues to reveal more species – in 1996 Dark Green Fritillary was observed bringing the site total to 31. A possible sighting of Chalkhill Blue was subsequently verified as an unusually pale blue aberrant female Common Blue. Horseshoe Vetch, the foodplant of the Chalkhill Blue does not occur on the site. Future surveying may reveal the westward spread of Essex Skipper, Silver-washed Fritillary as a result of coppicing in the ancient Dowlings Wood, or confirmation of the Wall Brown possibly seen in previous years.

Folly Farm will always surprise the patient and diligent observer.

Access to the site is open and there is a car park reached by track from the A368. Buses stop at Sutton Farm on routes from Weston super Mare, Bristol and Bath.

## 12. BROWN'S FOLLY ST793660
### Bath & North East Somerset

*Roger Edmondson, BRERC*

Two and a half miles east of Bath and just south of Bathford, lies Brown's Folly. This 40 hectare Avon Wildlife Trust reserve and SSSI lies on the west-facing slopes of Bathford Hill, overlooking the River Avon.

The oolitic limestone is covered in part by ancient and secondary woodland with some limestone grassland. The area is honeycombed with mines and quarries with the 19th century folly rising above them.

Ash dominates the woodland with Pedunculate Oak, Hornbeam, Wych Elm, Hazel and other broad-leaved trees. Many scarce plants can be found amongst the dominant Dog's Mercury, including Bath Asparagus and several species of orchid. Grasses dominate the open areas along with calcareous plants. However, the grassland is under threat from scrub encroachment.

Many grassland butterflies have been recorded including Grizzled Skipper, Dingy Skipper, Common Blue, Marbled White, Ringlet and Wall.

The Green Hairstreak and Brimstone are present in the scrub, whilst the woodland supports species such as Silver-washed Fritillary, Purple Hairstreak and Holly Blue

There are also historic records (1980s) of Grayling, White-letter Hairstreak, Brown Argus and Duke of Burgundy. Of these probably only the White-letter Hairstreak and the Brown Argus are now likely to be present.

This SSSI is owned and managed by the Avon Wildlife Trust. Turn off the A363 Bradford Road and take the minor road from Bathford to Kingsdown, taking the steep right hand turn to Monkton Farleigh. There is a car park on the brow of the hill and footpaths cross the site.

## 13. BANNERDOWN ST793685
### Bath & North East Somerset

*Roger Edmondson, BRERC*

To the north-east of Bath and Batheaston lies the 20 hectare plateau of Bannerdown. The site is mainly flat but falls away to the south into woodland and scrub.

Several disused quarries and a number of small fields exist on the slopes. The grassland on the plateau is tall, but the thin, calcareous soil and exposed rocky outcrops restrict the height of the sward on the slopes. This in turn provides a habitat for plant species such as Horse-shoe Vetch, Squinancywort, Autumn Gentian, Clustered Bellflower, Bee Orchid and

Pyramidal Orchid. Blackthorn is abundant on the site and scrub encroachment is an ongoing problem.

The grassland is the important habitat for the butterflies and a number of short-turf species are present including Dingy Skipper, Chalkhill Blue, Brown Argus, Common Blue and Small Heath.

In the rougher grassland are species such as Essex Skipper, Small Skipper, Small Copper, Marbled White, Wall, Ringlet, Gatekeeper and Meadow Brown.

Several other species are to be found in the adjacent trees and scrub including Green Hairstreak, Purple Hairstreak, Holly Blue and Brimstone.

There are public footpaths off the Fosse Way Roman Road at ST793688.

## 14. CLEAVES WOOD ST758577
### Bath & North East Somerset

*Roger Edmondson, BRERC*

Situated between the villages of Wellow, Norton St.Phillips and Hinton Charterhouse, to the south of Bath, lies Cleaves Wood.

This ancient and semi-natural broad-leaved woodland occupies a steep south-west facing hillside and has a network of calcareous grassland rides and clearings. It is dry and very well drained.

The broad-leaved trees consist primarily of Ash with Wych Elm and Oak plus Hazel coppice beneath. Some stands of conifers have also been planted.

The ground flora includes Common Rockrose, Wild Thyme, Wild Daffodils and a large quantity of Green Hellebore. Also present are calcareous plants such as Yellow-wort, Common Centaury, Autumn Gentian and various orchid species.

27 species of butterfly have been recorded here with the Duke of Burgundy being the highlight, with a series of records in the 1980's and 90's, but may now be extinct there. Other woodland edge species present are Green Hairstreak, White-letter Hairstreak, Brimstone and Holly Blue.

In the rides Silver-washed Fritillary occur but the last reported possible High Brown Fritillary seen in the wood, and for this entire recording area, was in 1992. Pearl-bordered Fritillary was last recorded in 1982 but Dark

Green Fritillary has been seen in the late 1990s.

Of the shorter grassland species, Dingy Skipper, Grizzled Skipper, Brown Argus, Common Blue all occur with Ringlet and Marbled White in the longer grass.

The other species recorded are Small Skipper, Large Skipper, Clouded Yellow, Large White, Small White, Green-veined White, Orange-tip, Small Copper, Red Admiral, Painted Lady, Small Tortoiseshell, Peacock, Comma, Speckled Wood, Gatekeeper, Meadow Brown and Small Heath.

This is a privately owned site, however there is a public footpath off Norton Lane at ST760573.

## 15. TUCKING MILL ST764615
### Bath & North-East Somerset

*Roger Edmondson, BRERC*

This site consists of a south-east facing meadow set in a valley to the south of Combe Down, Bath and north-east of Midford.

There is woodland on two sides of the meadow and scrub along the dismantled railway that skirts the north-west boundary.

The meadow is unimproved grassland with a rich flora that includes Devil's-bit Scabious, Black Knapweed, Bee Orchid and Pyramidal Orchid.

This site has all of the common grassland butterflies including Small Skipper, Large Skipper, Small Copper, Brown Argus, Common Blue, Marbled White, Gatekeeper, Meadow Brown and Ringlet. The more local Dingy Skipper is also present.

There are historic records of Marsh Fritillary, but this species has not been recorded at the site since 1982.

A Chalkhill Blue was also recorded on the site recently, but is thought to have been a vagrant.

Due to the amount of scrub and trees in the surrounding area, a few woodland butterflies have been recorded, including Brimstone, Speckled Wood, Holly Blue and Purple Hairstreak.

Tucking Mill is managed by the Avon Wildlife Trust. There is very limited roadside parking by the Tucking Mill Reservoir ST765615, but the site is best accessed from the footpath starting at Combe Down, ST762621.

# CHAPTER 3
# Conservation

## BUTTERFLIES AND BIODIVERSITY

*Tony Moulin and Rupert Higgins*

For more than two centuries butterflies have had a high profile and popularity with collectors and naturalists alike. In recent decades this popularity has extended to a wider audience and put them in a unique position to provide an insight into changing trends in man's interaction with the natural environment and his impact on wildlife and habitats.

This publication is testimony to a virtually unbroken sequence of observing and recording the fate of butterfly species in the Bristol region during the last two hundred years. Although recording on a systematic basis has only been undertaken in the last two decades we nonetheless have a reliable account of the changing fortunes of butterflies thanks to the earlier work in the area.

Butterflies are particularly sensitive to changes in their environment and consequently act as important biodiversity indicator species. As warmth seeking creatures the declines or increases in their numbers can not only be used to warn of habitat change but also help our understanding of climate change, particularly in relation to global warming. They are, in effect, part of an early warning system which, like the canary in a coal mine, can tell us if things are going wrong.

The presence and abundance of butterflies can help to indicate its health as a wildlife habitat. Butterflies and other insects are meticulous about what they require to complete each stage of their life cycle. Survival is not simply a question of whether the right larval foodplant is present. A continuity of appropriate land management will have created, for instance, the right growth conditions, sward height, degree of shade or openness, all of which maybe critical. It is not surprising therefore that butterfly "hot spots" are often coincidental with areas rich in other flora and fauna species. However, a moment of injudicious management, such as grass, hedge or scrub clearance, could destroy a small colony of butterflies for the next season or longer. The constant pressure on marginal habitats through "tidying up" roadside verges and hedgerows, eradicates suitable habitat permanently and unfortunately the reversal of this process brings no guarantees of a species returning in the future. A countryside bereft of butterflies is a likely indication of poor or inappropriate habitat management, which is probably also affecting other flora and fauna.

## National and Regional Trends – Changing Fortunes

There are 60 species of butterfly resident in the British Isles. The Butterflies for the New Millennium Atlas (2001) has, however, painted a picture of mixed fortunes for the national butterfly population. Those more mobile species with broader habitat requirements have fared better with some species extending their populations and geographic range. The northward extension in range of species like the Marbled White has been attributed to the climatic change brought about by global warming. Similarly the expansion of the Essex Skipper into our region may be explained in this way. Nationally the picture is less optimistic when considering the more sedentary species with very specific habitat requirements. Many of these habitat specialists have suffered serious decline over the last two decades. The increased profile and resources of the nature conservation movement over the last fifty years have failed to prevent this decline, although they have doubtless slowed it. The effort that has gone into nature conservation is reflected in the number of key butterfly sites that are now managed as nature reserves. Examples include Uphill and Walborough, managed by North Somerset Council and Avon Wildlife Trust; Troopers Hill, managed by Bristol City Council; and Dolebury Warren, Walton Common, and Goblin Combe, amongst many sites managed by the Avon Wildlife Trust. None of theese reserves has been set up specifically for its butterfly interest, but rather to conserve valuable habitat types.

The weakness of nature reserve-based nature conservation is demonstrated by the loss of butterflies from many of these sites, often despite considerable investment into survey and habitat management. For example, Duke of Burgundy has disappeared from Brown's Folly; Grayling from Trooper's Hill; Pearl-bordered Fritillary from Dolebury Warren; and the introduced population of Glanville Fritillary from Sand Point.

More recently large sums of money have been dedicated to supporting wildlife-friendly land management on sites not in nature conservation. The most important of these is Countryside Stewardship, which supports farmers who manage their land in a wildlife-friendly manner. These schemes have the potential to secure favourable management over much larger areas than can be managed as nature reserves. To date the butterfly species that have benefited locally are mostly the more widespread ones such as Marbled White and Small Heath. Nature conservationists have also devoted efforts to stemming the loss of habitats through using the planning system to direct development away from valuable sites. Avon Wildlife Trust and local authority ecologists, in particular, have been successful to the extent that no key butterfly sites have been lost to development in our area in recent decades. There has been an attritional loss of locally important sites, however. Amongst many examples are the destruction of Hawkfield Meadows in South Bristol, a site for many grassland species and of thriving colonies of Common Blue and Brown Argus near Temple Meads station.

Changes in land use and management practice as a result of farming and forestry intensification have also taken their toll along with the general "tidying up of the countryside". So-called improvement of grassland – the practice of adding large quantities of fertilisers to fields to increase agricultural yield, has resulted in the exclusion of almost all butterflies from large tracts of the countryside. Sites for species such as Marsh Fritillary have doubtless been lost before the naturalist community even became aware of their existence. Our region has escaped much of the large-scale coniferisation seen elsewhere in the country, but even so the butterfly fauna of many areas has suffered as native habitats have been planted with conifers. The worst damage has been caused at Goblin Combe where, away from the small Avon Wildlife Trust reserve, mixed downland and heath has been lost over a large area, and with it species such as Dark Green Fritillary.

Equally damaging is neglect. Many of our butterflies are thermophiles, which in the British climate are dependent on early successional habitats created by traditional management of either grassland or woodland. Economic pressures have led to many of these practices being abandoned. Formerly extensive grassland sites have been lost to, or at least severely fragmented by, scrub invasion and short sparse vegetation has been overgrown by tall-growing grass species. This has been the main factor in the disappearance of Adonis Blue from our area, losses of Chalkhill Blue from many sites, including the Avon Gorge, and the marked decline in Small Blue colonies. In woodlands the almost total abandonment of coppicing has led to well documented declines in fritillary species, which have been no less severe in our area than elsewhere, with only Silver-washed surviving as a woodland butterfly.

The agri-environment schemes referred to above, together with significant incentives for more wildlife-friendly forestry, offer genuine and exciting opportunities to reverse many of these trends, whilst ever larger tracts of land could be purchased as nature reserves if the National Lottery continues to support such applications by wildlife bodies. In coming decades we might see a real increase in the quality of wildlife habitats in key areas such as the western Mendips and the Gordano Valley. Already Avon Wildlife Trust has begun the process, restoring herb-rich grassland at Dolebury Warren and Folly Farm, and as a result both Dingy Skipper and Grizzled Skipper are breeding in what was once a kale field at the former site. If such schemes are successful, however, they might confront us with difficult choices. Even if we can re-create successful habitat for a species like Adonis Blue, is it realistic to expect natural re-colonisation? If not, re-introduction will have to be considered. Many entomologists have been rightly suspicious of such re-introductions and the examples of Marsh Fritillary and Glanville Fritillary in our area show how difficult it can be to establish viable populations of rare species, which *per se* have very specific habitat requirements. In the future there is likely to be greater pressure for re-introduction or, if climate change becomes severe, introductions of new species. If such schemes go ahead it is vital that they are backed by sound

science and this is one of the areas where even casual recording of butterflies and other insects can help to ensure that decisions are correctly informed.

Today one can find 39 species in the Bristol Region. During the 1990s, the Avon Butterfly Project produced new records for certain common and rare species in kilometre squares where they were previously unrecorded. Nonetheless the region is still poorer than twenty years ago due to the extinction of a number of species.

Sadly, mirroring the national trend, the region has lost three of its habitat specialists since the mid 1980s: the High Brown Fritillary, Pearl-bordered Fritillary and the Marsh Fritillary. The Duke of Burgundy may hold on at one site in north east Somerset. Species such as Chalkhill Blue, Small Pearl-bordered Fritillary, Dark Green Fritillary, Grayling and Small Blue give cause for concern, their precarious state pointing to the real threat of further species loss before the first decade of the new millennium is out.

Some species, the Marbled White for example, have extended their range. However, the increased number of kilometre square records for White-letter Hairstreak and Green Hairstreak probably results from the re-addressing of the under-recording in years prior to the project rather than a genuine increase in numbers. Both species are unobtrusive and the former is often found only as a result of specialised searches. It is true to state though that the habitats used by both species are in decline.

## Biodiversity Action Plans/Conservation

*Tony Moulin*

The very real possibility of national extinctions has led to the drawing up of an agreed list of 25 butterfly species most at risk to be included in the National Biodiversity Action Plan (BAP). Most of these target species are now extinct in the Bristol region and locally it may be too late to turn back the clock for those lost. It will be essential to ensure that Regional and Local Biodiversity Action Plans (LBAP) take into account the needs of species such as Small Blue, Chalkhill Blue and Grayling, whose habitats are considered fragile. During the Project, detailed work has been conducted on Marsh Fritillary and Small Blue.

Nationally the Marsh Fritillary had been highlighted for action under the Biodiversity Action Plan as a species in serious threat of extinction. Action was required to sustain existing populations and to establish reintroductions in areas where appropriate. By the end of 1991 the only known colony of the Marsh Fritillary in the Bristol region was to be found at Folly Farm, an Avon Wildlife Trust reserve in the Unitary Authority area of Bath and North East Somerset. English Nature sponsored the Avon Butterfly Project to produce a report in 1995 summarising the status of the Marsh Fritillary in Avon. By this time the butterfly had probably been lost, not having been recorded since 1993 at Folly Farm. Previous breeding colonies and areas where Marsh Fritillary had historically been found were also surveyed in 1995. No sightings were made. Consequently Avon Wildlife Trust was anxious to begin an assessment at Folly Farm regarding the possible reintroduction of the butterfly.

With funding support from English Nature a project was initiated in the winter of 1996/1997 to monitor the release of larvae and then pupae. Adult butterflies were observed in 1997 but the absence of sightings since 2000, suggests that although the habitat conditions were apparently suitable, breeding was not successful. The value of re-introductions is debatable with many dependent variables, the complexity of which is not fully understood. Success is rarely guaranteed. Such projects require perseverance and can be costly, requiring continuing funding for monitoring and habitat management. Long term solutions are needed to halt decline through measures designed to prevent habitat degradation and loss.

It is very important to carry on monitoring butterflies at regional level following the publication of this book. Certainly the Avon Butterfly Project has been successful over the last decade in raising awareness of the plight of butterflies and the need for butterfly conservation and recording, thanks to a diverse group of local people and the national and local work of Butterfly Conservation. However, it is important to note that while the Butterflies for the New Millennium Atlas project and the ABP have built up a picture of species distri-

bution, they have not been able to measure effectively species abundance. Assessing the quantity can only be achieved through dedicated and regular transect survey work. As part of the ABP this has been carried out in a limited way by a number of volunteers at key sites. The results still point to a depressing conclusion: although the distribution of common species throughout the region appears healthy, in reality the butterfly population is in all probability reducing. What is important is that more detailed monitoring of key sites should continue. Understanding the causes of population fluctuations is difficult. The abundance of any species on a specific site is affected by a number of factors. One has only to consider the Marsh Fritillary re-introduction to appreciate that single factors alone cannot account for its failure.

At Folly Farm a combination of factors was certainly at work. Changes in the habitat management between 1987 and 1991 together with cool and dull late spring weather in the early 1990s did not favour the Marsh Fritillary. In 1991 it was estimated that there were only two days in its flight period (end May/early June) that could guarantee breeding success (pers.comm. Martin Warren). Research also showed that in this period there were population crashes and extinctions at surrounding sites that probably made up an important "meta-population". The numerical fragility of a small population combined to make a recipe for impending disaster. The only Marsh Fritillary larval web found on the Folly Farm site in the autumn of 1991 was subsequently trampled by livestock after a new (and more appropriate) light winter grazing regime was instituted.

Despite extensive searching, no adults or larval webs were found in 1992. Yet four adults were recorded in 1993, demonstrating how difficult it is to monitor the presence of a species with a low population density. That was the last record for the site. The extinction of the Marsh Fritillary at Folly Farm closely followed that at Wetmoor, South Gloucestershire, where the loss in 1991 was possibly, at least in part, attributed to changes in land management.

Protecting species through the designation and creation of nature reserves is important. All the "best" sites in the region are protected in this way. It has, however, been witnessed at a number of excellent butterfly sites that these oases are not necessarily sustainable. The "lost worlds" of nature reserves have to be viewed in a wider context. The way forward requires an imaginative approach with extensions to reserves using wildlife corridors to link potential habitats.

Habitat creation can be successful provided a source population of butterflies is at hand. An experiment by Yatton and Congresbury Wildlife Action Group (YACWAG) to create field margins suitable as a Barn Owl corridor on its nature reserve in Congresbury, North Somerset, produced unexpected results. A survey recorded over 60 adult Large Skippers in a 150 metre stetch of rough grassland left uncut for three years. Previously the field had been intensively managed including fertiliser application with no margins left ungrazed or uncut. The source population had been extremely small and evidenced by an occasional record for adult butterflies on an adjacent track which had an unmanaged hedge one side. On a wider scale there is considerable potential for improving habitat for species such as the Large Skipper through less intensive roadside and hedge management.

The LBAP process could address these issues. Local authorities and the Highways Agency, for example, are in a good position to influence and improve management for biodiversity. Most flora and fauna face the same problems as butterflies and a reversal of modern trends in management will only come about where large tracts of land, or whole landscapes, are brought under sympathetic management through ownership by conservation bodies or financial incentives to landowners through agri-environmental or woodland management schemes.

Butterflies are beautiful creatures in their own right, but they have extreme value as a high profile indicator of the health of our local natural environment. Their conservation is considered to be nationally important. It is therefore hoped that this publication will put the regional situation into context, particularly highlighting the need for action to prevent further species decline and loss. To this end it is hoped that landowners, planners and regional decision makers will be encouraged to play their part in partnership with conservation organisations and environmental agencies. A garden, hedgerow, field or nature reserve without the sight of a butterfly is a sad place, and in all probability an indicator of a poor place for wildlife generally.

# CHAPTER 4

# Recording Butterflies:
# the history and use of butterfly data

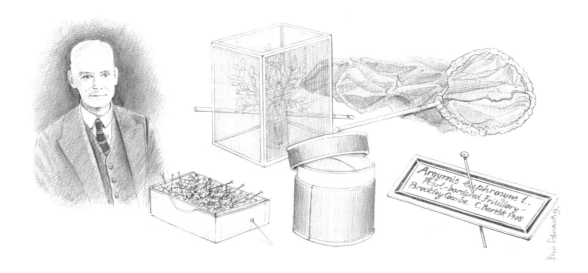

## HISTORY OF BRISTOL REGION COLLECTORS AND RECORDERS

*Ray Barnett*

There is little information available regarding butterfly collecting or recording in the region prior to the 19th century. Perhaps one of the earliest lepidopterists to be resident in the region was Eleanor Glanville (*c*.1654–1709). Although native to Yorkshire, she inherited property including Tickenham Court, situated between Bristol and Clevedon, which became her home. Eleanor Glanville reared butterflies and described the early stages of the High Brown Fritillary and Green-veined White butterflies, for example. The butterfly which bears her name, the Glanville Fritillary, was so called following her capture of specimens in Lincolnshire at the start of the 18th century. Her name has also been perpetuated in entomological circles over the centuries as her will was successfully challenged, after her death,

on the grounds that she had gone insane, one symptom being her interest in insects. The case was heard at Wells Assizes in 1712 and at least one respected entomologist of the day is thought to have testified in her favour, but to no avail (Bristowe, 1967; Salmon, 2000.). When Glanville Fritillaries were released by persons unknown at Sand Point in the 1980s, it is unlikely that they were aware of the close association of the species with the region, not because the butterfly had occurred in the region previously but through the residence of the discoverer of the species in the British Isles.

The early part of the 19th century saw an enormous growth of interest in, and study of, the natural world. Nationally there were a number of societies such as the Entomological Society of Great Britain, and the Linnean Society (based in London) that were developing, shadowed by the formation of many local, natural history societies. Impetus to insect recording in the Bristol region may have been given by the formation of the Museum of the Bristol Literary & Philosophical Institution in 1820 and then the formation of the Somersetshire Archaeological & Natural History Society in 1849 and the Cotteswold Naturalists' Field Club in 1864. However, the main emphasis for both the Museum and the Cotteswold Naturalists' at that time appears to have been the study of geology, following the pioneering work in the region by William Smith, for one. The Museum of the Bristol Institution, forerunner of today's Museum & Art Gallery, did include at that time the lepidoptera collection of Dr John W. Duck author of the 'Natural History of Portishead' but little else relevant to the butterflies of the region. Sadly, the collection has not survived.

It was the establishment of the Bristol Naturalists' Society in 1862 which saw entomology come to the fore in the region. The original seven members of the Society's founding committee included Stephen Barton, F.E.S. (1820–1898) and W. J. Feddon. Barton had collected British lepidoptera and coleoptera in his youth before moving to Australia in 1852 for a few years. On returning to Bristol he pursued mainly a fascination with foreign beetles and held office as President of the Entomological Section of the Society for over thirty years. Barton also acted as honorary curator of the insect collections in the Bristol Museum over a long period. Feddon too was an enthusiast for insect study and also for microscopy.

The high profile of entomology within the Bristol Naturalists' Society resulted in it being the subject of the first 'Section', formed in 1864. George Harding F.E.S. became Secretary of that Entomology Section from 1865 to 1896. He collected lepidoptera, chiefly in the vicinity of Stapleton, north Bristol, and was responsible for a number of observations reported in the Bristol Naturalists' Society Proceedings and the Entomologists' Monthly Magazine. At the start of this period much was already known about the butterflies of the region but the Section began its regular programme of field excursions to local sites such as Leigh Woods and Goblin Combe, for example reporting the Holly Blue as common at the latter locality on 4th June 1866. Over the winter season the Section's meetings included displaying specimens caught during the year, Mr Clarke exhibited a *'nice series'* of the Adonis Blue caught on Durdham Down, Bristol during the summer of 1866.

There is one figure that stands out, head and shoulders above the other members of the Bristol Naturalists' Society Entomology Section in the latter half of the 19th century, that is Alfred E. Hudd, F.S.A., F.E.S. Hudd was a member of the Society from 1864 until his death in 1920. As well as being very active in the field himself, he was responsible for the publication of a 'Catalogue of the Lepidoptera of the Bristol District' in parts within the Proceedings of the Society between 1877 and 1884. The complete list was then re-issued as a separate publication in the latter year. Hudd continued to collect and collate records after this date and his own annotated copy of the complete list is a valuable document still held within the Library of the Bristol Naturalists' Society. Early in the 20th century Hudd also contributed the lists of lepidoptera published in the Victoria County History of Somerset. He was also heavily involved in preparing information on the local lepidopteran fauna for the visits of the British Association to the city in 1875 and 1898. George C. Griffiths when celebrating the Diamond Jubilee of the Entomological Section (Griffiths, 1924) commented: *'Looking through the older records of the Section, one must be struck by the magnificent enthusiasm of its members for collecting locally. Many were the prizes found round Bristol for the first time, and the care bestowed on the* larvae*, and* pupae *enabled fine results to be shown at the meetings, and at the British Association, when at Bristol.'* It was Hudd and Griffiths (1914) who had previously contributed "Fifty Years of Entomology in Bristol", an excellent source of information on the entomologists of the day.

In the latter years of the 19th century there were a number of important figures who contributed their records to Hudd's lists of butterflies of the region. George Weare Braikenridge (1816–1882) amassed a splendid collection of local lepidoptera in the mid 19th century including the Wood White from Clevedon and Tickenham. His collection was given to the Bristol Museum and still exists but unfortunately none of his specimens have data labels on them. (This Braikenridge should not be confused with his father who was one of Bristol's great antiquary collectors and commissioned a stunning collection of watercolours of Bristol in the early years of that century as well as collecting beetles.) Henry and John Bolt, F.V. Jacques, Philip Vaughan, Mr Sircom, Robert Ficklin, W.H. Grigg, R.M. Prideaux F.E.S., Edwin Wheeler, C.J. Watkins F.E.S., F.D. Wheeler F.E.S., J.Mason, Rev. Joseph Greene, Alan Hill and I.W. Clarke were some of the major collectors and recorders of lepidoptera at this time. Perhaps the most famous name in this list is that of the Reverend Joseph Greene, author of 'The Insect Hunter's Companion' of 1870. It is little known that he was resident in Clifton between 1870 and 1890. Another, now well known name is that of Margaret Fountaine whose remarkable life was the subject of the book 'Love among the butterflies' (Cater, 1980). Between about 1893 and 1906 the family home for the Fountaine family was in Bath. However, Margaret Fountaine appears to have lavished all her attention on collecting butterflies in foreign climes at this time and did not herself take up residence in the region (Tony Irwin, pers.comm.).

It was George C. Griffiths F.E.S. who perhaps ranks alongside Alfred Hudd as one of the great names of the time. Griffiths replaced Barton as President of the Entomological Section of the Bristol Naturalists' and went on to hold office from 1899 to 1924. He too took on the mantle of Honorary Curator of the insect collections at Bristol Museum and was responsible, for example, for incorporating the collections from the Smyth family of Ashton Court.

Charles Bartlett did not hold office in the Bristol Naturalists' Society as President of the Entomological Section but as its Secretary, a post he held from 1896 to 1924. He put together an excellent collection of lepidoptera (and coleoptera) which was not donated to the City Museum in Bristol until after the Second World War. In this way it escaped the fate of so many older collections that were lost in the Museum when it was badly damaged by bombing in November 1940, and consequently it is still available for viewing at the Museum. Charles Bartlett lived at Henleaze Avenue in Westbury-on-Trym in Bristol for many years.

Between the two world wars a new generation of lepidopterists emerged. One such was Ian Robert Penicuick Heslop. Ian Heslop was born in India in 1904 but he came to Bristol whilst still young and attended Clifton College

where his interest in butterflies flourished. It was at the tender age of 14 years that he collected a Purple Emperor from Brockley Combe, something few have been able to do. After Cambridge he joined the Colonial Service and served in Nigeria. On vacation he would return to his home in Burnham-on-Sea in Somerset and would travel the country in search of butterflies and his favourite the Purple Emperor. In 1952 he returned to England for good and proceeded to take up a number of teaching posts. His Burnham home meant that he would still occasionally visit sites within the Bristol region, butterfly net in hand. A nationally respected figure he took part in a number of BBC radio broadcasts such as Nature Parliament and the likes of Baron de Worms, another famous name in national entomological circles, would regularly accompany him to favourite spots in summer. However, his report of a Large Blue to the south of Bristol caused considerable controversy. Following his death in 1970 his collection was donated to the Bristol Museum & Art Gallery, later to be re-united with his collecting note books when they too were donated in the 1990s.

The 1920s and 1930s also saw active collecting and study of butterflies by the likes of Alec Hamilton Peach (1875–1960). A series of the Marsh Fritillary taken by Peach in Leigh Woods in 1949 can be seen, for example, in the national collection in the Natural History Museum in London. Peach was President of the Bristol Naturalists' Society between 1951 and 1953 and in 1947 had started the annual reports published in their Proceedings summarising the important butterfly records of the previous year.

C.S.H. Blathwayt (Stephen) (1915–1991) was a dedicated lepidopterist who often visited sites with Cecil E. Bell, for example Leigh Woods and Wetmoor. Stephen Blathwayt's main interest focussed on the larger moths but he also put together an impressive collection of butterflies and holidays were regularly taken in the New Forest and other famous butterfly sites. Blathwayt's pedigree for this hobby was impressive as his father (C. H. Blathwayt) had collected butterflies and his uncle Francis Linley Blathwayt had contributed insect records other than lepidoptera to the Victoria County History of Somerset. The family home, Dyrham Park is now a National Trust property, and is situated to the north of Bath. Stephen lived most of his life in Weston-super-Mare and he continued collecting, particularly moths, up until the early 1980s. His collection and note books were donated to the Bristol Museum & Art Gallery on his death (Accession Number: 36/1991). Cecil Bell, as well as collecting and recording butterflies, took cine film of Marsh Fritillaries at Wetmoor.

During the Second World War the President of the Entomological section of the Bristol Naturalists' was J.W. Norgrove. His extensive collections are now in the Bristol Museum & Art Gallery. Just after the war saw the formation of the Bath Natural History Society which still flourishes. Its magazine for the summer of 1945 included an article on '*Butterflies that may be found in Bath and District*' by H. C. Rainbird and makes interesting comparison with today, Small Skipper being considered rarer than Pearl-bordered Fritillary for example! The Society has continued to include regular reports on the butterflies close to Bath, areas that have often been poorly covered by the Bristol Naturalists' Society.

Another local lepidopterist of considerable note was Norman A. Watkins who was resident of Stoke Bishop, Bristol and served as President of the Bristol Naturalists' Society between 1954 and 1962. He too was very active before the Second World War as well as after it. His collection was very impressive as it contained many fine examples of most British butterflies and remarkable aberrations. Some of his collection he passed to the Watson collection and following his death in the 1970s, the remainder went to the Natural History Museum, London. The former collection has now also been obtained by the Natural History Museum and so the Watkins collection has been re-united.

The archives of the Bristol Naturalists' Society contain a handwritten manuscript listing butterflies seen locally by J.F. Bird. Bird was resident at Redclyffe, Walton Park, Clevedon in the 1940s and 1950s and the list includes reference to his father's interest in butterflies (H.W. Bird).

John Burton worked at the Natural History Unit of the BBC in the 1960s, 70s and 80s and as well as being the author of The Oxford Book of Insects wrote the butterfly report in the Bristol Naturalists' Society Proceedings from 1962 until 1964.

Derek Foxwell began his long career as taxidermist and natural history conservator at Bristol Museum & Art Gallery in the early 1960s. As well as curating and conserving butterfly collections there, he also contributed important records, particularly in the 1960s. He too edited the butterfly report of the Bristol Naturalists' for a number of years.

Andrew D.R. Brown remembers many of the butterfly enthusiasts who were active postwar such as Norman Watkins. Brown made a significant contribution to study of the butterflies of the region by summarising the state of knowledge (again the area around Bristol both to the north and south, rather than the vice-counties) firstly in the proceedings of the Bristol Naturalists' Society, and then in a series of papers in the Entomologist's Record & Journal of Variation published in 1971.

Douglas Gordon Gibb was another butterfly collector in the 1940s, 1950s and 1960s. He lived at Patchway and Almondsbury during this time and collected for example at Patchway Woods which disappeared under developments in the 1960s. His collection was donated to the Bristol Museum & Art Gallery by his son in 1994 (Acc. No. 77/1994). Ken Poole and the late E. (Dixie) Dean, long time residents of Weston-super-Mare mainly collected and studied moths but, as with most moth recorders, also took an interest in the butterflies.

Since the 1970s and 1980s a number of names became synonymous with butterfly recording such as Graham Best and Barry Harper along with Geoff Sorrell, Bob Rowe and Trevor Silcocks, all members of the Bristol Naturalists' Society. At this time, Bryan Moore was acting as butterfly recorder for the Bath Natural History Society.

The 1970s also saw the formation of regional groups of the British Butterfly Conservation Society (now just called Butterfly Conservation). Gloucestershire has long been covered by Guy Meredith and hence as well as taking a leading role in that organisation, he contributed the butterfly section of the list of Macrolepidoptera of Gloucestershire (including North Avon) published in 1984. He has continued to produce maps and collate records for the county. The other local group that has been set up under Butterfly Conservation was the West Country branch. Originally encompassing Avon, Somerset and

Wiltshire, the latter county established a branch of its own during the late 1990s. West Country Branch of Butterfly Conservation manages a butterfly reserve at Bannerdown north of Bath, a haunt of the Chalkhill Blue.

A butterfly recorder who has added much information over many years has been Chris Wiltshire. A native to the region and researcher at the Long Ashton Research Station, he has studied butterflies, in particular at Wetmoor and the Lower Woods Reserve in South Gloucestershire. Chris has compiled species records for this reserve and carried out a transect survey for 15 years. He is expert in other insect identification, in particular beetles. He is a committee member of the Avon Butterfly Project.

The early 1980s saw the formation of the Avon Wildlife Trust which now owns, manages and has responsibility for many important sites for butterflies. It was that decade which also saw much activity within the Bristol Museum & Art Gallery where the Bristol Regional Environmental Records Centre (BRERC) had been set up and developed. Employed as staff and as volunteers with BRERC were a number of active recorders such as Andy Pym, and Lawrence Way, Ian Looker and Nick Lear. The Common Butterfly Survey of the 1980s was a scheme developed by BRERC which primarily aimed to raise the public profile of natural history recording, the Record Centre's work and the need for conservation of the environment as well as providing base data on the occurrence and abundance of a select few species. By definition it did not directly contribute to knowledge of the rarer species but as a means of promoting focussed interest in the local environment and harnessing the enormous potential of the general interest in butterflies it was extremely successful. Undoubtedly this led to a small number of individuals developing what had been a low key interest in butterflies into something more serious and of value to nature conservation and research.

The 1980s were also notable for an apparent flurry of activity in some circles of breeding and then releasing of captive bred butterflies into sites around the region. The major example is the release and establishment of the colony of the Glanville Fritillary at Sand Point. This is thought to be just one example of this practice which has gained much attention

because it was successful when so many other releases were not.

A.H. Weeks, known to all as John, was a Civil Servant who retired to Yatton in the 1970s and so was able to give his time to his hobby of watching butterflies. As well as making many important observations and records, his interest in the climate resulted in an annual report in the Bristol Naturalists' Proceedings from the 1980s until his death in 2000, linking insect activity to weather conditions. For a period in the 1980s and 1990s the expert micro-lepidopterist, David Aggasiz, lived at Dolebury on the southern edge of this recording region and submitted occasional butterfly sightings along with copious moth records.

Since the formation of the Avon Wildlife Trust (AWT) in the 1980s, as previously mentioned, it has consistently worked for the conservation of butterflies primarily by the purchase of its own nature reserves or through management agreements over other sites. Members of staff have contributed many important sightings of butterflies in this time and acquired considerable expertise and knowledge. AWT has played an extremely important role in focussing the conservation movement through its large membership. A majority of the best sites for butterflies are now AWT Nature Reserves or in joint management *e.g.* Wetmoor (joint with Gloucestershire Wildlife Trust). Conservation Officers at various times have played a significant role in butterfly conservation most recently John Martin (now with Department of Environment, Farming & Rural Affairs) and Tim McGrath. Rupert Higgins and Dawn Lawrence, independent ecological surveyors but also closely involved with AWT, have established an extremely broad knowledge of the wildlife of the region including the butterfly fauna.

As so often happens, individuals who are motivated to work or volunteer in the conservation movement become involved in most of the bodies coordinating this work. For example, Tony Moulin is a founder member of the Avon Butterfly Project and was Vice Chair of Avon Wildlife Trust from 1990–1996. His interest in surveying the butterflies of Folly Farm ultimately led him, with Philippa Burrell, then Manager of BRERC, to formulate the Project's aims and objects. His transect work at Folly Farm resulted in the rediscovery of Marsh

Fritillary in 1991 and 1993, and to add a further four species to the site's species list. He now manages part of the Cheddar Valley Railway Local Nature Reserve and has established a local registered conservation charity which has purchased land to create a nature reserve on Biddle Street SSSI. Philippa Burrell was closely involved in butterfly recording from the early 1980s until she left the region and notably summarised the status of the Marsh Fritillary in the mid 1990s.

Andrew Daw has had a life long interest in butterflies and been a contributor to the local recording schemes for many years. He has been an active member of the West Country branch of Butterfly Conservation and is a committee member of the Avon Butterfly Project. Kurt Vickery was a founder member of the Project, which benefited from his wealth of knowledge and skill as a butterfly photographer. Ray Barnett has curated the entomology collections at Bristol City Museum & Art Gallery since 1989. He started studying insects at an early age in Warwickshire, before first contributing records from the Bristol region as an undergraduate between 1979 and 1982. He has participated in many butterfly recording schemes including those in Warwickshire, Suffolk and Leicestershire. He has been a committee member of the Avon Butterfly Project since its inception and began the Bristol & District Moth Group.

The 1990s and start of the 21st century has seen much activity and notable recorders. Examples of individuals who have contributed many and important observations are Pat and Malcolm Oliver who have enthusiastically contributed regular records of butterfly species and their abundance on Cadbury Hill (Yatton/ Congresbury) Iron Age Hill Fort since 1993. The only previous significant recording on this site had been carried out by John Weeks in the 1980s. Their recording work resulted in the rediscovery of Brown Argus, Silver-washed Fritillary, White-letter Hairstreak and Wall Brown. A highlight was the observation of Small Copper albino aberrant in 1996. Jean Webb is a retired teacher who has regularly surveyed Dolebury Warren since the beginning of the project in 1991 and submitted an immense amount of information and data about this very important site. Keith Giles is responsible for the management of Walton Common SSSI, Avon

Wildlife Trust Reserve, and has set up a well established regular transect.

As well as the Project survey contributors themselves, other important contributions have been made by professional surveyors such as Martin Evans, Sarah Myles, Janet Boyd, Tony Robinson and Dave Gibbs (not to be confused with the earlier D.G.Gibb). The first three in particular have done much to improve the amount and quality of data from South Gloucestershire as part of commissioned survey work. Tony Robinson carried out regular transect work at Leigh Woods whilst working there as Warden for English Nature from the 1980s to the end of the 1990s. Dave Gibb concentrates on insects other than the well known butterflies but inevitably has recorded the latter as and when appropriate. Records and ecological data have also been obtained as a result of studies undertaken as part of University studies. Jerry Board carried out a detailed analysis of the habitat requirements of the Small Blue on Dolebury Warren and Rachel Corlett studied the impact of habitat management at Leigh Woods on butterfly populations.

Inevitably, in compiling such a list as this, individuals who perhaps should have been mentioned have been accidentally omitted, my apologies to all those such people.

## History of the Avon Butterfly Project

*Tony Moulin*

*The Common Butterfly Survey*

The roots of the Avon Butterfly Project lay in an earlier popular recording scheme, the Common Butterfly Survey. This was envisaged as a five year project, based at the City Museum and Art Gallery and administered by the Bristol Regional Environmental Records Centre (BRERC), which at that time was solely funded through Bristol Museums Service.

In the early years the Survey was funded by contracts from the Manpower Services Commission (M.S.C.), which provided for one full time and one part time surveyor. Later sponsorship came from other sources, including national initiatives of the World Wildlife Fund and Heinz Guardians of the Countryside scheme. The popularity of the Survey was evident with a peak of nearly 300 recorders. In just one year, 1988, the Common Butterfly Survey collected over 30,000 records – more data than the whole of the national network at that time. There is no doubt that it would have carried on beyond 1988 if funding had been available but the cessation of the M.S.C. scheme resulted in the Survey folding. Recorders were asked to continue to send in their records to BRERC. The Common Butterfly Survey had encouraged a lot of people to look at seven common species but other species had also been recorded and many were inspired to carry on with their recording work. However, it was not until 1991 that the Avon Butterfly Project was conceived, largely by Tony Moulin and Philippa Burrell, to carry on systematic regional recording throughout the then County of Avon.

It was decided that it would be good to resurrect a butterfly recording scheme but on a broader basis and with broader objectives. The Common Butterfly Survey had encouraged people to look at butterflies in their own back yards, but a need had also been identified to monitor butterflies at more sensitive sites, particularly rarer species. It had also been appreciated that there would be benefits if butterflies could be used as indicators of the health and status of habitats and to use this as a management tool to measure improvements in habitat management.

The Avon Wildlife Trust amongst its 27 reserves had some of the real butterfly hotspots yet there was no regular recording and BRERC itself had no regular input of data for these sites. So a project with a broader base, encompassing not only common butterflies but also encouraging people to go out and monitor butterfly populations elsewhere in the area, was considered to be a good idea.

## The Avon Butterfly Project

It had been realised that a lot of the richness of the butterfly diversity was showing serious signs of decline. The problem was that there was not enough detailed local information to help management of existing populations. Reliable and complete records were essential in this process, so the need to set up a more comprehensive database was considered the most important step, with the ultimate aim of producing a ten year atlas.

Tony Moulin and Philippa Burrell set out the project's broad aims and objectives and on 8th March 1991 a group of people were invited to consider the feasibility of the project. The meeting was held in the Jacobs Wells Road Avon Wildlife Trust offices with representatives from the Avon Wildlife Trust, Butterfly Conservation, BRERC and the Bristol City Museum and Art Gallery. The result was an enthusiastic endorsement of the need to set up the Avon Butterfly Project. The agreed aims and objectives are listed below:

### Purpose
*To co-ordinate the collection and collation of data on the butterfly populations of Avon and adjacent areas in order to further their conservation.*

### Aims
- *To encourage and assist all persons who have an interest in butterfly recording*
- *To build on present recording work and the work previously carried out through the Common Butterfly Survey*
- *To establish regular surveying at priority sites*
- *To monitor the status of rarer species*
- *To produce a full Butterfly Distribution Atlas by the year 2000.*

*Records can make a valuable contribution to:*
- *influencing land management plans at existing nature reserves and other sites of importance for butterflies*
- *identifying butterfly sites which need protection*
- *assisting in strategic local and country planning decisions*
- *national recording schemes.*

*The project will provide training as necessary including:*
- *identification workshops*
- *instruction in recording and field*

*techniques*
- *the opportunity to shadow an experienced recorder on site*
- *field meetings at special sites.*

*The project can also offer participants:*

- *access to existing records and to Bristol Museum's extensive collections*
- *the opportunity to gain detailed knowledge of a particular site and contribute that knowledge to key conservation reports*
- *annual feedback on the progress of the project.*

The Avon Butterfly Project committee was designed to have a diverse group of representatives to also include English Nature and the local authorities. This was considered very important in view of the broader objectives, particularly in relation to influencing decisions on habitat management in sites across the region. The original committee and subsequent membership is shown below.

The project aimed to improve and fill gaps in the information which existed about Avon's butterflies. It was not intended to replace the work of any groups or individuals. Indeed it was seen as a means of creating a more effective network. It soon became apparent that there were data sets held by a number of individuals and other groups and even within the Avon Wildlife Trust that had never been put into a centralised database.

The aim of the project was to provide a structure that would make the best use of local knowledge of butterflies to enable active conservation of sites and particular species. The importance of involving all interested people was recognised and therefore the project would be open to non-experts and established recorders alike. The project group arranged for a launch on Thursday 2nd May 1991 at the Ashton Court Visitor Centre. The launch included brief presentations by all the parties forming the project together with an opportunity for questions. Invitations had been sent out to all previous Common Butterfly Survey recorders, members of Bristol Naturalists' Society, Amateur Entomologists Society and the British Entomological and Natural History Society members. As a result, 35 people attended the

launch. 240 questionnaires had been sent out with the invitation and by June 1991 60 people had declared an interest in the project.

Since its inception the Project has had an active committee who have helped with various aspects including record validation and verification, writing the newsletter, organising field trips, identification workshops and arranging the AGM. The administration, record transcription, data entry and retrieval have been provided by BRERC. In particular mention must be made of Ralph Stabb who single-handedly has inputted a large percentage of the butterfly data. A recording pack was produced containing a variety of forms. One allowed regular recording on one site and another allowed for more detailed records for single site visits. The newsletter and AGM provided a means of updating recorders on any trends and information and amendments to the recording process.

Some of the field trips organised by the committee had an aim to target particular sites where regular butterfly monitoring was considered to be crucial. Invitations were therefore given to people to set up transects, in particular work on Dolberrow (Dolebury Warren) and Walton Common. A set of field visits with training in identification and monitoring was also offered.

As the project gained momentum after a couple of years the recorders were encouraged to record in kilometre squares where records had not been submitted. Also the project encouraged other agencies and recorders to release records that had been held before, some pre-dating the project, to help complete BRERC's historic records. The Avon Butterfly Project, together with the Avon Flora Project, which had been very active in the 1980s, have formed part of a strategy to develop active recording in the region. Other groups set up at about the same time as the Butterfly Project cover moths, hoverflies, reptiles & amphibia and more recently dragonflies and grasshoppers and crickets.

The Avon Butterfly Project has proved to be a worthy successor to the Common Butterfly Survey with approximately 200 active recorders. It has collected approaching 70,000 records in its ten plus years. The recorders who have carried out a regular transect over a number of sites and have provided detailed information giving a good insight into butterfly trends. A list of recorders who have contributed records for the Avon Butterfly Project is given in the acknowledgements section of this book.

It is hoped that the momentum that the Avon Butterfly Project has provided will continue beyond its first ten years shown in this publication.

*Common Butterfly Survey*
*Staff/Co-ordinators*

| | |
|---|---|
| Neale Mellersh | 1982–5 |
| Andrew Hawkins | 1982–6 |
| Geoff Carey | 1986 |
| Steve Manning | 1986–8 |
| Tony Murphy | 1987–8 |
| Andy Pym | 1988–9 |
| Philippa Burrell | 1988–9 |

*The original Avon Butterfly Project steering group*

Philippa Burrell (BRERC)
Cathy Wilson (BRERC)
Ray Barnett (Bristol City Museum and Art Gallery)*
Tony Moulin*
Antony Merritt (AWT)
Kurt Vickery (Butterfly Conservation)

Ten further years of the project also saw the following people as active committee members:

Phil Tolerton (Woodspring District Council)
Lisa Best (BRERC)
Chris Wiltshire
John Martin (AWT)
Simon Christian (English Nature)
Karen Turvey (BRERC)
Martin Evans (BRERC)
Jerry Board*
Sarah Myles (BRERC)
Stephen Parker (English Nature)
Rachel Corlett (BRERC)
Andrew Daw
Tim Corner (BRERC)

* current and past Butterfly Conservation West Country Branch Recorders

# USING THE AVON BUTTERFLY PROJECT DATA

*Roger Edmondson*

Many of us keep a log of our butterfly sightings. Some people record every species they see in a particular place and how many on each date. Others go further and record what the insect was doing. Some people note every butterfly they see throughout the year, the species, the number, the time, the air temperature, everything. Some just record interesting sightings, when they can. Embarrassingly, the writers lean towards the latter end of this scale but the point is, we all, and if you are reading this, that includes you, notice and take an interest in butterflies. If you write it down somewhere, or log it in something, then you have created a record. The question then is, what happens to that record?

In some instances, nothing happens to it. Some people note it down somewhere for their own interest along with the garden bird list and that is where it remains. Many others however, wish to create something more from their sightings. They have had the pleasure from seeing the insect and it is duly noted in their own diary or notebook and entered on their lists but who can you tell? Where can it go that it might have some significance?

The short and sweet answer is, us. The Bristol Regional Environmental Records Centre or to save time, BRERC.

BRERC want all of those records. The detailed ones. The occasional ones. If it was recorded in the Bristol region (the old county of Avon) we want it!

The question then remains, what do we do with it? The first thing we do is verify it. That sounds posh but all it means is we check it to see if the details appear to be correct. A basic tool in recording sightings is an Ordinance Survey Map. You and we need to know where you saw the butterfly. We check the Grid Reference or work one out if you haven't given us one to ensure the location is where you say it is. We look at the record to see if it is unusual or indeed, just plain wrong. That is a very rare occurrence, but Purple Emperors in a Bishopston garden are unusual. Either an identification mistake has occurred or someone is releasing them or a little more tonic is required in the gin.

We check the date. Butterflies have well known flight times and records a long way outside of that are unusual. It does happen though and we try to find out what is going on. Is it a second brood or an unusually early spring? We receive quite a few January records of hairstreaks and although it does not always say so, it nearly always transpires that someone has found the eggs.

Once verified, the details are transferred to the BRERC computer database. The species, the date, the number seen, the sex of the insect, how it was recorded, the grid reference and location, the recorder or recorders, a possible determiner, a reference number and a confirmation code. You may wonder what some of those are?

The first four are self-evident. For example; Purple Emperor, 03/February/2002, seven males. How it was recorded asks whether they were netted or seen in the field or what other method of recording was used. The grid reference is entered and a location should appear as a cross- reference. If not, then it's back to the maps. The recorders name or names is put in. A determiner means that if for instance a photograph has been taken and the species identified by someone else, their name is recorded. The reference number is an internal number so that we can trace the original paper document in future. The confirmation code is either 1, 2 or 3. The first means we have no reason to doubt the record and this applies to 99.9% of all records received. You say you saw an Orange-tip. It is the right time of year and the right place and we have no reason to doubt it. The second number means we do doubt it and it needs confirmation. Those seven fictitious Purple Emperors are very doubtful and need to be checked out before being accepted. The third number means we know the record is wrong. Someone else saw my Purple Emperors and confirmed that they were Starlings.

Once the record has been put in we have to check it again. We put hundreds of records on at a time and mistakes can occur. Someone different now checks that the data has been entered properly. All of this is time consuming but with the help of our volunteers we are managing to ensure a steady build-up of reliable data that can safely be used. We now

have hundreds of thousands of records on the database.

Now that we have this database of records, of what use is it? The records you submit sit alongside many others submitted by individual recorders, professional environmental surveyors, landowners, students, interest groups such as Bristol Ornithological Club and the Bristol Naturalists' Society and agencies such as English Nature, Environment Agency and the Avon Wildlife Trust. Together these build up a profile of which butterflies, birds, plants and other taxa exist in a given location. BRERC attaches further information to each record such as the local, regional and national status and distribution within 'Avon' of the species.

These records are then linked to the Geographical Information System (GIS) in use at BRERC, *MapInfo*, a powerful computerised mapping database. This allows BRERC to instantly map each record and to overlay them onto habitat, geological and sites information, also entered by BRERC. The mapped data can then be linked to other programs and databases that BRERC uses, such as three dimensional mapping and digital aerial photography. This enables a wide variety of ways and formats to analyse and present the data.

BRERC also holds an estimated several million records, in paper format, that date back to the nineteenth century.

These data holdings, computer and paper, are made available to, and are used by, all sectors of society for a multitude of purposes. Examples of purposes to which the data is used include; habitat and species management; informing the planning process and development control; background information for articles; ecological research into the requirements of species and habitats; strategic planning for biodiversity at national, regional and local levels; education; emergency planning; contaminated land strategies and pollution control.

Users include all of the wildlife agencies and groups in our region; local authorities; education establishments; community groups; professional ecologists and geologists; national bodies and organisations such as Joint Nature Conservation Committee, Butterfly Conservation, National Trust and the BBC; landowners; historians and the public. BRERC is an integral part of the National

Biodiversity Network and helped to develop the policies and standards that the network operates to.

All of this is made possible because people recorded something and passed the record on.

As a neutral umbrella organisation we are able to draw the recorders and users of information together.

There is a long tradition of our region being a centre for recording data and producing publications thereafter. Let's hope this will continue far into the future.

# CHAPTER 5
# Species Accounts

## *Ray Barnett*

The following species accounts have been compiled by reference to the known historic references (often reproduced verbatim), notebooks, local expertise and data on museum specimens, to build up a picture of the history of butterflies in the region. Species considered to have been reported in error are included for completeness. The results of the current (1991 onwards) Avon Butterfly Project survey are discussed to give a picture of the current status of those species known to be present.

The photographs of butterflies have been selected, wherever possible, from images actually taken within the Bristol region. Where this is so, the locality, date and photographer are given if known. If outside the Bristol region only the photographer is acknowledged. The region is blessed with a number of excellent insect photographers, apologies to them that some superb photographs were not selected because of the desire to show those actually taken in the region rather than elsewhere in the British Isles.

In cases where the butterfly species is now considered extinct in the region, or there are no recent (within ten years) records or the species is a rare migrant, then line drawings by Andrew Daw have been used to illustrate the species, rather than photographs.

The distribution maps and the graphs showing flight times, have been produced by the Bristol Regional Environmental Records Centre (BRERC) from the Avon Butterfly Project survey data using the *MapInfo* GIS system. Six figure and four figure grid references have both been plotted to show the distribution of the species at a glance. Historic

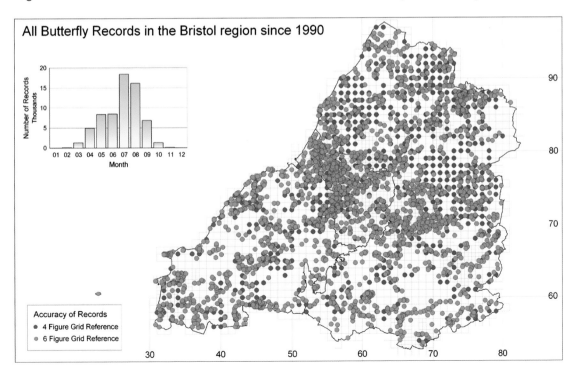

All Butterfly Records in the Bristol region since 1990

records (prior to 1990) have not been mapped.) The number of records including detail of the numbers of an individual species seen has not been considered sufficient to warrant plotting population densities on the maps or to plot numbers of individuals (rather than number of records) on the phenology graphs. (Records of ova, larvae and pupae have been omitted for obvious reasons from the graphs.) Encouraging more recorders to report numbers seen, may be one way in which the quality of data received may be improved as the Avon Butterfly project continues to monitor butterfly populations in the coming years.

The species are listed in the taxonomic order, and with the scientific names given, in the 'Checklist of lepidoptera recorded from the British Isles' by J.D. Bradley published in 2000 as the second, revised edition.

# HESPERIDAE

## Chequered Skipper   *Carterocephalus palaemon* (Pallas)

**National status: Resident, only in Western Scotland, extinct in England.**
**Bristol region status: Recorded in error in 19th century.**

The possibility of the existence of this species in the region was raised by its inclusion in a list of butterflies published in the Bath Handbook in 1888 (Morris, 1888). Following that, Hudd, in his annotated copy of his 1884 publication, noted that this inclusion had probably been in error. In the Victoria County History of Somerset, Hudd (1906) again included the record citing the author as Dr Terry who reported it as '*rare near Bath*', again Hudd expressed his doubt that the record was genuine but did note that a single specimen had been recorded in Gloucestershire. However, in his annotations to the 1884 list he had already recorded that two specimens (supposedly from Gloucestershire) were in the collection of C.J.Watkins. In the twentieth century Turner (1955) dismissed the Somerset (Bath) record and Meredith (1984) dismissed the two specimens in the Watkins collection, supposedly from Moreton-in-Marsh (outside the Bristol region), as probably not being Gloucestershire

specimens anyway.

Emmet & Heath (1989) indicate that this butterfly is thought to have occurred on the south coast of England and in the south west peninsula prior to the beginning of the twentieth century, away from its major stronghold in the East Midlands. It is well known that this butterfly became extinct as an English species in the mid-1970s but continues as a British species thanks to the colonies discovered on the west coast of Scotland at the end of the 1930s and in the 1940s.

Although it would seem that the larval foodplant, usually given as False Brome grass *Brachypodium sylvaticum* in England, would have been present in the favoured habitat, woodland glades and rides, there is no evidence to support the record listed in the Bath Handbook. Other environmental factors may explain its absence from apparently suitable habitat. Whatever the reason, there is no confirmed record for the region.

## Small Skipper *Thymelicus sylvestris* (Poda)

**National status: Common resident in England and Wales.**
**Bristol region status: Common and widespread.**

Martin Evans 29th June 1989

**Small Skipper** Chlorine Works at Frampton Cotterell

Hudd's comment in 1884 is interesting in that he states '*Local, and not common in the district.*' He also adds in a later annotation: '*Near Clevedon by the Rev. H. Tanner & Mr J. Mason. in litt. Rare.*' and then '*Used to be common in Leigh Woods and near Failand. RMP 1885.*' This suggestion that the butterfly was perhaps not as widespread as we always consider it must have been, is refined by Hudd in the Victoria County History of Somerset (1906) when he writes '*Common in some places but local*' and gives sightings as '*Bath, Bathampton, Clevedon, Leigh Woods and Weston*' within the Bristol region. Subsequent authors have never echoed this sentiment, all have considered it to be common, of frequent occurrence and often abundant. Perhaps the early observation reflects a relative reduction in its occurrence at the time and that com-

pared to many other species it still remained common. Certainly Brown in 1971, states '*occurs in any suitable habitat...including several localities within Bristol City itself*' and then '*nearly always common where it is found, and is frequently quite abundant.*'

The habitat for this small tawny coloured butterfly is rough grassland where the larvae will feed on Yorkshire Fog *Holcus lanatus*, or perhaps False Brome *Brachypodium sylvaticum* and Timothy Grass *Phleum pratense*, for example. All these grasses are common and widespread in the region (Myles *et al*, 2000) and so the butterfly is able to colonise many localities including woodland edge and rides, downs, roadside verges and even gardens. The current survey shows the butterfly to be fairly evenly distributed across the region and seems to reflect the distribution of

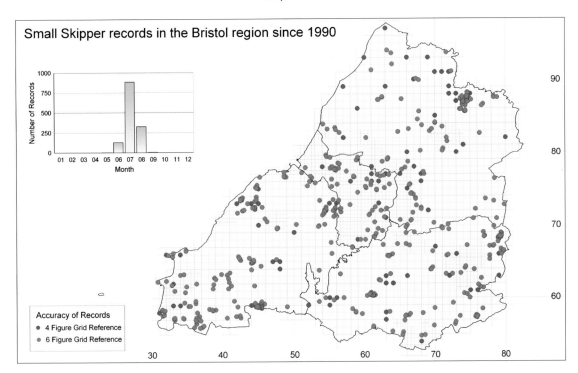

Small Skipper records in the Bristol region since 1990

recorders and recording effort. This would suggest that the Small Skipper may be encountered almost anywhere and continues to be widespread and common like its larval foodplants. The phenological data shows a small number emerging from late May through June in some years and then reaching a peak of emergence in mid-July before tailing off through August. In this respect the time of peak emergence follows that of the Large Skipper but is very close to that of the Essex Skipper. However, the sample for the Essex Skipper is very small. It is very likely that colonies of the Essex Skipper are hidden within records of the Small Skipper. The national survey of butterflies (Asher *et al*, 2001) suggests that the butterfly has expanded its range northwards in recent decades but makes the point that overall numbers may have dropped as available habitat has declined.

## Essex Skipper    *Thymelicus lineola* (Ochs.)

**National status: A common resident in south east England, thought to be expanding its range north and westwards.**
**Bristol region status: Occasional in the past, apparently increasing and establishing itself as a resident in small colonies since the 1990s.**

Andrew Daw   24th July 1994

**Essex Skipper** (showing all black tips to antennae)

This butterfly is not listed in Hudd's *Catalogue of the Lepidoptera of the Bristol District* (1877–1884) as it was only recognised as part of the British fauna in 1889. At that date specimens from East Anglia, at first thought just to be forms of the very similar Small Skipper, were recognised as being a distinct species (Hawes, 1890). However Hudd's later annotations to his manuscript, held in the Bristol Naturalists' Society Library, include a quote from Barrett's *Lepidoptera of the British Isles* Volume I, '*Two old specimens were found by Mr Barrett in the collection of the British Butterflies in Taunton Museum which had almost certainly been taken in the West of England.*' Hudd expanded on this in the Victoria County History of

Somerset (1906) stating that '*A specimen in the Taunton Museum collection was said to have been taken in the neighbourhood by the late Mr Rawlinson of that town (Bidgood).*'

Turner (1955), as well as again repeating this apparent Taunton record, reports '*recently been found to inhabit the north-eastern part of the county. [Somerset] Hinton Charterhouse (J.A.J.S.) 1947, 1952.*' [J.A.J. Smith of Bradford-on-Avon.] Meredith (1984) however, knows of no records for Gloucestershire and Brown (1971) has no records for the Bristol region. Moore (1975) recorded '*a small colony in the Hinton Charterhouse/Wellow area in 1972*'. He also stated: '*I have made extensive searches around Bath over a number of years* but this is the only colony which I have been able to locate.'

The Essex Skipper was found to be common in the south east corner of England, following its discovery at the end of the 19th century (it has always been widespread in continental Europe). This discovery, coupled with its name and the difficulty in distinguishing it from the Small Skipper, may have led to the false assumption that it only occurred in the south east. In fact it is likely that it has long existed at low concentrations across southern England, perhaps waxing and waning with changing environmental conditions. The undoubted concentration of the species in the south east is typical of a thermophilic species, one that flourishes where the climate is closer to that of mainland Europe, particularly with its hotter, drier summers. It represents a population that invaded the British Isles at a late stage after the retreat of the ice following the last ice age but before the land bridge to Europe was lost isolating our fauna.

Since the late 1980s there seems to have been a movement north and west of the species out of its traditional stronghold (Asher *et al*, 2001) but the evidence seems to suggest that it has been present in the Bristol region in very low numbers in the past. In addition to the Hinton Charterhouse record from the 1940s and 1950s, the collection of the late Ian Heslop, held at the City Museum & Art Gallery, Bristol, (Accession Number 226/1970) contains three specimens (numbers 2831–2833) caught on the 1st July 1929 on the '*Gordano moors*', south west of Bristol.

The first post-war records from the region that are known are from Weston-super-Mare Golf Course sometime between 1976 and 1982 and from Wetmoor as part of a Bristol Naturalists' Society survey, again around the end of the 1970s or early 1980s. Since then the current survey has produced records from over a dozen different sites. It includes a modern record from Hinton Charterhouse, forty-nine years after Smith's original sighting.

Records from the 1990s onwards are from a variety of rough grassland localities ranging from the unimproved *e.g.* Walton Common, to disused railway lines and surrounding fields. There is a strong concentration of the species in the east of the region, supporting the idea of increasing numbers invading from that direction. The larval foodplants Cock's-foot *Dactylis glomerata*, Creeping Soft-grass *Holcus mollis* and False Brome *Brachypodium sylvaticum* are widespread and common in the area (Myles et al, 2000).

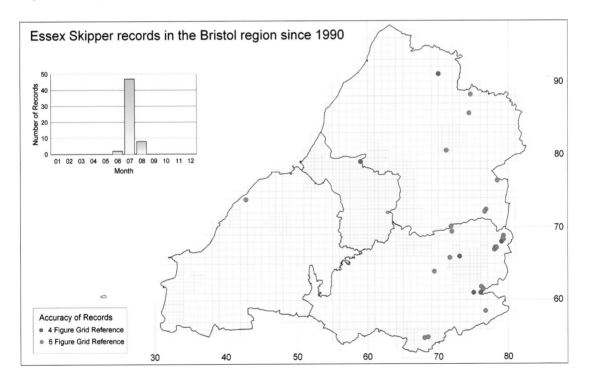

Essex Skipper records in the Bristol region since 1990

Accuracy of Records
● 4 Figure Grid Reference
● 6 Figure Grid Reference

Emmet & Heath (1989) suggest that this butterfly peaks in emergence later than the Small Skipper in mid to late August, although it is common for them both to be on the wing at the same time. The data from the Bristol Region survey does not support this, with the Essex Skipper peaking in late July and early August, but the sample is very small which may explain it.

In summary, it seems that the Essex Skipper has been present in the region in the past, perhaps maintaining low numbers masked by the much commoner, and very similar, Small Skipper. From the end of the 1980s and in the 1990s numbers have increased in line with the national trend, possibly due to milder winters and warmer summers during this time. The distribution map indicates that this increase is taking place from the east and south east as the national population expands from its

strongholds in that part of the country. This makes it a very interesting species for future monitoring and as a possible contribution to the body of evidence regarding the phenomenon of global climate change. Will this butterfly continue to be reported at new sites and in greater abundance? If so will it be possible to link that to national trends in population changes? Will the Essex Skipper replace and out compete the Small Skipper at some sites? Already at one site, Bathampton Meadows, in 1999 it was apparently commoner than the Small Skipper and that at a site that had been re-graded and sown with wild flower mix in 1997 or 1998 (J. Martin pers. comm.)! Furthermore, observations on its life cycle may help to establish exactly how the development of the butterfly in any of its stages is restricted by low temperatures, if indeed this is the reason for its limited distribution.

# Silver-spotted Skipper  *Hesperia comma* (Linn.)

**National status: A rare resident of south and south east England.**
**Bristol region status: An extinct resident, last recorded in the 19th century.**

A butterfly of closely grazed, unimproved calcareous grassland currently concentrated on the chalk outcrops of the south and south east of England, for example on the Chilterns. Emmet & Heath (1989) try to disentangle the early records of this butterfly from the Large Skipper. Confusion was generated by the application of the scientific name *comma* to both species in the 18th century. They suggest that the Silver-spotted Skipper was rare in southern England in the 18th century but became commoner in the 19th. This may explain why the only records from the Bristol region are those recorded by Hudd (1884) as '*"Among insects from Weston, and taken there I think. PHV". Mr Robt. Last is reported to have taken several specimens at Brockley in 1872.*' To this Hudd has later added the annotation: '*Near Clevedon by the Rev. H. Tanner in litt.*' In the Victoria County History of Somerset (1906), Hudd added "*Bath (Terry)*", to the reports from Brockley, Clevedon and Weston-super-Mare. But it is not on the list in the Bath Handbook (Morris, 1888).

In the 20th century the butterfly declined, particularly in the latter decades, perhaps correlated to the crash in rabbit populations with the myxomatosis epidemic which led to a reduction in its favoured short, limestone turf. In the last fifteen years or so of that century the butterfly staged a recovery due to careful management of the sites and the recovery of the rabbit populations (Asher *et al*, 2001). The larvae feed on Sheep's Fescue *Festuca ovina* on closely grazed sites, again it is a thermophilic species like the Essex Skipper. The prospect of an increase in populations, given a potential rise in average temperatures through global climate change, is tempered by the continued disappearance and isolation of suitably grazed unimproved calcareous grassland. The butterfly is not thought to have very good powers of dispersal. As a result it would seem very unlikely that the butterfly could become once again established in this region, even at low levels.

# Large Skipper   *Ochlodes faunus* (Turati)

**National status: Common and widespread in England, Wales and south west Scotland.
Bristol region status: Common and widespread.**

Nigel Milbourne   8th July 2001

**Large Skipper**   Mendip Hills

On the face of it the status of this species has not changed in over one hundred years. Hudd (1884) regarded it as '*generally distributed and common*' and, in so many words, that is how it has been reported ever since. Brown (1971) differs slightly in drawing a distinction between this and the Small Skipper placing the latter as overall more widely distributed and common. To state today that the butterfly is still generally distributed and common would be not to acknowledge how our fauna has been reduced in those one hundred years since Hudd and that the two identical statements are not really comparable.

The current survey has revealed that the butterfly is widespread and there is some evidence to suggest that numbers may have increased at the regularly surveyed sites, towards the end of the 1990s. The number of records received is very similar to that for the Small Skipper and the localities where it has been reported from are also very similar, no doubt reflecting recorder bias. But there seems to be little cause for concern over this butterfly.

This is the first of the orangey-brown, summer-time skippers to appear on the wing, in some years it can be seen in the last few days of May, being joined by the Small Skipper in late June and the Essex Skipper in July. All three can be on the wing together as the Large Skipper can persist into August but it is at its most abundant in June and July.

The larval foodplants usually quoted are Cock's-foot *Dactylis glomerata* and False Brome *Brachypodium sylvaticum*, both are very common in the region (Myles et al, 2000).

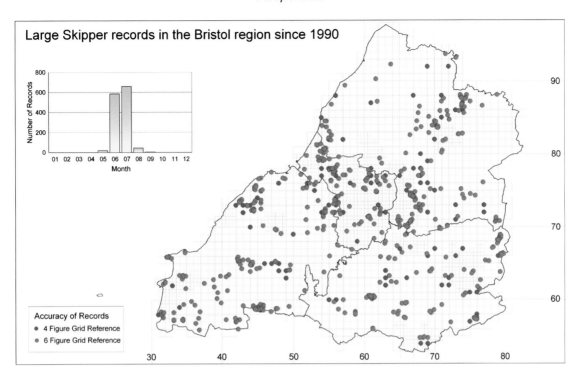

Large Skipper records in the Bristol region since 1990

Woodland edges and rides, meadows and hedgerows, indeed almost anywhere the larval grasses can grow unchecked, can support the butterfly. However, the butterfly can be frequent on sites where neither of these grasses is common and so it is likely to be using an alternative food source. Examples are grasslands dominated by Upright Brome *Bromopsis erecta e.g.* Dolebury Warren and Bristol's Downs.

## Dingy Skipper   *Erynnis tages tages* (Linn.)

**National status: Widespread throughout the British Isles but localised and declining.
Bristol region status: Localised in small colonies.**

**Dingy Skipper**   Sandford Quarry, North Somerset

Kurt Vickery  May 2000

Regarded by most authors in the last one hundred years as a common butterfly found throughout the region. Hudd (1884 & 1906) reported it as '*Common throughout the district*' and '*fairly common on downs and clearings in woods throughout the county*' respectively. This state of affairs seems to have stayed the case, certainly upto the post-war period of the 1950s as Turner (1955) regarded it as '*Generally distributed and common*' over the whole of Somerset and quoted records from the parishes of Portishead, Compton Dando and Blagdon. North of the River Avon, Richardson (1945) included a record of '*Portway 7.viii.1921 R.F.Bretherton*' which presumably represented a second brood, from the A4 in the Avon Gorge, quite an unusual event.

More recently Brown (1971) had '*little to say about this somewhat drab and "over-looked"*

*butterfly*' which he took to be '*holding its own.*' As Brown indicated, it is easy to miss this butterfly unless one is specifically looking for it. It can be confused by the uninitiated with common day-flying moths such as the Burnet Companion *Euclidia glyphica*, Mother Shipton *Callistege mi*, Latticed Heath *Chiasmia clathrata* and Common Heath *Ematurga atomaria*, although easily differentiated with a little practice. Furthermore its colonies are often fairly small and discrete. Sometimes it occurs on the wing with the Grizzled Skipper and the flight period of the two species is very similar.

The survey seems to show a fairly static picture in terms of numbers of known sites. Localities include golf courses, quarries and disused railways as well as the natural habitat of grazed, unimproved grassland, habitat which is declining locally and nationally. Limestone

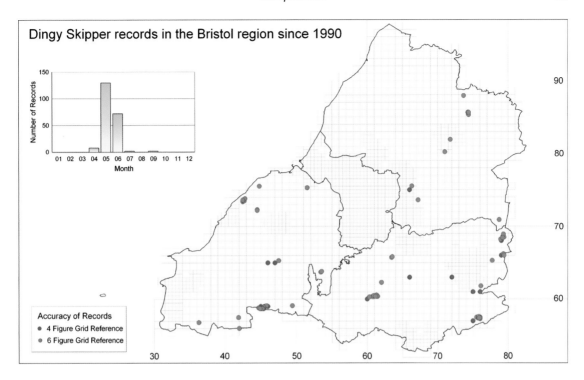

Dingy Skipper records in the Bristol region since 1990

Number of Records / Month

Accuracy of Records
● 4 Figure Grid Reference
● 6 Figure Grid Reference

downland is a particularly favoured habitat in this region. However, any warm sheltered scrubby, grassland sites may be suitable if they have the larval foodplants, trefoils, (in particular, Bird's-foot Trefoil *Lotus corniculatus*) and bare, open patches where the adult butterfly can perch. Such sites are declining, either through development or alternative land use or because lack of management and grazing leads to the shading out of the larval foodplants. In particular agricultural intensification, the process of replacing species rich grassland with species poor grassland, has been a major factor. Perhaps even more importantly, those that do remain become ever more isolated and therefore re-colonisation of sites that come back into management is very unlikely by natural means. At Wetmoor the Dingy Skipper used to be seen frequently until about 1992 when there was a gap of eight years before it was seen again. The opportunity for assisting butterflies such as the Dingy Skipper could include more sensitive restoration of quarries and other sites rather than importing topsoil in a mistaken attempt to improve the soil for plants.

It is disappointing, given the number of recorders involved in this survey, that more sites for the Dingy Skipper did not come to light. This may be partly due to the easily overlooked nature of the butterfly and its ability to exist at relatively low densities. However, there is a need now to do more to protect sites where this butterfly still occurs.

The phenological data from the current survey shows the peak of emergence of the Dingy Skipper in the Bristol region to be at the end of May. The earliest record is from 15th April in 1998. Emmet & Heath (1989) regard sightings in <u>late</u> April to only occur in '*advanced seasons when there may also be a small second emergence in late July and August; this is normal on the warm undercliffs of South Devon.*' The data from the Bristol Region shows that April records have been received in five years during the 1990s. The first brood is tailing off by the end of June but a record from 4th July, again in 1998, could have been a second brood. Even later records are 23 July 1976, 3 August 1994, 1 September 1994 and 25 September 1994. These must certainly be second brood records. It is likely that this trend may increase with the forecasts for climate change and this species will repay close monitoring.

# Grizzled Skipper    *Pyrgus malvae* (Linn.)

**National status: Widespread in England and Wales but localised and declining.**
**Bristol region status: Localised in small colonies.**

Andrew Daw  27ᵗʰ May 2000

**Grizzled Skipper**

'*Generally distributed and common*' in Hudd's day with '*The variety* malvae *occurs at Leigh.*' This situation had begun to change by the middle of the 20th century when Turner (1955) described its distribution in Somerset as '*Fairly common and widespread, but rather local, being found in the same small areas each year.*' Perhaps this is echoed on the Gloucestershire side when Donovan in 1942 described it as '*Frequent*' but Meredith had decided it was '*local*' by 1984.

Brown (1971) regarded it as '*much more sparsely distributed in the area than the previous species* [Dingy Skipper].' He mentioned Wetmoor and Goblin Combe as localities with strong populations. A search for specimens of the aberration *taras* Meigen in the 1960s had been fruitless.

Today, the current survey suggests a steady decline over at least the last ten years. In particular, there are no reports of the species from its former stronghold at Wetmoor since 1991. At that locality Wild Strawberry *Fragaria vesca* was the usual foodplant, which is still present. Another well known site, Goblin Combe, also shows a substantial decline although it is still thought to be present. To compensate for this there are records from the Walton-in-Gordano area as reported in the 1950s by J. Bird and it has also been found at a number of new sites particularly in the east and far east of the Bristol region.

Overall this is a butterfly which is closely associated with the Dingy Skipper even though its larval foodplants are different, usually Wild Strawberry, Creeping Cinquefoil *Potentilla rep-*

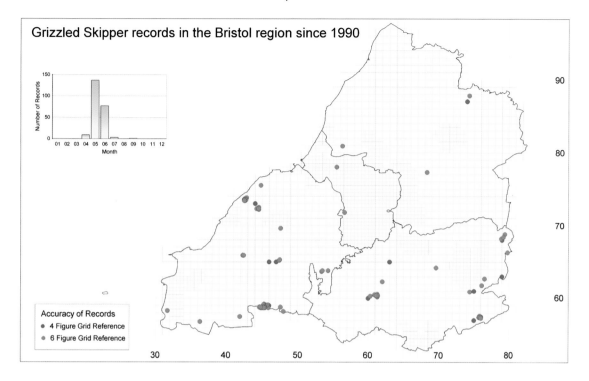

Grizzled Skipper records in the Bristol region since 1990

Accuracy of Records
• 4 Figure Grid Reference
• 6 Figure Grid Reference

*tans* or other low-growing Rosaceae. The two often fly together in May and June at the same sites as comparison of the distribution maps reveals. Records in April were at one time very unusual but, as with the Dingy Skipper, are probably becoming more common place. In particular 1997 accounts for a number of April records suggesting that environmental conditions enabled it to emerge early in numbers that year. Perhaps surprisingly the same was not true for the Dingy Skipper in 1997. There are two records which must have been due to a partial second brood, 3 August 1984 and 25 September 1994. Such a second brood occurs on the continent (Emmet & Heath, 1989) but has been considered in the past to be very rare in the British Isles.

As with the Dingy Skipper, identification can be confused with some day-flying moths, perhaps the Mother Shipton in particular. The downland habitats where the Dingy Skipper occurs often support this butterfly too. In 1999, for example, it was common on Dolebury Warren (J. Martin pers. comm.). Both will also be found on 'man-made' sites such as the disused railway lines at Radstock and the ex-industrial site at Pensford Colliery. As well as watching the populations of this butterfly carefully on unimproved grassland, where again it is vulnerable to 'scrubbing up' of the habitat, colonies may be lost by the trend to develop more 'brown field' sites such as the ex-industrial sites mentioned.

# PAPILIONIDAE

## Apollo    *Parnassius apollo* (Linn.)

**National status: Very rare immigrant.**
**Bristol region status: Doubtful 19th century record only.**

This spectacular butterfly, resident of mountainous areas in Europe, is thought to very occasionally reach British shores as a genuine migrant. The only known record for the Bristol region is that first reported in Barrett (1893). In that he states that one or two specimens had been recorded from near Portishead. The imprecise nature of the report is slightly worrying but it is perhaps possible that they could have arrived from Scandinavia or elsewhere naturally or perhaps more likely, have arrived courtesy of an accidental ship borne voyage. There are other examples where the early stages are thought to have been imported on horticultural imports elsewhere in the country and Portishead at the confluence of the Severn and Avon, on a direct route to the port of Bristol, would seem a logical place for such an occurrence.

# Swallowtail    *Papilio machaon* Linn.

**National status: British subspecies *britannicus* Seitz resident in the fens of the Norfolk Broads. European subspecies *gorganus* Fruhstorfer rare immigrant.
Bristol region status: Subspecies *gorganus* rare immigrant**

A.C.D.
2000

There is some hearsay evidence that the Swallowtail may have occurred as a resident species in the region at the beginning of the 19th century, as reported in Samouelle's Entomologist's Useful Compendium for 1819 p.235. '*It is very local, and occurs near Bristol*' Hudd (1884) added and went on, '*A friend tells me, on what he calls "only school boy authority" that* P. machaon *used to be found in the marshes near Aust, Gloucestershire.*' This is rather thin evidence and to counteract it Barrett (1893) states '*It has been taken in Somerset (and elsewhere) but not as a settled inhabitant.*'

If it ever did occur at Aust it is likely that this was a temporary colony of the European subspecies rather than the British form. Subspecies *britannicus* usually feeds on Milkparsley *Pseucedanum palustre* as a larva, whereas *gorganus* usually feeds on garden carrot or Fennel *Foeniculum vulgare* in this country, when it occurs. White (1912) does not include Milk-parsley as a native plant in the region. Meredith (1984) accepts the summary

of the situation by Bainbrigge Fletcher (1937) in which the records are rejected but has some sympathy with the idea that it just could have been present. Emmet & Heath (1989) accept that there have been instances of *gorganus* becoming temporarily established in England, for example at Deal in Kent between 1857 and 1869, however they apparently have not accepted the Aust records at all. Salmon (2000) does seem to accept that the records may have been genuine and of the European subspecies.

In addition to this, Chris Wiltshire has received a verbal report from a local resident to Lower Woods, Wetmoor in which he states that he saw Swallowtails in open areas near the Little Avon river when a small boy, presumably in the 1930s. It is unlikely that these are accurate though, as the foodplant is absent and there are no corroborating accounts.

Whether or not it ever was resident in the vicinity of Bristol, a number of examples of migrants from the continent are documented.

For example, Meredith (1984) states, '*Taken at Redland by Rev. Wm Ray in 18th century*' and Hudd (1884) and annotations reports "*A worn specimen was captured on the wing in June 1880, near Durdham Down, Bristol by a gentleman who gave it to W.W.A. Mann, in whose collection I saw it shortly afterwards. See Entomologist Vol. 14 p.66. Portishead October 1857 (AEH) Mr Knight of that place.*' In the Victoria County History of Somerset (1906) Hudd adds two other records '*In 1856 one was taken by Mr G.R.Crotch near Weston-s-Mare*' and then '*In 1864 Dr Terry records it as "rare near Bath"*'. Turner (1955) adds another sighting from Weston-super-Mare in 1906, but gives no details. The Bristol Naturalists' Society however, reported in their Proceedings for 1932 that they had cooperated with The Somerset Archaeological & Natural History Society in attempts to '*re-establish*' the Swallowtail in '*selected areas*'. Adult butterflies and eggs had been liberated at Shapwick Heath, south of the Bristol region, on the Somerset Levels. The attempt is not mentioned again so presumably failed. However those involved were obviously convinced that the butterfly had once occurred naturally in the county.

Since that time there appear to be no records until the current survey. During the 1990s there were reports of this beautiful butterfly from two sites in Bath in July of 1994; from Wain's Hill in the south west of the region and close to Bristol Grammar School in May and July of 1995 respectively; from a further two sites in Bath in July 1997 and from Dundry Hill, close to Bristol in 1999. None of the sightings has coincided with any other reports of the Swallowtail from across the country that might have given weight to affording these records the status of genuine immigrants. It is almost certainly true that they refer to individuals that have been bred in captivity and then released. The sightings at Wain's Hill, for example, may be due to an admitted escape of a number of individuals from glasshouses near the M5 motorway, where two individuals had bred specimens in 1994 (Tony Moulin pers. comm.).

In summary it is unlikely that there was a 19th century colony at Aust, in the late 19th and early 20th century there were occasional migrants from the continent but all recent records are considered to relate to captive-bred releases.

# PIERIDAE

## Wood White    *Leptidea sinapis sinapis* (Linn.)

**National status: Local and declining across England, Wales and Ireland.**
**Bristol region status: A rare resident in the past, no longer present.**

Historic records show that the Wood White has never been a common butterfly in the Bristol region. Hudd (1884) said that it was '*Not common in the district and very local.*' He cited a record from near Stapleton (P.H.V.) as well as single specimens near Clevedon and Tickenham reported by the Rev. G.W. Braikenridge and its inclusion in '*Mr Crotch's list of species – taken near Weston-super-Mare.*' Furthermore it was listed as from Bath reported by Dr Terry and as being in the Bath Handlist (Morris, 1888). Hudd's later annotation adds that Mr J.Mason had not seen the butterfly at Clevedon between 1884 and 1900, reflecting its rarity at that time.

In the 1980s there have been reports of the Wood White from Harry Stoke, South Gloucestershire (for example, Sorrell, Way &

Weeks, 1984) and occasional other records from the edge of Lower Woods, Wetmoor and elsewhere. In these cases, errors of identification are suspected as they have never been confirmed by separate witnesses. Indeed field surveyors in the mid 1990s recorded very small Green-veined Whites from this area, a possible source of misidentification for the Wood White.

The butterfly lays its eggs on foodplants such as Meadow Vetchling *Lathyrus pratensis* and Tufted Vetch *Vicia cracca*, both of which are common and widespread in the region (Myles *et al*, 2000). It seems likely that the butterfly's absence from the region is connected to the lack of suitable lightly shaded habitat in woodland rides and the distance from other colonies that could allow re-colonisation (south Somerset contains the nearest sites).

# Pale Clouded Yellow *Colias hyale* (Linn.)

**National status: Irregular and rare immigrant.**
**Bristol region status: Very rare immigrant.**

Confusion over records of the Pale Clouded Yellow has long existed and continues today. The pale form *helice* of the commoner Clouded Yellow is thought to account for many reports. Furthermore, the very similar Berger's Clouded Yellow was only recognised as a distinct species in 1945. Hudd (1884) recognised the former problem when reporting, '*I once saw a specimen in my garden in Redland which I believe was this species but not having captured it I may have been deceived by Helice PVH.*' Stainton's Manual lists Bristol as a locality and Hudd in his Victoria County History of Somerset (1906) includes Bath (per Dr Terry), Bedminster (a few specimens in 1900, Hudd) and Clevedon. The latter record is probably that reported in Harding (1899) as Clevedon 1885 J. Mason.

Records of the butterfly by the famed lepidopterist Ian Heslop were reported in Meredith (1984); '*Redland Green, two or three taken in a clover field and shown to me alive, vi or vii.11; Bristol Downs, one taken by a Clifton*

*College boy at the same time; Kingsweston, one taken in Trym Valley, 1922 and recorded by me in the* Field.'

There are no further records until after the establishment of the Bristol Regional Environmental Records Centre (BRERC) with four records from Bleadon in August 1983, and sightings in Sandford (July 1992), Banwell (July 1994) and Wrington (August 1997). These records are difficult to confirm absolutely, given the possibility of confusion with the much commoner, and similar, form *helice* of the Clouded Yellow as mentioned above. Emmet & Heath (1989) suggest that although 1983 witnessed a massive immigration of the Clouded Yellow into the UK this did not coincide with a similar increase in records of the Pale Clouded Yellow. It is very difficult to check old records and it is safest to say that it is likely that there have been occasional accurate sightings of the Pale Clouded Yellow but that it is of very rare occurrence in the region.

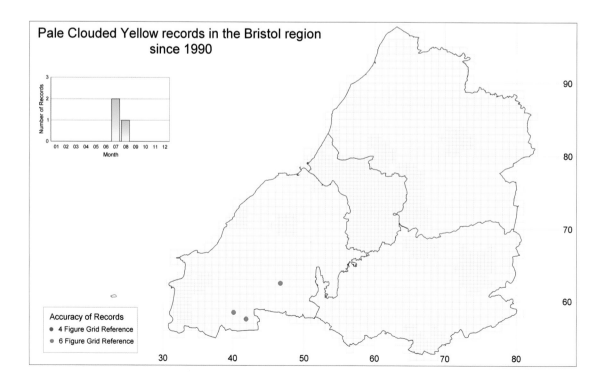

Pale Clouded Yellow records in the Bristol region since 1990

# Berger's Clouded Yellow *Colias alfacariensis* Berger

**National status: Very rare immigrant.**
**Bristol region status: No confirmed records.**

Given the difficulty of identification, confusion with the Pale Clouded Yellow, from which it was only differentiated in 1945, and the form *helice* of the Clouded Yellow, it is possible that records of those two other species could hide the presence of Berger's Clouded Yellow. There are, however, no claims for this butterfly otherwise in this region.

## Clouded Yellow   *Colias croceus* (Geoff.)

**National status: Regular immigrant.**
**Bristol region status: Occasional immigrant.**

Andrew Daw

**Clouded Yellow**

A famous visitor to our shores, notorious for its fickle appearance, some years absent others exceedingly common. The earliest record known from the region is by J. Allen Hill; '*Almondsbury House: Beginning of Oct on the flowers of a small species of dandelion on high pastures, scarce – Almondsbury 1849*' (Zoologist 1850 p.2882). Hudd (1884) picked out 1859 and 1877 as years when it was '*very plentiful*'. Nationally, 1877 and 1892 were considered the best for the species in the 19th century (Emmet & Heath, 1989). Locally the former year is recorded in the Proceedings of the Bristol Naturalists' Society as being noteworthy '*Owing to the extraordinary dearth of insect life*'. But, '*the extraordinary abundance of Collas edusa, which has swarmed to an extent never before recorded in England, having been by far our commonest butterfly through all the southern and eastern counties,*

*the general scarcity of other species making it the more remarkable.*'

1892 is represented by Hudd's annotations to his 1884 list with, '*Avon banks and Almondsbury several 1892 C.Bartlett.*' Charles Bartlett also saw a specimen at Bitton the following year on 28 April. The north Somerset recorders at the end of the 19th century were represented by '*Near Weston-s-M. GRC.*' and '*Clevedon periodically J. Mason 1884–88*' (Hudd, 1884 & later annotations). Hudd's Victoria County History (1906) mentioned '*The var helice has been recorded from Bedminster & Weston-super-Mare*' from the Bristol Region. Harding (1899) '*var helice Durdham Down Mr Geo Thompson in 1894. No previous record for Glos.*'

In the 20th century the years 1900, 1913, 1928 and 1937 witnessed good numbers across the country (Emmet & Heath, 1989) but there are no records from the Bristol region. The 1940s saw a number of good years culminating in 1947, still remembered as the Clouded Yellow year by the older generation of lepidopterists. The Bristol Naturalists' Society Proceedings recorded: '*Rarely have so many butterflies been on the wing during the late summer and autumn, and even those not interested in Lepidoptera must have noticed the general distribution in great numbers of the clouded yellow (*Colis croceus*). Probably the noted year of 1877 for this insect was surpassed.*' (Peach, 1948.) Turner (1955) says that the butterfly was abundant in 1947 in Somerset and for Gloucestershire Meredith (1984) records, '*Very plentiful all over the county in 1947, fairly common 1949.*' Bird (unpublished) listed the Clouded Yellow from Clevedon, Tickenham, Walton-in-Gordano, Yatton, Goblin Combe, Long Ashton, Wraxall and Churchill in the 1950s.

Following the great year of 1947, numbers generally were to remain low up until 1983. Brown (1971) summarised the records in between times, '*In 1964 this species was far more numerous in the Bristol area, particularly during August and September, when up to three butterflies would be seen in any one day.*

In June of 1967, the author caught a very battered female specimen at Wetmoor in Gloucestershire from which over one hundred ova were obtained. The larvae were successfully reared and the adult butterflies started emerging in August, with a substantial number of ab helice. Single specimens were observed at regular intervals during October 1969 at Sand Bay near Weston-super-Mare in Somerset, the last of which was noted on 17 October. So far we only have one record for 1970 and that is from the same locality.'

The Common Butterfly Survey organised by the Bristol Regional Environmental Records Centre from 1981 to 1986, had to report on the Clouded Yellow in 1983 even though it had not chosen that species to focus on originally. Records first started being received in mid-June but numbers built up mainly in late July and August. It was thought that these included true migrants along with a new generation of individuals, the progeny of the first arrivals to the south coast earlier in the year. In total 367 records were submitted to the scheme, largely scattered across the region perhaps avoiding the urban conurbations. Migrants are thought to be funnelled up the Bristol Channel on such occasions and sightings on

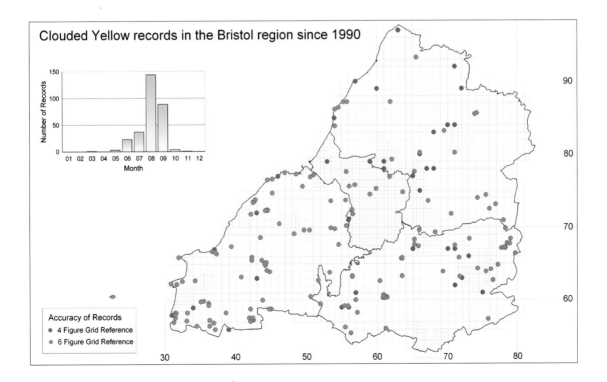

Steepholm at this time were of frequent individuals between 6 August and 24 September (Parsons, 1996).

During the 1990s the years 1992, 1994 and 1996 were reasonably good for the butterfly. The distribution map shows, as would be perhaps expected, that the butterfly can turn up anywhere in the region. Most sightings are in August and September but individuals in some years can be seen right from spring through to the end of the autumn. There are no records of local breeding but this is likely to have taken place. The number of records of the butterfly in the region over the period of the current survey is roughly equivalent to those received for the resident species Silver-washed Fritillary, Dingy and Grizzled Skippers, if that gives a further indication of its abundance.

It has been suggested that moderately good years for the immigration of the butterfly have been getting commoner in the last decade or two. Climate change has been put forward to support this idea. Given the very variable history of the immigration of the Clouded Yellow into this country only time will tell if this is a real phenomenon or just part of its pattern of boom and bust years.

# The Brimstone   *Gonepteryx rhamni rhamni* (Linn.)

**National status: Common resident throughout England, Wales and Ireland.**
**Bristol region status: Fairly common and widespread.**

Tony Moulin   August 1989

**Brimstone**   Yatton, North Somerset

The population of the Brimstone has apparently remained fairly stable in the region over a long period. All authors agree that the butterfly occurs regularly throughout the area but differ slightly over whether this actually makes it common. It does not form colonies but wanders considerably hence the difficulty in gaining an accurate picture of its numbers. To illustrate the point, Hudd (1884) called it '*Common throughout the district*' and yet in 1906 regarded it as '*Generally distributed, but not very common*'.

'*A remarkable specimen was captured by Mrs R. I. Iremonger in April 1920. It was resting on Virginia Creeper in her garden, The Parsonage, Langford, Bristol.*' The captor subsequently passed the specimen to the well known lepidopterist and illustrator F. W. Frowhawk who painted it in his book of 1938, *Varieties of British Butterflies,* along with the

above account of its capture. Mrs Iremonger noticed the butterfly because of the orange colouration over much of the wings. The cause of such an abnormality may be due to staining which occurred at the time the butterfly emerged from the pupa. Excess fluid, called meconium, that has not been utilised in the pupal stage, is ejected by the butterfly shortly after emerging. The very few other occasions when such forms have been reported nationally may also include examples artificially created by unscrupulous collectors, or those wishing to sell them to collectors.

By the 1970s Brown (1971) attempted to quantify the population density regarding it as '*widely distributed all over the Bristol area, but is rarely common.*' and '*Only on very seldom occasions do we hear of more than about eight butterflies having been seen on a particular day.*' He suggested that the larval foodplant,

Martin Evans  6th June 1989

**Brimstone** (larva)
Worle Hill, North Somerset

Buckthorn *Rhamnus cathartica*, was not common and that this could explain its low numbers locally. In fact both White (1912) and Myles *et al* (2000) regard Buckthorn to be widespread and rather common. The second known foodplant, Alder Buckthorn *Frangula alnus*, is much rarer, restricted largely to the Gordano Valley, south west of Bristol. Records of the Brimstone from Steepholm (Parsons, 1996): '*30th July 1983. 4 males and 2 females 7th Oct 1985. Three on 30th March 1991*' illustrate the nomadic quality of the butterfly as there is no larval foodplant present on the island.

In the 1980s the Brimstone was one of the subjects chosen for the Common Butterfly Survey (CBS) by the Bristol Regional Environmental Records Centre. The results showed interesting fluctuations year to year. In 1983, for example, there were twice as many records received as for 1982, although an increase in recorders could have accounted for this. The main emergence from hibernation in 1983 was from March with most being seen in mid-April. Of the new generation that year, the peak of sightings occurred in early August. The following spring there were twice as many sightings of the Brimstone as there had been of the same brood in the late summer of 1982. This is probably a common phenomenon and the data from the transect work at Wetmoor supports this showing a rapid peak in sightings in early April as individuals leave their hibernation sites. In the spring the male butterflies stand out as they emerge from hibernation and disperse across breeding sites. In the late summer the butterflies are less obvious amongst the greener landscape and are probably more engaged in feeding up on nectar nearer to over-wintering woodland sites. Females are also more likely to be mistaken for the Large White, which it resembles in flight.

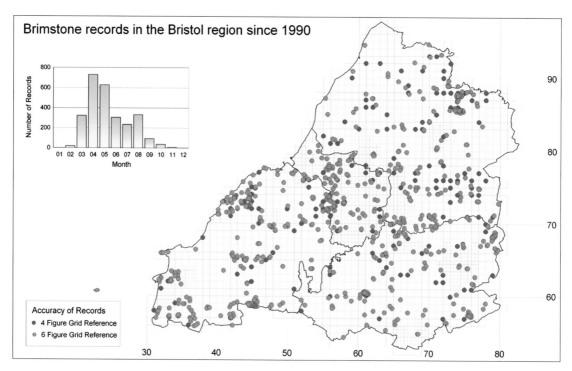

Brimstone records in the Bristol region since 1990

The CBS was also able to compare the numbers of records in the spring against other common species that over-winter as the adult butterfly. The conclusion was drawn that the Brimstone had a more successful hibernation over the winter of 1983/84 than both the Small Tortoiseshell and the Peacock. 1986 seems to have been a poor year perhaps due to severe weather over the preceding winter. Numbers of records for the year were less than for the previous two years added together. 1988 was even worse, this time mild and damp winter weather was suggested as perhaps a causatory factor! Environmental conditions probably do affect hibernation success but understanding the complexities of this impact is not easy.

In the 1990s the Avon Butterfly Project has received regular records, some very early in the year, and confirm that the status of the Brimstone has remained stable. Yearly fluctuations do not appear to be of concern to the long-term viability of the population. In general the peaks in reports of sightings are in March, April, May and into June. There is then a second peak when the new brood emerges in August. The relatively small numbers of records from the autumn suggest individuals enter hibernation early. The distribution map shows the widespread occurrence of the butterfly across the region.

# Black-veined White    *Aporia crataegi* (Linn.)

**National status: Extinct in Britain since the 1920s.**
**Bristol region status: Extinct by the 1880s.**

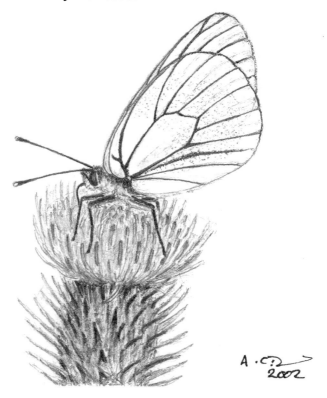

This fairly large butterfly, still widespread although declining in Europe, is thought to have become extinct in the British Isles in the 1920s. This loss has been suggested to have been primarily due to a combination of a series of wet autumns leading to a high incidence of disease. On top of this, increased predation by birds is thought to have accelerated the process (Pratt, 1983).

Locally, J.N.Duck even in 1852, regarded the Black-veined White to be *'About the wood. Very rare.'* in his book 'The Natural History of Portishead'. Hudd (1884) listed other records as *'Clevedon A.E.H.* [A.E. Hudd] *Worle G.H.* [G.

Harding] *Weston-s-M G.R.C.'* and *'Boiling Wells, Bristol. Scarce. S.B. Filwood F.V. Jacques.'* His general comment was that it *'Has apparently become very scarce in the West of England, not having been noticed lately in many of its old localities.'* To these he added Bath, courtesy of Dr Terry's list, when he published the Victoria County History of Somerset (1906).

Emmet & Heath (1989) suggest that the Black-veined White disappeared from Gloucestershire about 1887 and in Somerset give the last official record as 1857 although they speculate it may have clung on into the 1870s.

# Large White  *Pieris brassicae* (Linn.)

**National status: Common and widespread in the British Isles, resident and regular immigrant.**
**Bristol region status: Common and widespread as a resident and occasional immigrant.**

**Large White**   Winscombe, North Somerset

*Kurt Vickery   August 2002*

An instance where the definition of 'common' may have changed over the last one hundred years or so. In 1955 immigrant Large White butterflies are thought to have brought with them granulosis virus and from then on the resident population has never been as numerous as before (Emmet & Heath, 1989; Asher *et al*, 2001). Consequently Hudd's definition in 1884 of '*Common throughout the district.*' may have meant a considerably greater number of individuals than seen now. This may also be true given the modern use of chemical insecticides to control such 'pest' species as this butterfly. Hudd in his annotations to his 1884 list included the observation '*I have taken this species flying at night round a gas lamp. If disturbed at night I think all butterflies are attracted by light.*' Modern day moth recorders will also vouch that if butterflies are disturbed from their night roosts they will often remain close to a light source. In the case of the Large White, butterflies will often fly late in the evening, perhaps more so when migrating, and Hudd's sighting could have been due to such an event.

Testimony to the dispersal powers of this species is that Turner (1955) includes records from Steepholm Island. At the same locality, Parsons (1996) goes on to report '*First record: 1902. Frequent most years. Larvae on* Brassica napus, *1975; on* Reseda luteolata *1976 and* Lavetera arborea *(3) 1979.*' The Large White is familiar as a green and yellow larva feeding on the outside leaves of cultivated brassicas but it is equally at home on other members of the Cruciferae (Brassicaceae),

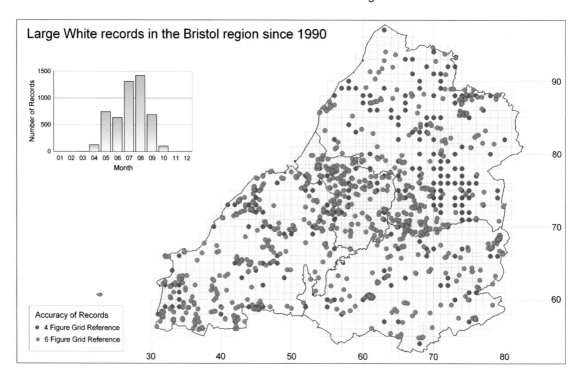

Large White records in the Bristol region since 1990

Leguminosae (Fabaceae), Resedaceae, Tropaeolaceae and Capparidaceae (Emmet & Heat, 1989).

Only Brown (1971) has previously attempted to identify peaks in emergence of the two broods in the region. He suggested the spring brood reached highest numbers in early June, on average, and the second brood in September, although no supporting records are quoted. He points out that this pattern seemed to alter in 1964 with the peak of the first generation in mid-May and the second in late July.

A.H. Weeks reported almost plague numbers in his garden in Yatton in the last week of July 1989 which had fallen by the beginning of August. This may perhaps reflect an instance of mass immigration. The 1990s survey data shows peaks in emergence which seem to concur with the observation of Brown (1971) for 1964, a relatively small peak in mid to late May followed by high peaks in early to mid August.

Further evidence of regular immigration in to our region was given by Brown (1971) as on 3 July 1970 about 50 individuals were seen apparently making landfall at Sand Point.

# Small White   *Pieris rapae* (Linn.)

**National status: Common and widespread in the British Isles, resident and regular immigrant.**
**Bristol region status: Common and widespread as a resident and sometimes immigrant.**

**Small White**   Madam Lane, Worle, North Somerset

A very similar species in profile to the Large White being both now and in the past a common and sometimes abundant butterfly. Larval foodplants again are cultivated brassicas as well as wild crucifers; Garlic Mustard *Alliaria petiolata* is commonly used across the region. The green larvae tend to avoid competition with the Large and Green-veined White by concentrating on eating the inner leaves of plants. Immigrants regularly supplement the resident population. Again Parsons (1996) reveals that there have been frequent records from Steepholm since 1902 but, unlike the Large White, there are no breeding records from there.

Historically the butterfly has always been considered to be an abundant species locally, commoner than the Large White, for example,

(Brown, 1971). However, by contrast, there are fewer records from Steepholm than for its congener. Hudd (1884) reported '*The earliest and latest dates of its first appearance, from 1864 to 1877 (as recorded by Mr Perkins) are "March 16th 1874" and April 24th 1866.*' With regard to the different broods Brown (1971) considered it '*stays on the wing longer during the second brood [than the Large White]. The butterflies are on the wing in nearly every month between April and October, and the various generations are difficult to distinguish owing to this fact.*' However some of the records from early in the year may possibly be ascribed to the common habit of the larvae of pupating in greenhouses or similar, with the result that the imagines are 'forced', emerging earlier than the rest of the population.

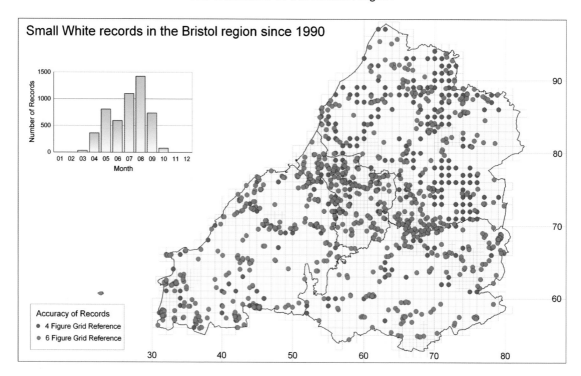

Small White records in the Bristol region since 1990

Data from the current survey confirms Brown's assertion that it may be seen in almost any month from spring to summer. However it shows very well that there are two broods peaking in mid May and late July, early August. It is though possibly that this still disguises third brood individuals. Sightings are concentrated in and around the conurbations reflecting recorder bias rather than a true concentration in those areas.

# Green-veined White   *Pieris napi* (Linn.) ssp. *sabellicae* Stephens

**National status: A common and widespread resident in the British Isles.**
**Bristol region status: A common and widespread resident.**

**Green-veined White**   Hill, South Gloucestershire

Martin Evans   2ND September 2002

As with both the Large White and Small White a very common species now and in the past, although sometimes considered to be not as abundant as the other two and being more restricted to damp places (Hudd, 1884 and Brown, 1971). Turner (1955) regarded its numbers to be reinforced by immigration but although it can be a mobile species, Emmet & Heath (1989) regard it as having '*no true migratory tendency.*' Parsons (1996) states that it was not recorded on Steepholm until 1954 and appears as an occasional visitor, the exception being an influx of 50 witnessed on 26 May 1990.

The predominantly green larvae are not found on cultivated brassicas but usually on crucifers such as Cuckooflower *Cardamine pratensis*, Garlic Mustard *Alliaria petiolata* and Hedge Mustard *Sisymbrium officinale*, amongst others, such as *Wavy Bitter-cress*

*Cardamine flexuosa*. Competition is avoided with the sometimes cannibalistic larva of the Orange-tip which is often seen on the same plant, as the larva of the latter feeds on the flowers and seeds rather than the leaves.

**Green-veined White**   Leigh Woods

Kurt Vickery   May 1989

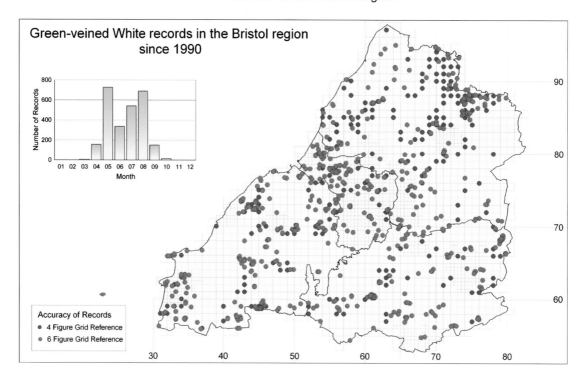

Green-veined White records in the Bristol region since 1990

Accuracy of Records
- 4 Figure Grid Reference
- 6 Figure Grid Reference

Brown (1971) comments that numbers fell in 1964 and adds a note that in central and west Gloucestershire superb examples of the females may be found with the black tip of the forewing merging into a soft grey.

The results of the Avon Butterfly Project survey show a very similar pattern to that of the Small White. The peak appearance of the two broods is in May and then in late July, early August. Again a third brood may happen in suitable years and explain the sightings in the late autumn. Overall the number of records received during the period of the current survey was roughly two thirds of the respective totals for the Small and Large Whites. It is likely that this is not a true reflection of the abundance of the species, it often being mistaken for the Small White in particular.

# Bath White    *Pontia daplidice* (Linn.)

**National status: A very rare immigrant.**
**Bristol region status: Very rare immigrant last recorded in the 19th century.**

A.C.2
2002

Although forever linked with the Region given its English name, the connection is very tenuous. Lewin (1795) is credited with the origin of the name *'from a piece of needlework executed at Bath by a young lady, from a specimen of this insect, said to have been taken near that place.'* Even two hundred years ago the provenance of the butterfly that acted as the model for the piece of work seems to have been in severe doubt. What is more, this was not the first reference to the butterfly as it had been known as an irregular visitor to the British Isles since probably 1699 (Emmet & Heath, 1989) and had been assigned various other names at different points in time.

The records we do have from our region are as follows *'A specimen of the Bath White was captured many years ago, near the Bristol Royal Infirmary, by Dr Dyer. Mr H.C.Harford.*

*(Communicated by Mr Harding)'* and *'A specimen taken near Bath, is recorded by Lewin,* Magazine of Natural History *for 1831. "One captured by J.S.M. in a field near Keynsham in 1818, was in the cabinet of Mr Miller, of Bristol." Dale in* Mag. Nat. Hist. *for 1831. Mr Barton informs me this last named specimen used to be in the collection of the Bristol Museum and I have discovered lately an old specimen of* Daplidice *(which I believe to be the one referred to) among the Exotic species in the cabinet there.'* (Hudd, 1884). Hudd's later annotations to his list include *'Near Bath, Handbook Bath/1888/p.256'* and *'Specimen "Leigh Woods 1832" in Nat. Mus. of Wales in Cardiff'*. (The Keynsham record was erroneously listed in Turner (1955) as being from 1918.) Sadly the specimen found by Hudd in the Bristol Museum collections was probably

destroyed when the Museum was badly damaged by bombs in November 1940.

Given the above it is surprising that the only record of the Bath White in the Victoria County History Of Somerset (1906) is of the Keynsham specimen. The four or five records above are the only known sightings from the region. Even in 1945 when a mass immigration did take place into the British Isles, none have been reported from the Bristol region.

# Orange-tip *Anthocharis cardamines* (Linn.) ssp. *britannica* Verity

**National status: Common, resident throughout the British Isles.**
**Bristol region status: Common and widespread.**

Martin Evans    20ᵗʰ May 1992

**Orange-tip**   Elmsley Lane, Kewstoke, North Somerset

An unmistakable butterfly, at least as the adult male, and hence impressions of abundance can be relied upon. It appears that the Orange-tip has been fairly common as long as recording has taken place in the region. Brown (1971) believed that it had been increasing from 1968. He recorded the capture of a partial gynandromorph (half male, half female) by D.G.Gibb at Wickwar in 1967, which is now in the Bristol Museum collection (Accession Number: 77/1994).

The Common Butterfly Survey monitored populations from 1982 to 1988 and identified the annual brood as building up from early April, peaking in mid-May and then declining in June. 1983 was noted for a cold late spring and that was thought to be the reason for a peak in early June. Records from late July and August were ascribed to the Green-veined White being mistaken for the female Orange-tip, given that many recorders were not established lepidopterists but recruited from the general public. On average the results suggested that the peak of appearance occurs two or three weeks earlier on average than elsewhere in southern England. The number of records received by the CBS in 1985 was the greatest of the first four years of the survey. A female Orange-tip was confirmed on 2 July but at Brent Knoll, Somerset, just outside the recording area. 1986 was an even better year but the peak of records was considered late, in mid-June. Again confirmed sightings stretched into July with individuals reported on 1, 2 and 3 July, this time from within the region. Finally in 1988 the peak occurred back in mid-May with the last sighting on 21 June.

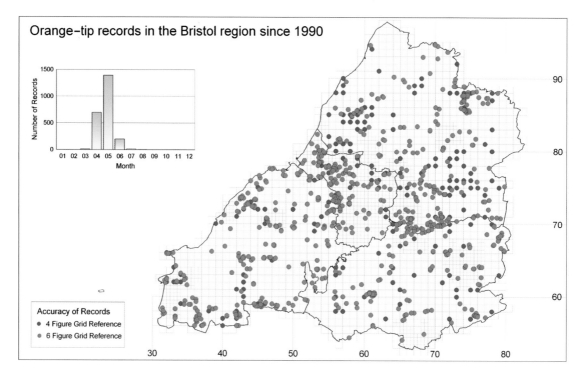

Orange-tip records in the Bristol region since 1990

Accuracy of Records
● 4 Figure Grid Reference
● 6 Figure Grid Reference

Phenological records for 1893, published in the Bristol Naturalists' Society Proceedings for that year, include a record from Leigh Woods of 3rd April by G. C. Griffiths, consid-

**Orange-tip** (larva on Garlic Mustard)

ered a very early record for the butterfly. However the Avon Butterfly Project's survey, one hundred years later, includes many records for April and even a few from March. The earliest is from 13 March 1991, a remarkable date even given the suspicion that climate change is altering the emergence pattern of many insects. It is possible that such individual occurrences may be due to accidents of pupation where the development has been enhanced by the pupa being in a particularly favourable position. Despite this the survey results show that on average emergence is well underway by mid April each year.

Foodplants used by the Orange-tip include a variety of crucifers but most often Cuckooflower *Cardamine pratensis* and Garlic Mustard *Alliaria petiolata*. Seedpods are the main source of food although the larva is notorious for eating other larvae it may come across in the early instars. The main foodplants are not present on the island of Steepholm but the butterfly has been seen there during 1983 (Parsons, 1996).

The butterfly has been observed ovipositing on Garlic Mustard, Honesty *Lunaria annua* and Dame's Violet *Hesperis matronalis*, for example, in city centre gardens and no doubt

**Orange-tip** (ovum)
Days Hill, Weston-super-Mare, North Somerset

**Orange-tip** (pupa)

allotments and rough ground support the butterfly in the urban environment. Furthermore Wild Turnip *Brassica rapa* has now been reported as a foodplant at Claverton near Bath and it is likely that Oil-seed Rape *Brassica napus* is also being utilised (Sutherland, 2001). Chris Wiltshire has seen oviposition on Aubrietia *Aubrietia deltiodea* in a Westbury-on-Trym garden in the early 1990s, following the larvae up to full grown, feeding on the seed-pods.

The distribution map of the current survey reflects the widespread occurrence of this distinctive butterfly across the region and particularly its preference for moving along linear topographical features.

# LYCAENIDAE

## Green Hairstreak    *Callophrys rubi* (Linn.)

**National status: Local resident throughout the British Isles.**
**Bristol region status: Local, isolated colonies.**

Kurt Vickery   May 1988

**Green Hairstreak    Midger Wood, Gloucestershire**

Always considered to be widespread, sometimes common but at localised sites. Duck (1852) considered it rare at Portishead but Brown (1971) summed up the generally agreed situation as, *'easily overlooked. Where it does occur it is rarely plentiful, and in some places it is on the decline.'* This could be considered to still reflect the position today. Its disappearance at well known sites may be assigned to a decline in the available habitat, for example it was lost from the Wetmoor list before 1983. However in this case it is still known relatively nearby, close to Wickwar.

The fact that this little green and brown butterfly can be easily missed may explain the relatively small number of currently known sites. A colony exists in the Avon Gorge for example, but in this space, which is very popular with the public, how many people will have noticed this? There are concentrations along the Mendips and in the vicinity of Bath. Small colonies can exist in relatively small locations. The single brood, and therefore relatively short time to record the butterfly, may contribute to the lack of records. However the paucity of records is of concern and efforts should be made to search for more colonies or to establish whether the distribution map is a true reflection of the extent of the populations in our region.

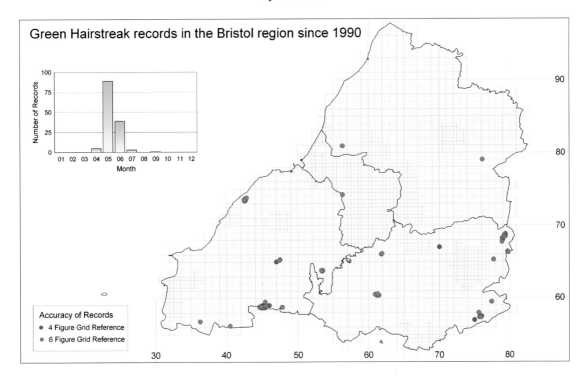

Green Hairstreak records in the Bristol region since 1990

Accuracy of Records
● 4 Figure Grid Reference
● 6 Figure Grid Reference

Any sites of herb-rich grassland with some scrub, where the larval foodplants such as Bird's-foot Trefoil *Lotus corniculatus*, Rock-rose *Helianthemum nummularium*, Gorse *Ulex* spp. and Broom *Cytisus scoparius* amongst others, occur should be considered potential sites to be searched in April and May. In particular Hawthorn *Crataegus* spp. bushes should be inspected closely as the male butterflies are very fond of perching on such shrubs in the sunshine and using them as vantage points from which to fly short distances to presumably, hopefully intercept passing females.

The survey during the 1990s has shown that although the peak of emergence is mid May it may be seen well through much of June. Emergence in April is also of regular occurrence it would seem. An individual at Dolebury on 23 July 1995 by Tony Moulin may represent the occasional example emerging as a second brood.

# Brown Hairstreak    *Thecla betulae* (Linn.)

**National status: A declining resident now confined largely to two or three major areas of England, Wales and Ireland.**
**Bristol region status: Very rare resident perhaps over-looked.**

**Brown Hairstreak**

One of the country's most elusive butterflies, the adults are notoriously difficult to find as they spend most of their time on the tops of trees and bushes. The butterflies, which feed on honeydew secreted by aphids, are also only very active when temperatures reach greater than about 20 degrees Centigrade. The latter is a considerable restriction given that they are on the wing from August into October.

Recording of the species was revolutionised by the discovery that the eggs could be found more easily than the adults by searching the larval foodplant Blackthorn *Prunus spinosa* in winter.

19th century records are, as might be expected rather few. Hudd (1884) reported *'An old school fellow, Mr F Harvey, informed me many years since that he had captured a specimen of the "brown hair-streak" near Brockley Coombe. In reply to a letter I wrote him on the subject, Mr Eustace Button of Clevedon writes me- "In the school 'Manual,' where captures are recorded, I find entered 'T. Betulae caught at Yatton 1861." I think you would be safe to include it in your list, as I feel sure it has occurred in the neighbourhood."'* In the Victoria County History of Somerset (1906) Hudd adds *'Recorded from "near Bath" (Terry)'*.

There is one report by the dipterist d'Assis Fonseca, of the butterfly at Leigh Woods, presumably in the mid 20th century.

In South Gloucestershire Meredith (1984) has no records but the database at the Bristol Regional Environmental Records Centre and the Proceedings of the Bristol Naturalists' Society reveal that the butterfly was present

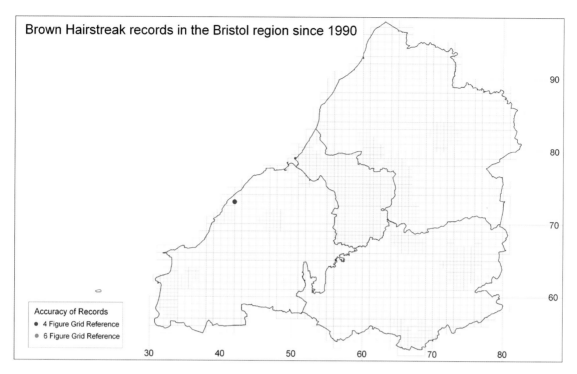

Brown Hairstreak records in the Bristol region since 1990

Accuracy of Records
● 4 Figure Grid Reference
○ 6 Figure Grid Reference

at Inglestone Common in the 1980s. Larvae were beaten from Blackthorn in 1979 (Harper, 1981). Sadly the Wetmoor guide (Anon, 1994) states that although it had been present there it is thought to have become extinct at the Common sometime before 1983. A look at the site today suggests that lack of management of the Blackthorn may be to blame for its demise there. Thomas and Emmet (Emmet & Heath, 1989) explain that the eggs are preferentially laid '*on the bark of Prunus twigs at the base of a spine or the junction of one- and two- year old growth.*' they go on to say '*In Britain most ova are laid on hedgerows which are regularly cut.*' This has the down side that many eggs are there-fore destroyed, a probable cause of the decline of the species in many parts of the country, but if carried out in rotation it does generates that junction of one-and two- year old growth that the butterflies prefer. At Inglestone Common the Blackthorn has been left untouched and the consequent predomi-nance of old woody twigs may account for the apparent loss of the Brown Hairstreak. There have been concerted efforts to rediscover the butterfly at the site but all to no avail. The local council's management of the Common

and rides ceased two or three years before the last record of the Brown Hairstreak, this seems more than just a coincidence and may also be linked to the decline of the Nightingale at this site.

South of the Bristol region, particularly in the south of Somerset and Devon, searches for the ova of the Brown Hairstreak have been very fruitful in recent years and this is now one of the main concentrations known of in the country. One would perhaps expect then that the butterfly would be found in the south of our region, if anywhere. The only known confirmed site during the 1990s was south west of Bristol when a small number of eggs was found on a small scrubby Blackthorn in February 1995 on calcareous downland. Despite numerous searches since then, no adults or other ova have ever been found. Given the secretive nature of the butterfly it is likely that it may still be present there although the lessons of the disappearance at Inglestone may not have been learnt, despite the fact that the site is a nature reserve. It is also possible that there are other localities where the butterfly occurs awaiting discovery, particularly in the south of the region. The BRERC database includes a couple of reports from the Clevedon area from the early 1980s, but these are unconfirmed. Asher, *et al* (2001) state that the butterfly is difficult to protect as colonies range over large areas not just within a particular site and so conservation of the landscape (with blackthorn at the right stage of growth available) is a requirement.

# Purple Hairstreak   *Neozephyrus quercus* (Linn.)

**National status: Local resident across the British Isles, apparently increasing.**
**Bristol region status: Local but widespread.**

Purple Hairstreak

Hudd considered the Purple Hairstreak to be *'Generally distributed and common in oak woods'* (Hudd, 1884). He also made the observation *'plentiful in oak woods, where the curious larvae are sometimes to be found in abundance on the leaves round the trunks of the trees'* (Hudd, 1906). Turner (1955) considered it *'by no means confined to woodland.'*

By contrast, Brown (1971) considered it quite scarce compared to the White-letter Hairstreak, in distribution and numbers. He stated: *'From time to time this species has turned up in considerable numbers near Goblin Combe, but none has been noted in recent years. In 1964 a single specimen was seen in some woods near Weston-super-Mare but none have appeared since that time. Up to 1965, larvae and adults were occasionally found in Leigh Woods on the Somerset side of*

*the Avon Gorge and it is likely that this species still occurs there.'* He went on to add: *'The chief problem with this attractive little butterfly, in the Bristol district at any rate, is the availability of suitable habitats which are rapidly being reduced in number.'*

This pessimism appears to have been unfounded and in recent years the Purple Hairstreak gives the impression of having increased in numbers. The 1990s survey results certainly support Turner's assumption that it can be found on oaks in hedgerows and open parkland. The full grown larvae can sometimes be beaten from oak trees they feed on in late May. Chris Wiltshire has even observed oviposition on Holm Oak *Quercus ilex* in the Avon Gorge. The adult butterflies, like many hairstreak species, feed on honeydew and do not visit flowers, contributing

**Purple Hairstreak**
Leigh Woods, North Somerset

Kurt Vickery

Chris Wiltshire 1st March 1984

**Purple Hairstreak** (ova)
Long Ashton Research Station

to the difficulty of recording them. However to counteract this, butterfly recording at the end of the 20th century saw many bird-watchers changing their attention from the feathered flyers to the scaled ones. This has seen not only the introduction of a much more focussed attitude to recording but also the application of high quality optical equipment in the form of close-focussing binoculars. Scanning oak trees with the latter, in order to see the Purple Hairstreak may have added to the apparent increase of records.

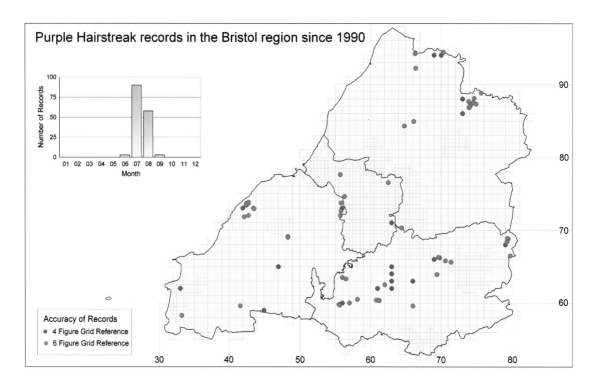

Purple Hairstreak records in the Bristol region since 1990

Currently known strongholds include Leigh Woods, Lower Woods, the Gordano Valley (including Walton Common) and the Brockley/ Goblin Combe woodlands for example. In some years adult Purple Hairstreaks may be seen from the third week of June but more normally most are seen from mid July through to mid August. A few may linger on into the first days of September.

# White-letter Hairstreak    *Satyrium w-album* (Knoch)

**National status: Widely distributed resident throughout England and Wales.**
**Bristol region status: Local, scattered populations.**

Kurt Vickery

**White-letter Hairstreak**    Leigh Woods, North Somerset

Once again the difficulty of finding hairstreaks, as they often ignore flowers and stay on trees feeding on honeydew, has contributed to the paucity of records. Despite this Hudd (1884, and later annotations) records ' *"Used to occur on Durdham Down." S.Barton. One at Westbury in 1876 T.H.O.P. One at Hill near Berkeley in 1867 H.J.F. Larvae common at Coombe Dingle, near Bristol in 1869 F.D.W. Combe Dingle CB. – CGB -47. Brockley Combe AE..H. Weston-s-m G.R.C. Local and scarce. Clevedon J.M. Clevedon scarce J.M. and Cleeve Court (R.W.P). Larvae abundant at Brockley in 1888 Mr Harding and A. Mayes. Near Bath. Handbook 1888 p.256. "Its extreme western limit seems to be at Weston-s-M, Somerset" G.S.B. Lepid – I. 48.'* In 1906 Hudd refined this to *'Not very common except near Bristol, Brockley Coombe and Weston-*

*super-Mare where the larvae are sometimes abundant on wych elms.'.*

Interestingly Brown (1971) was not convinced that it was still common at Weston-super-Mare: *'This butterfly has recently been discovered in several places within Bristol itself, which is a very good sign. On either side of the Avon Gorge, this species has been seen from time to time, but mostly high up in the Wych Elm trees. In 1966 a larva was beaten from a low branch of one of these trees and later on a butterfly was seen on some nearby bramble blossom. To the north of Bristol not far from Henbury, specimens have been noted much more frequently, and various evidence points to the fact that it may be on the increase. At Whorlebury Hill near Weston-super-Mare, single specimens have been found occasionally, not only as adults but also*

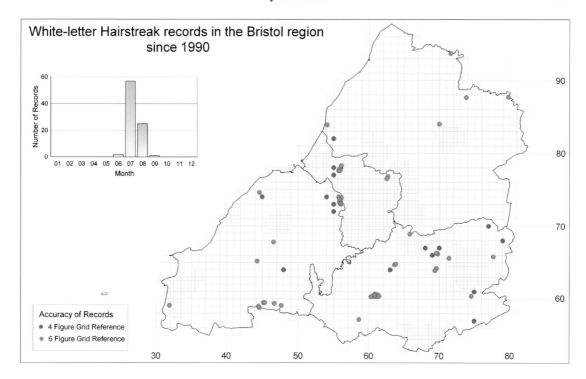

White-letter Hairstreak records in the Bristol region since 1990

*as larvae and once a pupa. However, it often appears to be absent from this locality.'* Brown also went on to say that the White-letter Hairstreak had been recently found in some of the unspoilt areas between the Cotswold Hills and the Severn Estuary and that he regarded it as *'well established in the Bristol area, and at present is in no kind of danger.'*

The latter comment was written just before the devastation of the larval foodplant, elm trees *Ulmus* spp., due to the arrival of a virulent strain of Dutch Elm Disease during the 1970s. Meredith (1984), as well as listing a number of records from the northern half of the Bristol conurbation, expressed the opinion that the butterfly population had collapsed as a result of the disease. In fact the elm favoured by the butterfly, Wych Elm *Ulmus glabra* has faired better than Common Elm *Ulmus procera* and certainly in the last fifteen years the butterfly has survived well despite the original fears for its future.

The difficulty of spotting the butterfly is still the biggest limitation to establishing the true distribution of this species in the region. It was only added to the Wetmoor list in 1990 (Anon, 1994), for example, where it may have been present for many years previously. However, that record is from a single Wych Elm which had become infected with Dutch Elm Disease by 2002. Looking specifically for the butterfly along woodland edges and hedgerows with much Wych Elm in the early morning or late afternoon on hot days in mid to late July may be the best way to find new colonies. A little experience at where to look for this secretive species can be very helpful.

The current survey results show the widespread distribution of the butterfly across the region. The concentrations of records reflect the well recorded wildlife reserves, for example Folly Farm to the south of Bristol and it is present still on both sides of the Avon Gorge. The butterfly is present in Weston-super-Mare and along the Mendip ridge. More sites are awaiting discovery.

# Small Copper    *Lycaena phlaeas* (Linn.) ssp. *eleus* (Fabr.)

**National status: Common resident throughout the British Isles.**
**Bristol region status: Common and widespread.**

Martin Evans    13ᵗʰ August 1983

**Small Copper**    Hutton, North Somerset

The Small Copper has been a common member of our butterfly fauna for well over one hundred years at least. Hudd (1884) considered it common, Turner (1955) felt it was probably less abundant than it had been but still very common locally. The capture of aberrations was a fairly regular event as per this species elsewhere in the country, eg *'var radiata Tutt a specimen bred from Bristol stock, gen. 3 (C.L.B. Proc Brist. N.S. XXVIII p.42).'* (Meredith, 1984).

Brown (1971) also referred to variations in appearance, *'At Kingsweston Down, a healthy brood is observed in each generation every year, with a good proportion of ab.* caeruleopunctata, *the form with a series of blue markings on the hindwings. Sorrel being the larval foodplant abounds here, since the grass is cut back each year and there also being a large*

*number of anthills in the vicinity. In an orchard not far away, the Small Copper is equally plentiful, even though cattle are regularly allowed to graze there. This butterfly is often bred by the author, from larvae collected in a number of localities, and it is of interest that the abovementioned variation appears in as much as eighty or ninety per cent of the resulting brood.'* He adds *'On the whole, the prospects look good for the Small Copper in our part of the world, its only real enemies being disease and parasites.'*

As well as Common Sorrel *Rumex acetosa*, Sheep's Sorrel *R. acetosella* is often utilised as a larval foodplant and hence the butterfly is a feature of so-called waste ground, railway sidings, rough grassland and other such places. The first known record from Steepholm was in 1954 (Parsons, 1996) but

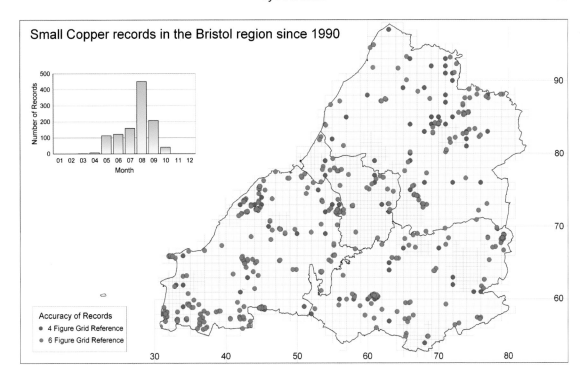

Small Copper records in the Bristol region since 1990

sorrels are not known to grow there. Parsons postulates that ragwort could be used as an alternative larval foodplant but this is perhaps rather unlikely.

The current survey shows it to be particularly well represented on the Mendip edge, in the Gordano Valley and elsewhere still very widely distributed. It is likely that it is not as abundant as it once was due to a steady decline in suitable habitat. The phenological chart for the duration of the survey reveals peaks in emergence in mid May and August with a third brood reinforcing the second in September and lasting on into October. Albino forms have been seen near Yatton and at Folly Farm during the 1990s.

# Large Copper    *Lycaena dispar dispar* (Haw.)

**National status: Extinct resident.**
**Bristol region status: Reported in the 19th century, probably in error.**

Allan (1966) accepted that the Large Copper did occur in the Somerset Levels at least until 1857. However by that time the butterfly was already extinct in most of the East Anglian counties that were its stronghold, and the last British record is from Norfolk in 1864. On that basis the Somerset reports are open to question.

The suggestion that the butterfly may have also occurred within the Bristol region in the past is based on Hudd's report of 1906 in the Victoria County History of Somerset: '*It was reported but I could not ascertain particulars that a specimen of the Large Copper was taken near Clevedon about 1869 or 1870. Not being able to find either the exact date or the name of the captor I did not record it in my Catalogue of the Lepidoptera of the Bristol District but it is quite possible I think that it was found there. The late Mr G.R.Crotch recorded a specimen from near Weston-s-Mare in 1856 "C. dispar fell ignobly slain by the hat of a friend who kindly made the spoil over to me in utter ignorance of its rarity (Intelligencer ii. 165; iv. 21).*" This is the record, ascribed to 1857, that Allan accepted.

Turner (1955) regarded these records as '*most improbable*' although he considered that an extinct population at Langport, on the Somerset Levels, was a possibility. This is reinforced by the existence of specimens in the Somerset County Museum at Taunton, but they are unlabelled. One could postulate that individuals might have wandered from such a small population into the Bristol region. However this butterfly is thought to be very sedentary and restricted to an aquatic environment where the larvae feed on Water Dock *Rumex hydrolapatham*. This plant is widespread in the region. However no Large Coppers were ever reported from the north Somerset moors such as in the Gordano Valley and elsewhere. Consequently, the conclusion that Turner reached was probably the correct one and the records from Clevedon and Weston-super-Mare are very probably erroneous.

# Long-tailed Blue    *Lampides boeticus* (Linn.)

**National status: Rare immigrant**
**Bristol region status: Very rare immigrant (only one record known).**

There is just one known record, from Bloomfield Road, Brislington, a specimen of a worn female taken at Sweet-pea blooms on 20 July 1952 (Cooper, 1952). It is possible that others may have been over-looked as the butterfly is small and easily missed. The British examples are thought to originate from summer breeding in central and southern France (Emmet & Heath, 1989). In recent years there has been an increase in sightings in England, perhaps due to accidental importations, but this may be a butterfly that might be found in future in the region.

## Small Blue  *Cupido minimus* (Fuess.)

**National status: Localised resident, throughout the British Isles but declining.**
**Bristol region status: Rare, at a few remaining sites.**

Martin Evans 1982

**Small Blue**  Worle Hill (south side), North Somerset

The Small Blue requires sites where the larval foodplant, Kidney Vetch *Anthyllis vulneraria* occurs along with reasonably tall grass where it prefers to perch. Consequently unimproved, calcareous grassland is the only habitat where it will be located. Its intolerance to variation in this habitat type is less than that of the Chalkhill and Adonis Blues but nevertheless it is still very vulnerable and can be lost from sites relatively quickly.

Limestone grassland is a feature of the Bristol region but the quality and quantity has declined and very rapidly so in the last part of the 20th century. In Alfred Hudd's day he regarded the Small Blue as '*widely distributed, but very local, being found in some localities only in the corner of a field, or a space of a few dozen yards on a hillside*' (Hudd, 1906). Localities at that time included Brockley, Bath,

Clevedon, Portishead, Weston and Durdham Down in Bristol. This was still largely the case by the 1950s although it disappeared from the Gully on Durdham Downs at some point around this time.

It is surprising that little notice seems to have been taken of this diminutive butterfly. For example, Brown (1971) knew of it from Weston-super-Mare and on the Cotswolds but otherwise noted '*we have very little information concerning the Small Blue.*' One would have expected its sites along the Mendip edge to have been noted. R.Angles had though reported finding the Small Blue at Haw Wood, Filton on 6th and 20th August. If identified correctly this would have been second brood examples and the second brood is notoriously small in number. A possible source for such butterflies has been suggested as Mount

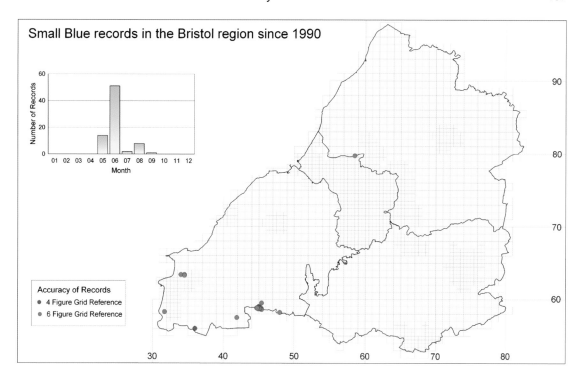

Small Blue records in the Bristol region since 1990

Skitham, a south facing grassland site which has supported Green Hairstreak for example (C. Wiltshire, pers. comm.), but there is no trace of the larval foodplant currently and it has become scrubbed up. J. Muggleton (pers. comm.) points out that the adults can be hard to find and that looking for the eggs can be more productive. This may also explain the lack of sites in Brown's paper.

Records held at the Bristol Regional Environmental Records Centre for the 1980s suggest that the Small Blue was thinly scattered over the region at that time, particularly in the south. In the 1990s however, there seems to have been a dramatic decline. More than half of the recorded sites of the 1980s no longer support this species. This loss may be due to the degradation of the available habitat. Lack of grazing and disturbance of the soil leads to the Kidney Vetch disappearing as it requires bare patches of earth to colonise. Over-grazing can adversely affect the plants' ability to flower and can lead to direct loss of larvae as they actually feed in the inflorescence. The loss of rabbits through myxomatosis affected this butterfly as rabbits are undoubtedly beneficial in keeping the habitat and sward to the butterflies' liking.

In 1994 Jerry Board carried out a behavioural study of the population of Small Blue at Dolebury Warren on the Mendips (Board, 1995). His findings were of great interest in that they identified areas of the grassland being used for different purposes by the butterflies. Unfortunately this is one of the populations that has crashed and is now considered to be probably extinct at the site. However the butterfly has fluctuated at the site previously and was considered extinct, for example, in the early 1990s. Populations produced adults on the wing throughout June with a much smaller second brood

**Small Blue**

apparent in some years in August and even one individual on the 1 September in 1991. If it has disappeared from Dolebury the suggestion has been made that the levels of sheep grazing may have contributed to this as the stock preferentially eat the flowers of the Kidney Vetch. Future management of such sites should consider winter grazing only.

There is every possibility that this species will shortly become extinct in our region or indeed is already now extinct. The fragmentation of suitable habitats makes natural colonisation or re-colonisation unlikely.

# Silver-studded Blue  *Plebejus argus* (Linn.)

**National status: Widely scattered resident across England and Wales in localised colonies, probably declining.**
**Bristol region status: Always rare, not recorded since the early 1980s.**

A very sedentary butterfly restricted to localised colonies where numbers can get high. Four different subspecies have been recorded from the British Isles, two of which are, or have been, very restricted in distribution: ssp. *caernensis* only found on the Great Orme of North Wales; and ssp. *masseyi* only found in Lancashire and Westmoreland, but now extinct. The two remaining subspecies are ssp. *cretaceus* restricted to chalk and limestone downland, now nearly extinct, and ssp. *argus* only found on heathland. The former subspecies is usually considered to be mainly found in the south east of England, whereas the latter is more generally distributed. Consequently the few scattered colonies that have existed in our region have usually been assigned to ssp. *argus*. However the sites where these colonies have been

recorded from could have supported either subspecies being limestone grassland but with heathland. In the 19th century Hudd (1884) quoted Durdham Down and Stapleton in the northern part of the region and also '*Weston-s-m. E.S. & G.R.C.*' and in a later annotation, '*fairly com. in one locality at Clevedon Mr J.Mason 1900.*' Newman (1874) includes Brockley and gives A.E. Hudd as the source. By the Victoria County History of Somerset (Hudd, 1906) Bath had also been added.

This state of affairs remained the case until 1950 when A.M. Emmet reported it from Combe Dingle in Bristol where no suitable habitat for either subspecies is present. The reputation of the recorder leaves misidentification as highly unlikely but the source of the butterfly remains a mystery. The only other recent records are from Wetmoor. The Wetmoor Guide (Anon, 1994) reports '*Three males in the Horton Trench in 1979 (reported from Hawkesbury Upton in the 1950s and Horton Common in the 1960s)*'. The origin of those earlier records is still to be traced, but the 1979 sighting was by C.W.V.Gane, in late August, of three males. One was reportedly sent to the British Museum (Natural History) for confirmation and subsequently given to his brother J.V.Gane. There appears to be no record of this at the Natural History Museum and the location of the specimen now is not known.

The impression then, is that in the 19th century there were a few scattered colonies on calcareous downland sites (with limestone heathland) of either ssp. *cretaceus* whose larvae feed on Bird's-foot Trefoil *Lotus corniculatus* or ssp. *argus*, larvae on gorse *Ulex* spp., heaths *Erica* spp. or heather *Calluna vulgaris*.

The Wetmoor records of the second half of the 20th century, have apparently some validity as there is a series over time even though the habitat seems unlikely. But the colony must have always have been very small and, like elsewhere in the region, the butterfly is now thought to be extinct there.

# Brown Argus    *Aricia agestis* (D. & S.)

**National status: Widespread resident throughout England and Wales.**
**Bristol region status: Widespread and increasing.**

24ᵗʰ August 1986    Martin Evans

**Brown Argus**    Sand Point, North Somerset

To the casual observer the Brown Argus may be overlooked as a female Common Blue. However butterfly enthusiasts over time have kept fairly accurate records of its true distribution in the Bristol region. Turner (1955) for example when writing about the whole of Somerset stated *'Moderately common locally, particularly in the northern part* [of Somerset] *Clevedon, Walton-in-Gordano (J.E.H.B.) 1919.'*, the northern part being within the region examined in the current survey. Duck (1852) records *'Generally distributed. Variable.'* referring to its occurrence around Portishead and Hudd (1884) wrote *'Throughout the district, common but rather local. Some curious varieties have been taken.'* Unfortunately he does not elaborate on the latter.

In the 1950s the occurrence of the Brown Argus at calcareous downland sites was reflected by the sites that J. Bird recorded it at: *'Walton-in-Gordano, Clevedon, Tickenham, Kenn, Goblin Combe, Brockley Combe, Rowberrow.'* The 1970s saw a similar situation as Brown (1971) reported *'As with the species just described* [Duke of Burgundy], *the Brown Argus is mainly confined to the western slopes of the Cotswold Hills in Gloucestershire, where its colonies are none too strong. At Kingsweston Down just to the north of Bristol, a few of these butterflies are seen each year, despite frequent clearing of the long grass. In North Somerset the Brown Argus occurs in a wide variety of habitats where it also flies in greater numbers. Once again, Goblin Combe is one of the strongholds while the other colonies seem to be centred around the western end of the Mendip Hills.'*

An interesting record is from the island of Steepholm (Parsons, 1996), with a single

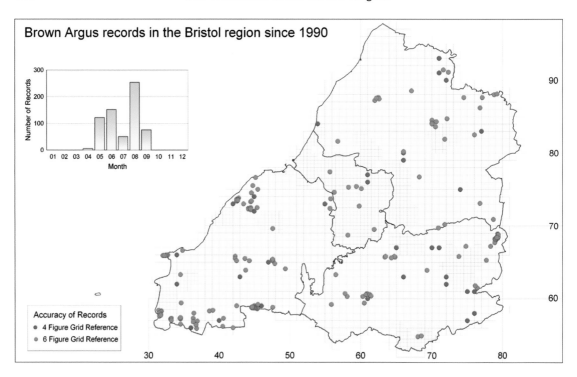

Brown Argus records in the Bristol region since 1990

sighting on 10 Sept 1988 and Parsons suggests this may be explained as '*an itinerant (from Brean Down?).*'

In the period of the current survey the butterfly has apparently maintained good numbers on suitable habitats throughout the region, for example at Goblin Combe, but with perhaps a concentration on the Mendips and in the Gordano Valley. It also certainly seems to be increasing in numbers and exploiting new larval foodplants in the form of native species of *Geranium*. Cut-leaved Geranium *Geranium dissectum* for example, has been seen being used as a foodplant in long grass at Horwood Farm, west of Lower Woods (C. Wiltshire, pers. comm.). Previously the accepted foodplants have been Common Rock-rose *Helianthemum nummularium*, Common Stork's-bill *Erodium cicutarium* and Dove's-foot Crane's-bill *Geranium molle*. Given that these are **usually** low-growing plants of calcareous habitats, Brown's comment that the Brown Argus had survived at Kingsweston Down despite the removal of long grass should perhaps have been **because** of that removal. In recent years the butterfly has disappeared from that site, probably because those larval foodplants have been crowded out by lack of

grazing, or other management, to keep the sward height down. Furthermore the Brown Argus has been lost from many urban "wasteland" sites as they have been re-developed. Asher *et al* (2001) suggest that increases in Brown Argus populations can be correlated to warm, dry summers and to the availability of non-rotational set-aside fields. The latter may be a more important factor in the central and eastern parts of England.

The increase in populations will be worth further monitoring to establish which larval foodplants are being used at new sites and whether the increases are continuing. Aside from the early mentions by recorders of interesting forms, there is no other information available on the type of forms recorded then or any more recent aberrations found.

The phenological data shows clearly the double brooded nature of the Brown Argus. The highest number of records are from the first brood in May which survives throughout June. The second brood appears to have strong numbers on the wing for a longer period, from late July into September. It is possible that a third partial brood may also be occurring in certain years, masked by the remnants of the second.

# Common Blue    *Polyommatus icarus icarus* (Rott.)

**National status: Common and widespread resident throughout the British Isles.
Bristol region status: Common and widespread**.

**Common Blue**    East Harptree Woods, North Somerset

A very common member of the butterfly fauna in the 19th century, Hudd (1884) reports, '*Abundant everywhere. The "small variety scarcely larger than L. Alsus* [Small Blue]*," recorded from Wotton-under-Edge by Mr Perkins, has also been taken on Durdham Down late in the autumn. It may be a third brood.*' Turner (1955) though considered it to be '*less common than formerly.*' This did not stop Bird (unpublished) listing twelve sites for it in north Somerset at around this time.

By the 1970s, Brown (1971) considered it '*widespread and can be observed in a variety of habitats over the two vice-counties. In West Gloucestershire, it is particularly common at Wetmoor.*' With regard to south of Bristol he remarks: '*The western end of the Mendip Hills appear to be another good locality for this species, where there extensive areas of open*

*limestone downlands with well-cropped turf and an abundance of flora.*' As a final thought he adds: '*There appears to be little in the way of local variation.*'

This still remains the commonest of the blues that feed as larvae on herbaceous plants. Bird's-foot Trefoil *Lotus corniculatus*, Greater Bird's-foot Trefoil *Lotus pedunculatus*, Black Medick *Medicago lupulina*, Restharrow *Ononis* spp. and White Clover *Trifolium repens* are amongst the plant species it can utilise in this form. As a consequence it can colonise and survive in quite small patches of rough grassland. For example, in the centre of Bristol it occurs in low numbers in Castle Park, where areas of archaeological interest are left unmown and fenced against the public. So called 'urban commons' such as these are also becoming rarer as development of 'brown

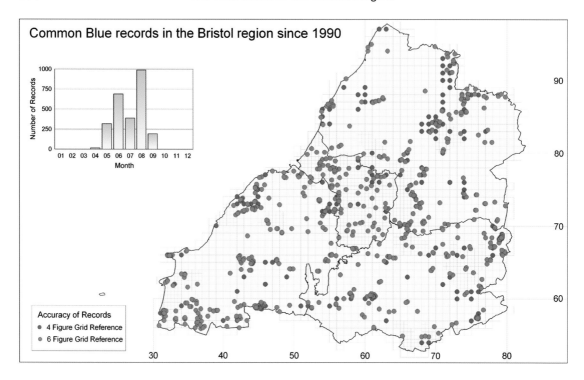

Common Blue records in the Bristol region since 1990

field' sites increases and several city centre sites are known to have been lost. Individual butterflies have also been recorded reaching Steepholm, the first record dating back to 1912 with others in 1976, 1983 and 1991 (Parsons, 1996).

Although the survey shows it still to be widespread, there is cause for concern. The density of Common Blue populations has undoubtedly been reducing. It is a species that illustrates well that utilising butterflies as a means of monitoring the health of the countryside must include more information other than just presence or absence. The use of pesticides and intensive farmland management techniques is a probable reason for the weakening of colonies. Lack of management and grazing on protected sites also leads gradually to a reduction in the vitality of colonies as the leguminous larval foodplants become shaded out.

The situation in our region echoes the national position where undisturbed neutral grassland has declined by approximately 98% in the last half of the twentieth century with consequent reductions in invertebrates that live in such habitats. Even road verges and quarries, which in some parts of the country provide a refuge for Common Blue colonies, appear to be losing this butterfly in and around Bristol.

The Common Blue usually has two broods in the Bristol region peaking around late May and early June and then in August. The often smaller examples of the third brood referred to by Hudd only appear in years when the summer is prolonged. This explains the sightings that go on into October. In all broods we do seem to have a very high percentage of females which come close to ab. *caerulea*, in which they exhibit upperwing markings that are nearly as blue as the male but with a chocolate border and prominent orange lunules.

# Chalkhill Blue   *Lysandra coridon* (Poda)

**National status: Resident of calcareous grassland in southern England in localised and declining colonies.**
**Bristol region status: Very rare and threatened.**

Martin Evans   4th September 1986

**Chalkhill Blue**   Uphill Quarry, North Somerset

Together with the Small Blue and Adonis Blue, the Chalkhill Blue makes up part of the triumverate of blues restricted to unimproved calcareous grassland. In this case the larvae feed exclusively upon Horseshoe Vetch *Hippocrepis comosa* and a glance at the Flora of the Bristol Region (Myles *et al*, 2000) immediately reveals how restricted the plant is in the area. It occurs scattered across the area with concentrations in the far north west on the edge of the Cotswolds, around Bath (particularly to the south) and then with pockets close to Bristol, near Clevedon and near Weston-super-Mare and finally on the Mendip edge. This distribution is probably not that different to that recorded by White in The Bristol Flora (1912). However it disguises the reduction in the

number of sites within these areas and the reduction in concentration of the plant's occurrence at these sites.

To maintain strong populations of the Chalkhill Blue butterfly the presence of Horseshoe Vetch in its own right is not enough. The plant must be plentiful but also the grassland must be grazed not only to prevent the plant from being shaded out and eventually disappearing but also to ensure that solar radiation reaches the sward and bare patches of soil and creates a relatively hot environment which is favourable to the butterfly. Furthermore the larva has a loose association with ants, like a number of lycaenids. Secretions from the larva are milked by the ants and their presence is thought to confer a degree of protection against predation and parasitism. Even the pupa, which lies on the soil surface, continues to secrete chemicals which the ants find attractive.

Already, at the end of the 19th century, Hudd (1884 and later annotations) was concerned that the butterfly was losing out; '*Glos. This species seems to be found throughout the county on limestone hills and downs, though it has of late disappeared from some of its old localities. Stapleton, Durdham and Coombe Downs (1885 R.W.P), Bristol. Somerset. Leigh Down, scarce, Weston-super-Mare A.E.H. G.R.C. Batheaston Col. B.*' The colony on the Downs at Bristol illustrates just how different that place would have looked then with a sward of flowering downland plants, unlike today's green playing field. In the 20th century the Chalkhill Blue was lost from the Downs themselves and post-war only managed to survive there on the steep sides of the Avon Gorge itself. Sightings actually on top of the Downs became a rare event as Meredith (1984) records, '*Gully, Bristol few 1941–2 (J.W.N.); Sheepscombe few in 1938,39 much more plentiful in 1942, minor varieties. Used to be extremely common on the old rifle range Avon Gorge and have seen it as far afield as waterworks on Durdham Down (Heslop).*'

In the Gully, within the Gorge, the butterfly was '*fairly common on grassy slopes*' according to Norgrove in 1947 (Peach, 1948) but died out in the early 1990s as the habitat became scrubbed up. C. Wiltshire recorded eggs at the top of the Gully in 1985 and later adults that same year at the bottom of the Gully. The last adults were seen in 1990 and 1991 by Rupert Higgins and John Martin.

A similar tale of reduction of habitat can be seen across the region from the Second World War leading to just a very small number of suitable sites remaining at the end of the 20th century. Localities that J. Bird saw the butterfly on before the 1950s disappeared rapidly e.g. '*Tickenham, Portishead Down, Walton Moor.*' Stephen Blathwayt was familiar with the Chalkhill Blue at Worlebury Hill near Weston-super-Mare, for example in 1954 where he took the aberration named *obsoleta*. Brown (1971) summed the situation up as '*Along the coastal areas around Weston-s-Mare, this species is seen every year. It is feared, however, that this butterfly is on the decline as it is elsewhere in the country, due to the cultivation and destruction of habitats, particularly for farming purposes.*' As an example of the latter, Brown and C. Wiltshire discovered a larva of the Chalkhill Blue on a patch of Horseshoe Vetch on Henbury Golf Course, Bristol in 1966. The site is now woodland.

The Chalkhill Blue is known to occasionally wander away from its colonies, for example the Lower Woods Guide (Martin, 1998) records '*One and possibly two males in Horton Great Trench, these are not likely to have bred here as the site is unsuitable for its foodplant* Hippocrepis comosa *(Horseshoe vetch), the nearest examples of which grow some two kilometres away.*' The first record known of from the area is from 5th August 1967 by A. Kennard at '*Inglestone Common*'. In 1974 J. Muggleton confirmed that the 1967 record refers to the nearby Hawkesbury Hill. The butterfly continued to be present at that locality at least until 1970. Indeed the foodplant is still present there. The specimens noted above from Horton Great Trench were seen by C. Wiltshire and consisted of two sightings of male butterflies on 30th July 1992. A further sighting by the same observer in the same Trench was of a female Chalkhill Blue on 12th August 2000! Perhaps these were wanderers from Hawkesbury Hill or from the well known site for the butterfly at Saddlewood Roughs, near Midger Wood or some other colony yet to be discovered. Sadly apart from Saddlewood Roughs, there would appear to be very few places left where such a colony could exist and also to where wandering individuals could establish new colonies.

Butterfly collectors and recorders have long sought out the Chalkhill Blue in search of the many aberrations and forms that can occur. In particular the spotting on the underside can vary and become altered into streaks or other marks. The larger the colony the greater the chance of such variations being thrown up. Meredith (1984) includes the following, '*Sheepscombe a specimen with a pronounced black bar along inner margin of f.w. undersides 10. viii.52 (Thom). Sheepscombe one approaching ab fowleri South 27.viii.62, two ab fowleri 12, 28.viii.63.*' The aberration *fowleri* South is one of the over four hundred forms given names (Bright & Leeds, 1938) and affects the upperside, where the black border of the wing is replaced by white. No other reports of such forms are recorded even

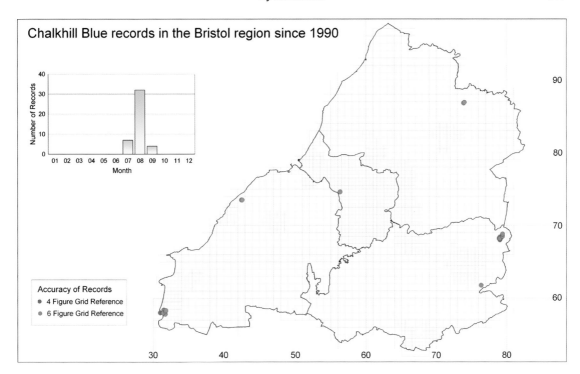

Chalkhill Blue records in the Bristol region since 1990

though the local recorder C.S.H. Blathwayt, was very keen on collecting them. Like many butterfly recorders he was tempted to visit the well known localities in the south of England where populations were greatest and with a history of aberrations, rather than concentrating on smaller colonies of the butterfly close at home.

In general, Brown's fears have been realised and the remaining colonies of the Chalkhill Blue of any size must be considered under threat in our region, despite being on nature reserves. The remaining concentration is in the Weston-super-Mare area. At these localities, despite Local Nature Reserve status

and grazing with Soay Sheep in late summer, which has reduced the rankness of the vegetation, the colonies remain small. The colony at Bannerdown, north of Bath is also very small if it still exists and yet there have been recent sightings at Tucking Mill on the west of the city of Bath. Research into the best management for the butterfly at its remaining sites and then the provision of adequate resources to achieve that must be a priority. Otherwise this splendid butterfly will follow the Adonis Blue and Silver-studded Blue, similar specialists of particular habitats, into extinction within the Bristol region and no longer be able to be seen on the wing in early August.

# Adonis Blue   *Lysandra bellargus* (Rott.)

**National status: Rare resident of calcareous grassland in southern England.**
**Bristol region status: Always a very rare butterfly and now extinct in the region.**

The Adonis Blue sits between the Large Blue and the Chalkhill Blue in terms of having evolved to become very specialised and dependent upon particular environmental conditions. Consequently although it has not become extinct in the country, unlike the Large Blue, it has become very rare, even rarer than the Chalkhill Blue.

The habitat required by the Adonis Blue is similar to that for the Chalkhill as they both feed as larvae on Horseshoe Vetch *Hippocrepis comosa*. The difference lies in that the Adonis requires shorter turf which not only results in higher temperatures at ground level but also enables the ants *Mrymica sabuleti* and *Lasius alienus* to survive. (The former of the two ant species is the favoured one for the very close symbiotic relationship exhibited with the Large Blue.) The larva of the Adonis Blue is attended by the ants which

stimulate glandular secretions which the ants drink. The ants will bury the larva just under the soil at night and will also bury the pupa (Thomas, 1983). The benefit to the butterfly is believed to be protection against predation and parasitism.

Closely grazed calcareous grassland with high concentrations of Horseshoe Vetch and the appropriate ant colonies in the warm south of England are therefore the only places where the butterfly can survive. Historically there seem to have been few places local to Bristol that met those criteria. The Bristol Naturalists' Society Proceedings for 1866 include: *'Mr Clarke exhibited a nice series of Lycaena Adonis, captured during the summer on Durdham Down. This beautiful species had appeared in some abundance this summer, and had not been recorded as having occurred in the district before.'*

Hudd (1884 and later annotations) has the following, *'Glos. Clifton, Durdham and Coombe Downs, and Henbury A.E.H. Stapleton G.H. Local but sometimes common. "The females seem to be lighter in colour at the coast of Dorset than in Kent or Gloucestershire." C.G.B. I. 83. Somerset. Not recorded from this county though it probably occurs on the downs south of the Avon. Radstock, 1900. Liveth. Bath Int. 25. 246. Weston-super-Mare – Int. II 165.'* Whereas Newman (1874) only gives, *'Taken in the Gully at Durdham Down in 1868 but not reported since, W.H.Grigg. Clifton, A.E.Hudd.'*

The existence of the Adonis Blue on the Bristol Downs continued through the first half of the 20th century but as with other species the only suitable habitat that remained was on the slopes of the Avon Gorge. Meredith (1984) reports, *'Gully Bristol few 1941–2 (J.W.N.).'* and goes on to give these extra sites *'Coombe Dingle end of Henbury Golf Course links 1918 (Heslop). Filton one 17.vi.63 (R.Ayler)* [presumably an error for R.Angles], *Charfield 13.v.65, 7.viii.65, 14.viii.65 Mrs M.Knight, BNS Inglestone about 12, 13.v.65 Mrs Knight BNS.'* and ends by stating *'No colony known.'*

It is possible that some of the latter records may be as a result of what Brown (1971) identified as probable confusion with the Common Blue, leading to claims where no foodplant has been found. He also stated: *'We have been sent in other observations of the Adonis Blue from the region around Wickwar, but we have yet to check up on this.'* Furthermore Brown was sceptical of reports from the south: *'regular reports come in of sightings along the coast near Weston-super-Mare. The habitat appears suitable but we still doubt these observations due to the abnormal times during which this butterfly has been noted.'* However there were a couple of sightings that did pass muster from Somerset including one from: *'a Roman encampment south of Clevedon'* and Brown accepted that record. His conclusion was *'obviously on the decline in the Bristol area as elsewhere in the country, and every effort is needed to protect it.'*

In fact it would seem that by the 1960s this butterfly was in serious trouble in the region. Burton wrote in 1965: *'The continued destruc-*

*tion of habitat is, however, a real threat to the recovery of those local species with specialised requirements such as the Adonis Blue.'* (Burton, 1965). Myxomatosis probably assisted in its decline as the habitats became unsuitable for its requirements. The only records known from the latter part of the century are: Filton Golf Course R.Angles 1962/3; Cadbury Camp E.Clay 1964; Charfield M.Kendall 1965; Sand Point R.Angles 1969; Weston Golf Course A. Pinches 1976–1982; Charmy Down Airfield B.S.Harper 1980. The origin of some of these sightings is intriguing as the localities were not all suitable even at that time, and the butterfly is not known to wander far from its colonies. The mis-identification problem has already been mentioned. To those who have never seen the blue colouration of the Adonis Blue male, confusion with brightly coloured male Common Blues is quite possible. The females are almost indistinguishable from the female Chalkhill Blue.

The records given as from Inglestone by Mrs Knight and Charfield by M. Kendall in 1965 are considered to be due to mis-identification of the Common Blue, or even Chalkhill Blue, as the records refer actually to Hawkesbury Hill rather than Inglestone Common. This is thought to be the possible origin of wandering Chalkhill Blues sighted at Wetmoor and has certainly held the larval foodplant for both these species.

As well as the above records, the Adonis Blue was recorded on cine film by Gordon Brown (father of A.D.R.Brown) in 1963 at Coombe Hill, Wooton-under-Edge just over the border from the Bristol region.

In summary this rare butterfly was found in a few localities but suffered a decline, nationally and locally post-war and finally had disappeared from the Bristol region by the 1980s. Following the success of the re-introduction of the Large Blue to localities in the south west, there have also been attempts to re-establish the Adonis Blue at sites before its populations drop too low, some of which surround the Bristol region. These have met with mixed success but form part of a national Biodiversity Action Plan for the butterfly aimed at preventing further reductions in the butterfly's distribution.

# Mazarine Blue   *Cyaniris semiargus* (Rott.)

**National status: Extinct resident by 1904.**
**Bristol region status: Less than half a dozen ever taken, all in the 19th century.**

The only records from our region are those quoted in Hudd (1906) and Heslop (1955). The former states, *'Recorded by Lewin: "The last week in August, 1763, I took two or three, flying in a pasture field at the bottom of a hill near Bath" (Insects of Gt. Britain p.80). Near Bath (Crotch); a specimen from Leigh Down near Bristol was caught about 1867, and was in the collection of Mr W.H.Grigg of Bristol.'* (Leigh Down is land now partly occupied by Long Ashton Golf Course and Failand.)

In the first half of the 19th century there were a number of records from the rest of Gloucestershire and it is possible that the few sightings around Bristol and Bath represent spill-over from those colonies. It is considered to have never been a common resident, except perhaps in Dorset, and to have become extinct in the country around the start of the 20th century, the Gloucestershire colonies having disappeared by 1865 (Emmet & Heath, 1989, Asher *et al*, 2001).

Heslop claims to have been familiar *'with the specimen and the place of actual capture'* of an individual dated 1916 from the *'Gloucestershire side of the Avon'*. He also states that *'one was taken by a school-fellow, and seen by me fresh-killed in his tin, in 1921'*. On this evidence Heslop thought that a colony could have survived in the vicinity of Bristol up until this date. However, these specimens have never come to light and if correct are perhaps more likely to be due to releases. The butterfly is not known to migrate commonly.

# Holly Blue   *Celastrina argiolus* (Linn.) ssp. *britanna* (Verity)

**National status: Common resident expanding its range over England, Wales and Ireland.
Bristol region status: Common, but numbers vary from year to year.**

Andrew Daw   26th May 1998

**Holly Blue**

The reports from different authors about the status of the Holly Blue have varied over time. Duck (1852) considered it '*Generally distributed. Common*' in and around Portishead. Similarly Hudd (1884) states '*Common amongst holly and ivy throughout the district.*' and then in his later annotations: '*Common everywhere in gardens of late years (CB).*' By contrast Turner (1955) thought it '*Uncommon but widespread: much less common than formerly, and irregular in appearance.*' Meredith (1984) joined him by stating '*Widespread but uncommon*' but recognised '*Common in some years especially the first brood.*' Brown (1971) thought it to be '*Although very widespread, the Holly Blue is never common and is usually observed in one and twos. The greater part of our records comes from within Bristol itself, and in a few places it seems to be on the*

*increase. Little more can be said than that, since we have no idea what controls the strength of this species in the Bristol area. Its various foodplants are abundant nearly everywhere, and the only possible explanation is the dependence upon the weather conditions, which are on the whole mild and damp in comparison with the rest of the country.*'

The fact is that currently it is believed that the Holly Blue population varies cyclically and that parasitism is more likely than the weather to be to the cause. Numbers build up year on year but the larvae are parasitised by the ichneumon wasp *Listrodomus nycthemerus*. As the butterfly numbers build, so numbers of the parasitoid similarly are able to follow this increase. At some point this causes the butterfly population to collapse. Naturally the ichneumon wasp then has prey that is very hard

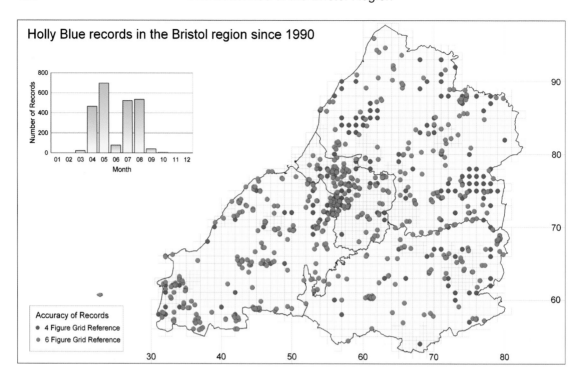

Holly Blue records in the Bristol region since 1990

to find and its numbers correspondingly crash. The butterfly numbers start to build again and so the process continues. Very good years in the mid-1990s followed the very poor ones of 1993 and 1994.

The Holly Blue is usually thought of as concentrated within the urban areas perhaps as the main larval foodplants (Holly *Ilex aquifolium* in the spring and Ivy *Hedera helix* in the autumn) are so regularly grown in gardens, parks, cemeteries and so on. However the distribution map from 1990 onwards shows that it is also widespread across the Bristol region. The good years of the 1990s may have been due to a combination of a reduction in the parasitoid with milder winters and warmer summers favouring the butterfly. During years of great abundance observations have shown that eggs will be laid on plants other than just

Holly or Ivy. For example, oviposition has been witnessed on Buddleia *Buddleja davidii* in a Bristol garden and the species regularly uses a variety of larval foodplants on the European mainland.

The Holly Blue has been regularly seen on Steepholm since 1954 (Parsons, 1996) but with no Holly present if breeding it must be using an alternative foodplant in the spring.

The butterfly is reported from Bristol in large numbers in good years which may also reflect the concentration of recorders in the city. The ability to identify the butterfly relatively easily due to its characteristic flight high around trees and bushes may add to the numbers of records. The size of the two broods varies as Meredith suggested, the spring brood in late April and May showing greater numbers than the summer brood from mid July to mid August.

# Large Blue    *Maculinea arion arion* (Linn.)

**National status: Extinct resident since the 1970s, various reintroductions.**
**Bristol region status: Extinct in the region since about 1860, but one reported in 1945.**

A.C.ᴿ
2002

The Large Blue holds a special place in the British butterfly fauna, sadly because of its disappearance from these isles in the 1970s. Its remarkable, highly specialised lifecycle has been often described in the butterfly press. The larva feeds on Wild Thyme *Thymus polytrichus* ssp. *britannicus* in its early instars before being taken into the subterranean nest of an ant, usually *Myrmica sabuleti*. Within the nest it feeds on the eggs, larvae or prepupae of the ants and in return secretes "honeydew" upon which the ants feed. Pupating within the nest, the butterfly emerges and crawls up to the surface to expand its wings and fly off. The ants require very short sward and without them the butterfly does not survive. The loss of grazing from sites where the butterfly occurred, either through the impact of myxomatosis on rabbit numbers or otherwise, is thought to have been the main cause of its extinction in this country.

The British distribution of the Large Blue was highly restricted for the last 150 years of its natural occurrence at which time it was only found in the counties of Northamptonshire, Gloucestershire, Somerset, Devon and Cornwall. The concentration in Gloucestershire was in the Cotswolds, mainly between Gloucester, Stroud and Cheltenham and the butterfly died out there in the 1960s. In Somerset very small colonies were found in the Langport area until the late 1950s. (Emmet & Heath, 1989).

The records from the Bristol region reported by Hudd (1884) are: ' *"Hills near Bath."* – *Lewin, quoted in Newman's "Butterflies" p.140. L.arion is marked on Mr Crotch's list from Weston but without locality. Near Bath Handbook 1888 p.256. "Hills near Bath"* – *Lewin.*' The last record is dated in the Victoria County History (Hudd, 1906) as being from 1795. It seems that the butterfly was probably last actually seen in the area in about 1860 (aside from the 1945 record) and that it was always of very rare occurrence here. There are no known specimens from our region and no reference to whether their appearance could be attributed to perceived differences between specimens from the Cotswolds and those from the south west peninsula. The time of emergence each year between these two geographically separated groups has also been remarked upon, the Cotswolds butterflies emerging earlier in the year than those further to the south west. This is considered to be due to the higher temperatures experienced on the southerly slopes of the Cotswolds compared to the cooler coastal combes of Corwall and Devon (J. Muggleton, 1973 & pers. comm.). Again there is no evidence to point to the time of emergence of butterflies close to Bristol.

There is one other record of this butterfly from the region. In The Entomologist journal for 1945, Ian Heslop wrote: '*I was reclining on a clump of heather in order to rest a lame foot when I was astonished to see a Large Blue come flying towards me. It gave me an excellent view of itself as it fluttered over some flowers at two paces distance while I was struggling to my feet; it was in absolutely fresh condition.*' (Heslop, 1945.) Heslop's diaries (now held at the Bristol Museum & Art Gallery) reveal this locality to be Brockley Combe. The entry concerning this event on 8th July that year is brief: '*Charles de W. accompanied. We saw an **arion**! (see letter to Entomologist – copy in file), the driver, Mr Herring, saw what can only have been an **iris**.*'

In his later article, written in 1949, Heslop described how in that year he had searched again for the Purple Emperor in Somerset with J. E. Herring and had by chance encountered the Large Blue at two sites. Five specimens were seen at two localities, both in the south of the county, outside the Bristol region, and one specimen was captured. Heslop postulated that the species might be able to survive at low densities across an area rather than at specific sites and offered that as an explanation, not only for those two localities, but also for the Brockley Combe occurrence four years previously (Heslop, 1950). The alternative view is that the butterflies all wandered from a central colony, perhaps that had survived since the reports from the 1830s and 1840s from near Langport. (Heslop's specimen is in the Bristol Museum & Art Gallery collections and as such is the only Somerset specimen from the 20th century.)

There has never been another record, before or since, from Brockley Combe or anywhere very close at hand. Brockley Combe is, and was, a well frequented locality by entomologists. Heslop, and Baron Charles de Worms who accompanied him in 1945, were highly respected and competent entomologists. Could they have made an error of identification? Or could the butterfly have represented a small colony somewhere nearby? Baron de Worms confirmed to J. Muggleton (pers. comm.) by letter in 1973 that he had indeed seen the specimen distinctly which establishes the record as genuine. It concurs with the experiences of lepidopterists in the 1940s in the Cotswolds where many completely new sites for the butterfly were found but which did not survive long after discovery. (J. Muggleton, pers. comm.)

In the 1990s the programme of re-introducing the Large Blue to the British Isles, which began in the 1980s using Swedish stock, has met with some success at a number of sites. It is highly unlikely that sites within the Bristol region might be used within this programme but local butterfly enthusiasts do not have that far to travel to see the butterfly flying freely again. If it was considered, there are sites that could be suitable with high concentrations of the foodplant, such as Hellenge Hill nature reserve, near Weston-super-Mare, already a site for the Chalkhill Blue.

# Duke of Burgundy    *Hamearis lucina* (Linn.)

**National status: Local resident of southern England.**
**Bristol region status: Rare, possibly extinct.**

**Duke of Burgundy**   Midger Wood, Gloucestershire

The delightful little Duke of Burgundy has always been a rare butterfly in our region. There are only a handful of sites at which the butterfly has been seen although there are well known colonies just to the north of the region in Gloucestershire and south into Somerset. The well known locality of Saddlewood Roughs in Gloucestershire, was at one point classed within the County of Avon but then the boundaries were re-drawn and it was excluded. The Bristol region area follows the boundaries of Avon as at its demise.

In 1884 Hudd listed '*Warleigh Wood, near Bath G.W.B.*' and in his later annotations: '*Near Bath Handbook 1888 p.256.*' On Hudd's authority Newman (1874), also included Weston-super-Mare.

In the 20th century Meredith (1984) reports, '*Wickwar (C.L.B. Proc BNS XXVIII 42: 191, 263), Wickwar 28.v.49, 6.vi.49, 29.v.50*

*(C.S.H.B.)*' indicating an established colony but the Guide to the nearby Wetmoor reserve (Anon, 1994) only gives records from 1980, one in April seen by C.W.V. "Bill" Gane and another on 10th May by Dr Hartill. Two of those specimens from 29th May 1950 are still in the Blathwayt collection at Bristol Museum & Art Gallery (Accession Number 36/1991).

South of Bristol and Bath, eight were seen at Goblin Combe in 1964, but no others have ever been seen there subsequently (Brown, 1971). This paper omits the record of 19th May 1948 by Dr Earnest Neal at Priory Wood near Blagdon (C.W.Wiltshire, pers. comm.). The Bath Natural History Society Magazine of 1977 includes a record of the Duke of Burgundy from Norton St. Philip by Bryan Moore. Several were reported from Newton-St.-Loe in 1981 (Sorrell & Weeks, 1982) but not seen since.

Kurt Vickery

**Duke of Burgundy** (aberration),   Midger Wood, Gloucestershire

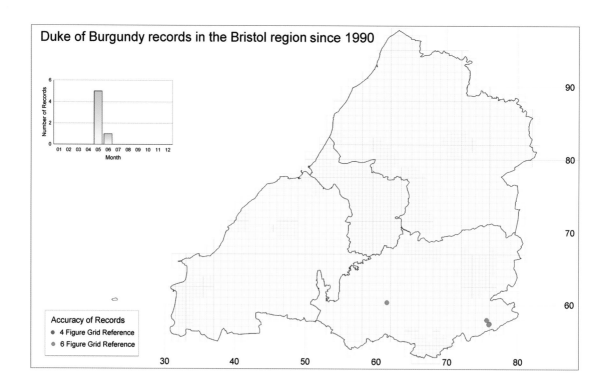

During the period of the current survey there has been a report of an individual butterfly at Folly Farm nature reserve in 1991 but, despite regular butterfly surveys, no other examples have been seen. There has only been one known colony in the 1990s and that very small, known from the edge of a privately owned wood, south of Bath. The Duke of Burgundy was first reported from here in 1982 (Sorrell, Way & Weeks, 1984). Only small numbers were ever seen at this site and sadly none has been recorded there since 1998. The open grassland site has been scrubbing up and therefore the favoured habitat, open but sheltered sites where the larvae feed on Cowslips *Primula veris* or Primrose *Primula vulgaris*, has virtually disappeared. It is possible that the colony had originally been linked to the Warleigh Wood colony mentioned by Hudd in the 19th century as the woodland to the east and south of Bath could have harboured other colonies between these two sites. Alternatively the butterfly populations may have moved around the area gradually as long as they could move from suitable habitat to suitable habitat. The fragmentation of habitats now makes such possibilities almost non-existent.

# NYMPHALIDAE

## White Admiral    *Limenitis camilla* (Linn.)

**National status: Local resident in southern England.**
**Bristol region status: Local in woodland.**

**White Admiral**    Leigh Woods

Kurt Vickery    July 1988

The White Admiral is one of a small number of butterflies that actually increased in abundance during the 20th century. Before that, this magnificent butterfly was largely restricted to the central southern counties of England. Hudd, in 1884, noted the one record from the Gloucestershire side of the region and the one accepted record from the Somerset side: '*Glos. The only specimen which has (so far as I know), been recorded from the county, was captured by Mr Crawford, on the bank of the Avon below Cook's Folly* (Avon Gorge) *more than twenty years ago. Mr Harding tells me he saw the specimen a few days after its capture,* and has no doubt of its having been taken in the locality named.' In his later annotations he adds: ' *"There is even a record of one specimen in Gloucestershire, but no recent captures seem to be recorded." C.G.B. I 120 Int. IV p.139. Taken by Mr J.B. Crawford of Cotham in July 1858 in Cook's Folly Woods. A rather worn specimen. Somerset. I have heard on* doubtful *authority that several specimens of the "White Admiral" were taken in Brockley Wood, by a local collector, many years since but have failed in verifying the statement. A. Iris was also said to have been taken there by the same collector.'* Hudd's annotations con-

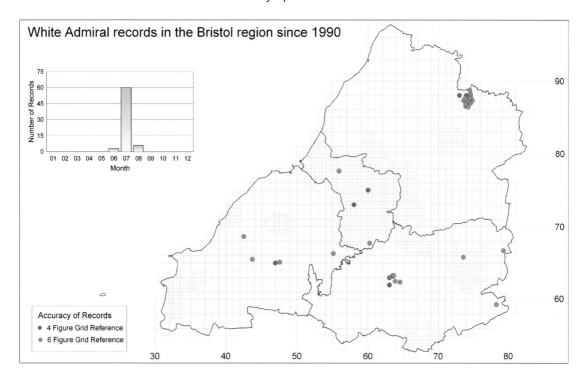

White Admiral records in the Bristol region since 1990

It was during the 1930s and 1940s that the butterfly started to expand its range across more of southern England. This is thought to have been due to the butterfly's preference for woodland that has lightly shaded areas within which the female lays its eggs on Honeysuckle *Lonicera periclymenum*. The decline in woodland management and, in particular the reduc-

**White Admiral** (larva)
Wetmoor, South Gloucestershire

tinue: '*Weston-s-M 1856 G.R.C. Int. II 165 and IV p.21. One by Mr Crotch at Weston 1856. One by Mr Bidgood from Newton Fitzwarren, one by Mr Swanton in Griff Wood near Bratton Seymour.*'

tion in coppicing, suited the butterfly at this time and it was assisted by a series of warm Junes which reduced the length of the final larval and pupal stages and resulted in less bird predation (Emmet & Heath, 1989). This increase was noticed by local naturalists and the appearance of such a splendid butterfly in the area even resulted in an article in the Bristol Evening Post in which H.C.E. Brucker reported it from Pensford on 15th July 1946 (published in the paper for 18th July). J.Bird listed it from Tickenham and Clevedon on 29th June 1943 as well as Walton Common in 1955 and he listed the following reference '*Bickenhall fairly common, local (Turner, J L Soc B. E. May 1950).*' Turner (1955) added one more record: '*Hinton Charterhouse (J.A.J.S.) 1952.*' and Meredith (1984) completes the records from this time with '*Wickwar several vii 1949, 1.vii.1950 (C.S.H.B.).*'

In 1971, Brown however did not seem to be that familiar with the species only reporting it within the Bristol region from Wetmoor. He obviously regarded it as likely that other colonies were awaiting discovery as he expressed concern over the impact of the blasting through the Tickenham ridge near Clevedon, taking place to pave the way for the construction of the M5 motorway, on likely sites. The history of the White Admiral at Wetmoor is one of colonisation from at least the 1960s and a small but constant population continuing to the present day. Another reliable colony can be found in Lords Wood near Pensford, the likely source of the 1946 record which appeared in the local press.

In recent years, there has been a suggestion that the butterfly is perhaps declining locally. Lower Woods and Lords Wood are the two main colonies with scattered sightings across the region representing small populations or wandering individuals. If there has been a decline it is unlikely to be due to the small amount of coppicing that has been re-instated in some woodland nature reserves but could be due to conifer plantations, which can support the butterfly in the middle stages of growth, becoming too mature and hence unsuitable. However even at the main sites, such as Wetmoor, the butterfly does appear to be less abundant than previously too. A further suggestion is that the increase of deer populations is accompanied by grazing of young honeysuckle, the butterfly's larval foodplant. If this decline is real, and there is little evidence to support this claim or not, it may also be linked to unfavourable weather at crucial times in certain years. This is another butterfly which can be relatively easily monitored in its known sites and could repay close study.

# Purple Emperor    *Apatura iris* (Linn.)

**National status: Local resident in southern England.**
**Bristol region status: Always been a great rarity.**

Andrew Daw   19th July 1998

**Purple Emperor**

This magnificent butterfly has always been very elusive in the area. The Victoria County History of Somerset (Hudd, 1906) summarised the few records from the 19th century as: '*A few recorded from Brockley Woods in 1870 (Last), Brockley Coombe (I.W.Clarke), Clive* [a misprint for Cleeve] *Coombe (F.D.Wheeler) and woods near Winscombe (T.H.Ormston Pease).*' Apart from an additional record reported in the Entomologist for 1952, Turner (1955) suspected the butterfly was likely to be extinct in the whole of Somerset.

Brown (1971) reported that in 1969 '*the late Mr I.R.P. Heslop informed us that he had rediscovered it at one of its old haunts in North Somerset after a gap of fifty-one years. Due to the isolation of this habitat it is presumed that the Purple Emperor has survived there all this time, but has obviously been previously over-looked. The author visited the locality again this year, but no butterflies were seen. The area in question is quite inaccessible in places, where large oaks and other deciduous trees grow on the sides of a steep valley. Vertical cliffs protrude from the valley sides and these are adjacent to some deserted quarries, mostly overgrown. For some distance around the thick oak forest spreads out until the boundaries of the Forestry Commission's plantations take over. From this it can be seen that the Purple Emperor could be flourishing anywhere within this region, and it is just a question of finding the master oak (or oaks). There appear to be very few dangers to its future existence, the only threat being the gradual encroachment of the Forestry Commission.*'

The description of the site given by Brown is reminiscent of Goblin Combe. In reality, the

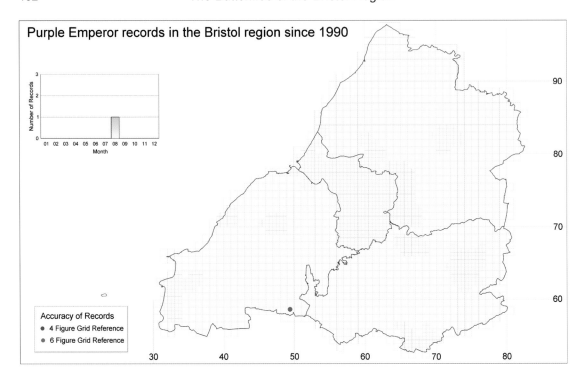

Purple Emperor records in the Bristol region since 1990

locality where Ian Heslop took a Purple Emperor, on 22nd July 1969, was the nearby Brockley Combe. He recorded the event in his notebook in the following manner: '*The Purple Emperor having been so widespread and abundant this year, I decided to make a detour to this old locality on my way back from Romsey for the last time. I parked my car at the head of the wooded portion of the Combe and walked down the road. I had not gone very far before I was astonished and delighted to see the familiar shark's-fin silhouette on drying horse-droppings on the road. I dropped the net over it, a female, without difficulty. She obliged me by laying six eggs when sleeved on a cut spray of sallow: she then died suddenly and rather mysteriously while still in almost perfect condition. I returned five of the resultant larvae to sallows in Brockley Combe in October; and resolved to try to bring the other one through.*'

In fact Heslop had seen the Purple Emperor once before at Brockley Combe, in 1918. The male specimen he took on the 9th August that year is still in his collection that is held at the City Museum & Art Gallery, Bristol. Again in 1945 there was another sighting there as Heslop recorded in his notebook for 8th July 1945 (at the same time as a Large Blue was apparently seen there by Heslop): '*the driver, Mr Herring, saw what can only have been an iris*'.

The large gaps between records from the site gives hope to the possibility that the butterfly could still cling on in small numbers even though it has never been seen there since 1969. However, this optimism may be tempered by the way the Combe has dramatically changed since the 1960s, largely due to the coniferisation that Brown had noted, which was also to contribute to the disappearance of so many fritillaries. Despite this there are still lepidopterists who might echo Hudd's comment from 1884: '*I feel no doubt the species does occur at Brockley*' even though in that case he had had no report for 14 years and the next record from the site came 48 years after the last. As it is now 34 years since the butterfly was last reported from Brockley perhaps it is time it put in another appearance?

North of Bristol, Meredith did not know of any records prior to 1984. However there had been unconfirmed records from Wetmoor in the 1970s and in 1989 a female Purple Emperor was positively identified at this woodland. The high degree of squirrel damage to sallows, resulting in open crowns, reduces the suitability of the habitat at this site, (M. Oates pers.comm.)

In the 1990s there have been a couple of records from south of Bristol, but these have been ascribed to the probable release of captive bred examples as in each case the habitat is unsuitable. The last recorded site is Burrington Combe where again the habitat is not ideal but the sighting was confirmed. Alternatively these individual records may represent wandering specimens as the butterfly is considered to be highly mobile, at least in some years (M. Oates pers. comm..).

The Purple Emperor is a butterfly of large woodlands where the larvae usually feed on Goat Willow *Salix caprea* or Grey Sallow *Salix cinerea*. Asher *et al* (2001) suggest there may have been a slight expansion of the butterfly in some areas in latter years following the gradual declines of the 20th century. It is possible that the few recent sightings relate to that or could be due to unauthorised releases and attempted introductions. Further searches at Lower Woods and Brockley Combe would be worthwhile.

# Red Admiral    *Vanessa atalanta* (Linn.)

**National status: Regular immigrant throughout the British Isles, now overwintering regularly in southern England.**
**Bristol region status: Regular immigrant, varies in numbers year to year, overwintering.**

John Aldridge   July 1988

**Red Admiral**    Wooscombe Bottom, Bath & North East Somerset

The Red Admiral has apparently always been a common immigrant to our region, present in reasonable numbers most years. On occasion the numbers of individuals reaching our shores, from southern Europe and northern Africa, can be very impressive. Brown (1971) singles out '*1964 and 1969*' as they '*stand out conspicuously, owing to the immense numbers of these butterflies which were observed during the late summer and autumns of those years. Clumps of Michaelmas Daisies and other plants were literally covered with them and they stayed with us right up into the middle of November*'.

The Common Butterfly Survey of the 1980s revealed a pattern whereby the main influx of Red Admirals arrived usually in late June with a rapid increase in numbers a month or so later as the progeny of the arrivals emerged. A second peak of numbers in August and September suggested a second brood reaching adulthood or these peaks could be explained as further influxes from the continent. 1982 and 1987 were the best years during that survey (1982–1988) with a dramatic slump in 1988. These good years did not coincide with that splendid year of 1983 for another well-known migrant, the Clouded Yellow, but did follow a similar pattern to the Painted Lady. Some sightings in the autumn of 1984 were tentatively ascribed to possible reverse immigration *i.e.* a trend for adults to move southwards perhaps triggered by reducing day length. More recent observations in the 1990s have confirmed this behaviour.

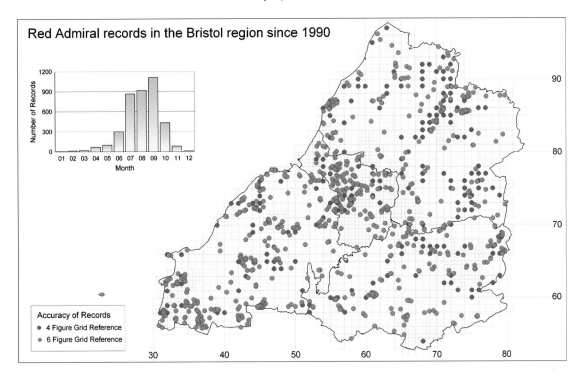

Red Admiral records in the Bristol region since 1990

In the last twenty years or so it has been suggested that this species has been successfully hibernating as winters have become less severe. However, Turner in 1955 mentioned that the butterfly could be '*Noted in every month of the year.*' Undoubtedly immigration can occur at any time of the year in small numbers and this can explain winter sightings. The direct observation of Red Admirals disturbed from hibernation sites however, for example from ivy on 1st January 2001 in Bristol, has justified the claim that this is a new and genuine phenomenon. Asher *et al* (2001) report that all stages of the butterfly can survive the winter.

Parsons (1996) provides further evidence of the immigration of the Red Admiral when stating '*Records of 50+ frequent*' with regard to the island of Steepholm and yet '*Breeding sparse & rarely successful.*'

The foodplant of the butterfly is usually Common Nettle *Urtica dioica* but the larvae are less often noted than those of the gregarious Small Tortoiseshell and Peacock, as they are concealed within folded leaves.

As the distribution map shows the Red Admiral is familiar to all butterfly recorders in the region and can turn up anywhere, as you would expect with a migrant and resident using nettle as a foodplant. The flight time graph reflects the build up of immigrants from May and June followed by home bred individuals joining the armada from July through to October.

## Painted Lady    *Vanessa cardui* (Linn.)

**National status: Regular immigrant throughout the British Isles.**
**Bristol region status: Regular immigrant, varies in numbers year to year.**

Kurt Vickery   September 2002

**Painted Lady**    Winscombe, North Somerset

As with the Red Admiral this butterfly has always been a regular immigrant from North Africa each year. However, unlike the former species it has always been considered unable to enter a hibernation phase, existing in warmer climes as a continuously brooded butterfly. Hence, the impression that in recent years the Painted Lady has not been able to adapt to the milder winters we have experienced as effectively as the Red Admiral. Asher *et al* (2001) though report that a marked individual was recorded overwintering at Hayle in Cornwall during 1997/8 so perhaps this is a possibility and worth looking out for in future years.

The numbers of individuals which make the journey to our shores seems to vary more than the Red Admiral, as Turner (1955) mentioned '*A very irregular immigrant: sometimes abun-*

*dant, and in some years scarce or even absent*'. Brown (1971) picked out 1964 and 1969 as years when the butterfly was particularly abundant, as was the Red Admiral. The peak of sightings was in the spring, in contrast to the Red Admiral's numbers building towards the latter part of those years. The Common Butterfly Survey of the 1980s showed again a parallel between the Painted Lady and Red Admiral with numbers declining dramatically after the good year of 1982 and then building again from 1985 to 1987.

Again this butterfly has been regularly reported on migration from Steepholm (Parsons, 1996) but on one occasion breeding has been detected once utilising Tree-mallow *Lavetera arborea*. The usually quoted foodplants for the larvae are thistles *Cirsium* and *Carduus* spp., but Common Nettle *Urtica*

**Painted Lady** (larva)
Madam Lane, Worle, North Somerset

Martin Evans   June 1982

**Painted Lady** (pupa)
Madam Lane, Worle, North Somerset

Martin Evans   July 1982

*dioica* and Mallows *Malva* spp. will also be used.

During the current survey there have been two good years for the butterfly. 1994 was notable for good numbers but nothing led any-one to predict the enormous numbers which visited the whole country in 1996. In the Bristol region records from 455 sites were received and some truly exciting sightings reported, fields apparently moving with the sheer abundance of this butterfly. International analysis of the phenomenal immigration in 1996 (Asher *et al*, 2001) suggests that these numbers are linked directly to favourable environmental conditions in the north of Africa from where individuals disperse very rapidly northwards.

Analysis of the data from all observations sent in over the survey's period shows on average a peak of records in June and then a gap before another peak in early August slowly declining into October. This blip between the first appearance of immigrants in June and the summer abundance is much more pronounced than in other immigrants reflecting the more haphazard way in which the populations vary from year to year.

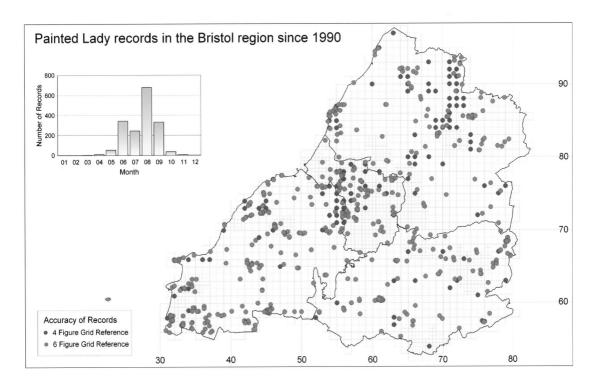

Painted Lady records in the Bristol region since 1990

Accuracy of Records
• 4 Figure Grid Reference
• 6 Figure Grid Reference

# Small Tortoiseshell    *Aglais urticae* (Linn.)

**National status: Common resident throughout the British Isles.**
**Bristol region status: Common resident.**

Martin Evans    1982

**Small Tortoiseshell**    Loxton Estate, North Somerset

This is perhaps the archetypal British butterfly familiar to most people as the common but attractive butterfly, subject of campaigns to preserve nettle beds near habitation to help the butterfly breed. In fact the gregarious larvae feed on both Common Nettle *Urtica dioica* and Small Nettle *Urtica urens*. The adult butterflies prefer to oviposit on small plants on the edge of nettle beds in relatively open situations and egg-laying is determined by temperature as recorded in Bristol being restricted to between 10.00am and 2.00pm during March/April (Emmet & Heath, 1989). Nettles grow on soils that have high levels of nutrients such as phosphorous and potassium and consequently grow close to human habitation and agricultural land. This, coupled to the nationwide distribution of the butterfly and its appearance from hibernation early in the year,

has led to it occupying such a high profile in the public appreciation of our butterfly fauna. It is not unusual for the Small Tortoiseshell to be discovered hibernating within houses as well as in sheds and other such structures.

This impression of abundance has not changed significantly in the last two hundred years, Hudd (1884) for example stating '*Abundant everywhere.*' More recently, Brown (1971) drew attention to occasional years when climatic conditions seemed to favour the butterfly and to allow a third brood of this normally double-brooded species. In particular he mentioned '*1964 was one such year when it was probable that a third generation took place; in mid September no fewer than 150 individuals were noted at Blagdon Lake in North Somerset, where they were visiting Water Mint flowers on the shore. In 1968 a* similar occurrence took place and the butter-flies "swarmed" everywhere during the second generation. Earlier in the year larvae were to be found in profusion, and several good aber-rations were bred from collected wild stock. Specimens remained on the wing throughout the autumn, and the last one was recorded from Charfield in Gloucestershire on 24th November.'

During the 1980s Common Butterfly Survey the Small Tortoiseshell was the most common of the species studied during 1982, 1983 and particularly 1984 when yet again groups of up-to 200 individual butterflies could be seen feeding on Water Mint *Mentha aquatica* at Chew Valley. In 1985 numbers were extreme-ly low in early summer and this was suggest-ed to be a response to awful weather in early to mid-June killing the offspring of the over-wintered butterflies. However Asher *et al* (2001) contradict this theory suggesting that numbers improve with high rainfall in May and June and that fluctuation is more likely to be related to conditions the previous autumn when the butterflies were preparing for hiber-nation. By the start of September in 1985 the second brood was three weeks late but good weather then gave rise to a dramatic resur-gence and good numbers appeared well into October. The final years of the Survey were not very strong for the Small Tortoiseshell.

It is perhaps surprising that apart from Brown's reference above, there are very few records of aberrations from our area. One example though was the record from Whitchurch in 1995 of ab. *semi-ischnoides*, a form thought to be produced after the pupa has been exposed to unusually high tempera-tures reducing the deposition of the black pig-ment melanin.

In recent years numbers have fluctuated without any spectacular increases but at the start of the millennium concern has been expressed that numbers may have suddenly dramatically decreased, an impression remarked upon nationally as well as locally. This is likely to be just a blip in a species which does fluctuate in numbers and, if a real obser-vation, may be related to poor weather at cru-cial stages in the life cycle such as those seen in 1985. However, the concern raised comes at a time when the general degradation of the natural environment is apparently leading to significant declines in population density of other "common" species such as the House Sparrow. There is no room for complacency

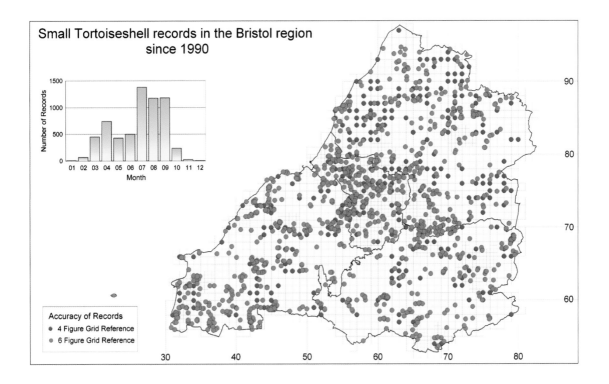

as insects' rapid life cycles mean that declines can impact very quickly upon their national status. The Small Tortoiseshell is not a particularly common sight on the masses of buddleia bushes in the centre of Bristol for example and yet nettle is still common and widespread. Regular monitoring of this butterfly could be beneficial as a means of monitoring the general health of the local environment given its ease of identification and popular image.

Despite all this the Small Tortoiseshell was still the butterfly for which most numbers of records have been received during the period of the current survey. That data shows the main sightings of butterflies out of hibernation from March through into early May. The first generation following that is mainly on the wing from mid June to mid July. The second brood flies from mid to late August, through September before sightings taper off as the butterflies enter hibernation.

# Large Tortoiseshell   *Aglais polychloros* (Linn.)

**National status: Extinct resident since the 1980s, rare immigrant.**
**Bristol region status: Extinct resident, probably since the early 20th century.**

As a breeding species the Large Tortoiseshell was probably commonest along the south and south eastern coasts of England before its demise in the 1980s. It had always varied in abundance with resident populations probably reinforced by immigration from the continent giving rise to good years and bad years.

In the nineteenth and early twentieth centuries the butterfly was found sparingly in the Bristol region. Duck's little book on the natural history of Portishead (1852) for example considers it '*About the wood*'. Hudd (1884) concluded '*Generally distributed throughout the district, but rather local. Mr Vaughan says, "common some years in all its stages."*' His later annotations include: '*A few on Clifton Down 1881 & 2 R.M.P. Scarce at Clevedon 1884–99 J.M. Weston & Bathampton J.G.R. Bath, Bathampton, Clevedon.*' In the Victoria County History of Somerset (1906) he added, '*Mr Braikenridge tells me it used to be com-*

*mon at Clevedon fifty years ago. None have been seen there of late.*'

In the north of Bristol, Meredith (1984) records '*It disappeared from the Trym Valley where it had been rather scarce and uncertain about 1918. Westbury-on-Trym iv. 1918; Avon Gorge on the old rifle range 1919 (Heslop Entom LXXX p.218).... It has been reported from N. Avon.*' In that article (Heslop, 1947) the author also elaborated on North Somerset sightings: '*The species used to occur at Clevedon; I heard of its still being there in 1918 (in August of which year also I saw a specimen fresh-taken by another collector in Kewstoke Woods, Weston-super-Mare); but it must have disappeared from this locality soon afterwards.*'

Since that time the records have been few and far between and perhaps spurious. In the mid-1960s a dead specimen was picked up on Henbury Golf Course but its origin remains uncertain (C. Wiltshire, pers. comm.). Singletons were reported from Hartcliffe in Bristol and Thornbury in the summer of 1981 (Sorrell & Weeks, 1982). In the 1980s a colony of the Large Tortoiseshell was renowned from Bourton Combe just to the south west of Bristol. The Bristol Naturalists' Society Proceedings carries records from this site from 1982 to 1985 inclusive. In reality these were butterflies which were almost certainly the result of captive releases with the specific intent of establishing the butterfly in the area. This coincided with attempts to 'put down' a number of different butterflies species, the most successful being the introduction of the Glanville Fritillary to Sand Point.

During the 1990s there were three sightings of this butterfly which if mis-identification is ruled out (often large Small Tortoiseshells are reported as this species by the novice) then again captive bred releases are the most likely source unless stray immigrants have reached this part of the UK. The latter scenario seems to be receeding as the populations in northern Europe are reported as declining (Asher *et al*, 2001). The period of 1945 to 1948 was one of an upsurge in records in the UK and is assigned to genuine influx from abroad but interestingly there are no records at this time from the Bristol region. On the face of it, this region should be able to support the Large Tortoiseshell as the usual larval foodplant, Wych Elm *Ulmus glabra*, is a very common woodland tree but in reality the butterfly was always a rarity and has probably been extinct in the region since the first half of the twentieth century.

# Camberwell Beauty  *Aglais antiopa* (Linn.)

**National status: Rare immigrant.**
**Bristol region status: Very rare immigrant.**

The Camberwell Beauty is a striking insect which visits this country on occasion from the resident populations in Europe and in particular Scandinavia. Consequently, there is a preponderance of sightings from eastern England but nevertheless individuals do occasionally make it as far west as the Bristol region, and even beyond. In 1884 Hudd summarised sightings thus: '*Several specimens of this beautiful rarity have been recorded from the district.*'

*Glos. Mr Robert Mayes has one in his collection, which was captured by his father, near Durdham Down, more than twenty years since. A specimen was taken near the Gully, Durdham Down, in August, 1872 by Mr Clark. 'My friend Mr Hill, saw a fine specimen of V. Antiopa near the Berkeley Road Station, on August 5th, 1875 but did not succeed in capturing it.' J. Preston in "Entomologist," VIII*

*p. 220. "One was seen by Mrs Harding, at Downend, in August, 1877." G.H. "Goblin Coombe, near Bristol." James Francis Stephens in the "Zoologist," Vol. III., p. 945. His account is so good I give it verbatim. "While entomologising in Goblin Coombe, a romantic glen near Cleeve, Somerset in August last (1844), a fine specimen of this beautiful insect settled on a rock before me, and 'ere I could secure it, it took flight and ascended a lofty precipice; in a few moments it reappeared almost in the original spot, but again took flight down the precipice, and finally eluded my grasp, to my great mortification."' A specimen was taken near the Bourton Railway Station (G.W. Rail) about August, 1866.'* The later annotations state: ' *Near Bath Handbk Bath (BA. 1888) p. 256. One near Flax Bourton, 1866. (2) near Bath (Terry). One Goblin Combe (Stephens).*' Only one of

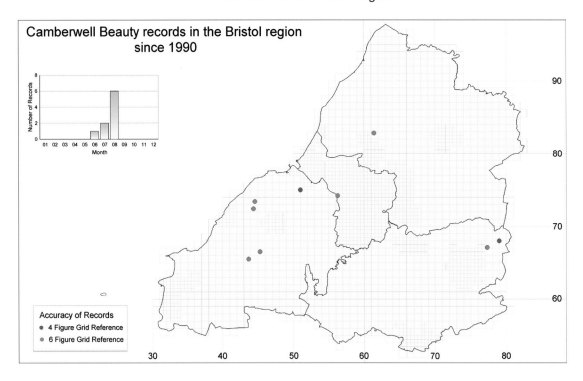

Camberwell Beauty records in the Bristol region since 1990

these sightings coincides with famed Camberwell Beauty years when numbers were recorded across the country, namely 1846 and 1872.

There was a single sighting of a Camberwell Beauty reported in the 'Report of the Entomological Section' within the Proceedings of the Bristol Naturalists' Society for 1940, as extracted from the Bristol Evening Post for 4th April of that year: '*a specimen of* Nymphalis Antiopa *was seen in his garden at Lodway – Easton-in-Gordano- by Mr W.H. Kettlewell*'. The note recognised the scarcity of spring records of the migrant.

Nothing more is heard of the Camberwell Beauty in our region until 1966 as Brown (1971) summarised '*we were fortunate to receive a report of this rare migrant from Scandinavia, when we heard that a single specimen had been found in a mercury vapour trap at Winscombe in North Somerset. This incident took place on 25th September, and it is of interest to note that there was a dense fog in the air that night, the visibility being down to fifty yards.*' Somewhat suspiciously a further record of the Camberwell Beauty from the vicinity of Winscombe is reported by Grose (1972). This specimen was seen and photographed at Barton, near Winscombe either in July or August, 1971.

In the 1980s there have been three records followed by nine in the 1990s, including four in 1995 which was an excellent year for immigration of this species with 350 butterflies reported across the country (Asher *et al*, 2001). Of the other records it is very difficult to judge whether these are genuine migrants or captive bred releases.

## Peacock   *Inachis io* (Linn.)

**National status: Common resident throughout the British Isles.**
**Bristol region status: Common resident.**

Martin Evans   1982

**Peacock**   Wesley Drive, Worle, North Somerset

The unmistakeable Peacock butterfly has apparently always been '*Common everywhere*' (Hudd, 1884). The historic authors have not had much else to say about it except Brown (1971) expanded on the observation with '*This species too (like the Small Tortoiseshell) appears to be capable of sudden peaks, although judging from our records this phenomenon is far less frequent. It was observed fairly commonly throughout the 1960s, but was likewise affected by the hot summer of 1968. However it was nothing like as common as the Small Tortoiseshell (*Aglais urticae *Linn.) and the maximum number counted on any one day was about fifty.*'

Along with the Small Tortoiseshell, its larvae are a common sight massed on Common Nettle *Urtica dioica*, which is the usually recorded foodplant. The very black colour and more spiny nature of the caterpillars distinguish them from those of the Small Tortoiseshell and nettles in more sheltered positions are usually chosen (Baker, 1972). Again like the Small Tortoiseshell this butterfly breeds in close proximity to human habitation, feeds on garden flowers as an adult and often hibernates in houses and other buildings. Close observation will show that the hibernating butterflies move around their chosen winter home, one week in one corner of a room the next in another. After hibernation the butterfly seems to be more frequently met with in the countryside in the spring rather than in the town. Unlike the Small Tortoiseshell there is only one brood per year and so the progeny from the over-wintered generation emerge in mid to late summer and then are much more frequently seen

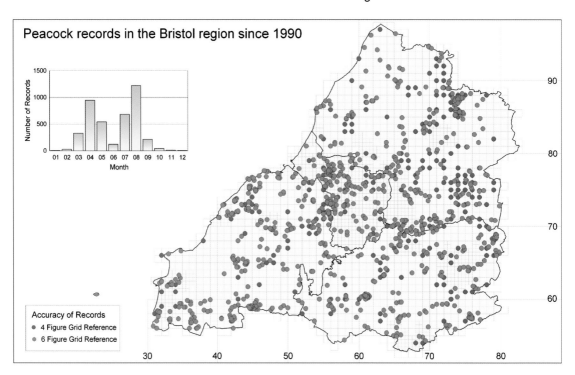

Peacock records in the Bristol region since 1990

feeding on nectar rich plants in gardens, before entering hibernation.

Not surprisingly the Peacock was a subject of Bristol's Common Butterfly Survey, numbers seemed to stay fairly buoyant with 1985 the best year, however there was a decline after that which follows the national trend with low returns from 1986 to 1988. It is still common and widespread and there does not appear to have been a drop in numbers, as suspected for the Small Tortoiseshell, at the end of the 1990s.

# Comma *Polygonia c-album* (Linn.)

**National status: Common resident of England and Wales.**
**Bristol region status: Common resident.**

Kurt Vickery    September 2000

**Comma** Winscombe, North Somerset

Although the Comma is considered today to be a common member of the butterfly fauna of most of England this has famously not always been the case. Very widely distributed in the early nineteenth century the populations then crashed dramatically to shrink down to pockets along the Welsh borders and to a few sites in the south east by the turn of the twentieth century. In this respect the northern part of the Bristol region was on the edge of the area which became its stronghold at this time. The decline can be seen in the late nineteenth century records, Hudd in his annotations to his 1884 publication listing the following: '*Almondsbury J.A.H. Near Almondsbury by M – . Bristol. Very rare at Clevedon 1884–99 J.M. Leigh. Bathampton (R). Henbury (James). Combe Dingle, Brockley & Portishead (CB).*' and then going on to comment '*Still occasion-*

*ally found, but much scarcer than formerly A.E.H.*' By 1906 in the Victoria County History of Somerset, Hudd was able to include '*It has been abundant this year (1901) in Gloucestershire, and several specimens have been seen in my garden at Clifton.*'

In fact, the expansion of the Comma's range following this decline is generally put at around the time of the First World War (1914–1918) and it has continued ever since apart from a slow down or minor contraction in the 1950s. This may explain Turner's comment '*Does not appear to be increasing here, as in some parts of the country*'. Whereas, Bird could list Clevedon, Tickenham, Leigh Woods and Walton Moor as localities for the butterfly around this time.

By the 1970s the expansion of the Comma's populations had been resumed in

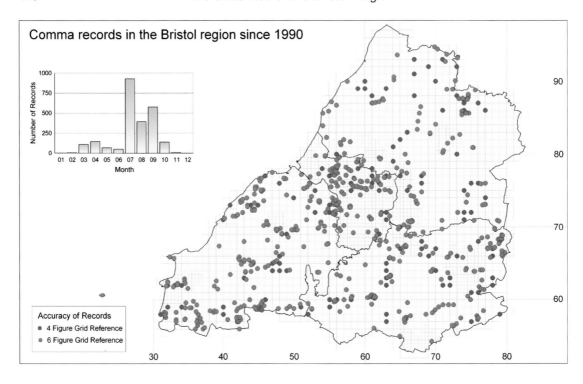

Comma records in the Bristol region since 1990

earnest and Brown (1971) was able to report *'fortunately, as in other parts of Britain, its distribution is increasing. This species is never common, and on average only one or two specimens are seen at a time. Occasionally, however, considerable numbers are met with, such as at Wetmoor on 17 April 1968, and again in Goblin Combe on 29 July of this year* [1970]. *In the Bristol area, the first specimens usually appear on the wing in early April following hibernation, and these then deposit their ova giving rise to the first generation in July. It is the butterflies from this first generation possessing the pale undersides that are known as a. hutchinsoni. From August onwards the second generation is on the wing, and these may be around until late in October when they finally go into hibernation.'*

The hibernation of this butterfly differs from the other two common related species the Small Tortoiseshell and Peacock in that it is usually undertaken in or around trees in woodland and there is little association with habitations. This may be considered surprising as Common Nettle *Urtica dioica* is the often quoted foodplant of the larvae. However Wych Elm *Ulmus glabra* is potentially being utilised more frequently and searches for the larvae on this foodplant could reveal interesting information.

The full extent of the remarkable turn around in fortune for the Comma can be seen by its inclusion in the Common Butterfly Survey (CBS) of the 1980s. The results revealed a fairly constant but thinly distributed population in our region. The butterflies emerging from hibernation mainly in March and giving rise to the first brood in July and August. (Larvae developing whilst day length

**Comma** (larva)    Hutton, North Somerset

Martin Evans   22nd June 1983

is increasing emerge as the form *hutchinsoni* with greater scalloping of the wing edges and paler upper and undersides to the wings (Asher *et al*, 2001).) Some butterflies from the first brood are known to enter hibernation along with the second brood individuals that peak in late September. The CBS indicated a local decline in numbers after 1982 before re-building to becoming abundant in 1986 before dropping again in 1988 as a result of periods of cold and wet weather.

The Comma has been seen regularly on the island of Steepholm since 1978 but breeding has not yet been detected (Parsons, 1996).

The dramatic swings in fortune of this but-terfly over the last couple of hundred years make it an interesting species to monitor. In particular establishing exactly what plants it favours to oviposit on may repay study. In the 1990s, the Comma has done well in terms of numbers. Furthermore, the results of this sur-vey closely follow those of the Common Butterfly Survey regarding the time of appear-ance of the different broods. It is quite likely that the Comma is the source of a few erro-neous reports of fritillaries, as the rapid flight and orange/brown colouration can mislead the unwary.

# Small Pearl-bordered Fritillary    *Boloria selene selene* (D. & S.)

**National status: Localised resident in England, Wales and Scotland.**
**Bristol region status: Very rare and declining resident.**

Andrew Daw  16th June 1989

**Small Pearl-bordered Fritillary**   Dolebury Warren, North Somerset

The violet-feeding fritillaries are butterflies that give great concern at present over their future in the British landscape. The Small Pearl-bordered Fritillary is a butterfly that has always been restricted to a somewhat specialised habitat namely grassland with either Common Dog-violet *Viola riviniana* or Marsh Violet *Viola palustris* upon which its larvae feed. The latter is a very rare plant in our region (White, 1912 and Myles *et al*, 2000) and unlikely to have been used as a foodplant consequently.

In the late nineteenth century the Small Pearl-bordered Fritillary was a localised species which occurred in some of the same localities as the Pearl-bordered Fritillary but as Hudd (1884) pointed out is '*rather more local, and appears about ten days later in the season.*' He added at a later date: '*Scarce at Clevedon J.M. 1888. Brockley (C.B.).*' By the

Victoria County History of Somerset (1906) Hudd was expressing concern that both species '*have become very scarce in the northern part of the county, where they were once common.*' This state of affairs was echoed by Turner (1955) stating '*more frequent in the south* [of Somerset] *than the north.*' However C.S.H. Blathwayt recorded the butterfly at Walton Moor in the Gordano Valley, nearly every year from 1953 to 1957.

The only record in the nineteenth century from South Gloucestershire appears to be from Wickwar by Watkins (Meredith, 1984). This may in fact be Wetmoor where it was certainly present a century later in the early 1980s (and was recorded in 1989) but is considered to have been lost as a breeding species in 1989 (Martin, 1998). It is surprising that Brown in 1971 did not list any known sites

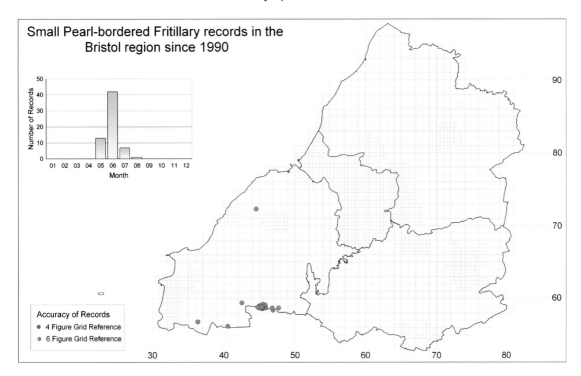

Small Pearl-bordered Fritillary records in the Bristol region since 1990

from South Gloucestershire given that recorders such as C.S.H. Blathwayt found it there, for example, in 1949 and 1950 but did state '*In Somerset, the butterfly is usually met with in the same haunts as the Marsh Fritillary (Euphydryas aurinia Rott.), ...but is never common. Goblin Combe, mentioned earlier, is an ideal locality for this species, and it is observed there in abundance every year.*'

So the impression we have is of a localised butterfly which was found at a few sites south of Bristol and perhaps just one site in the north of the region. These sites were by and large characterised as grassland and clearings within, or on the edge of, woods. In the nineteenth century at least the Small Pearl-bordered Fritillary was less common than its congener the Pearl-bordered Fritillary as shown, not only by the comment of Hudd above, but also by the predominance of specimens of the Pearl-bordered in historic collections of butterflies.

The picture in the last twenty years of the twentieth century is sadly one of great decline for this already localised species. Currently the butterfly is only known from one or two sites on the Mendips on the edge of the Bristol region, although it is known from other sites along the Mendips just outside the remit of this

publication. At Dolebury Warren though, it has managed to retain considerable numbers; over ninety were seen there on a visit in June 2000 (M. Evans, J. Boyd and J. Martin, pers comm.). However, this must not be seen as too encouraging as the trend both locally and nationally is for the butterfly to be lost from sites quite rapidly. The habitat that is necessary for the butterfly is not only for the larval foodplant to be present but also for there to be open sunny areas, a factor probably related to developmental rates of the larvae and/or activity and behaviour of the adult butterfly. The intensification of agriculture which has reduced available sites and the reduction in traditional management of woodland, most noticeably the virtual cessation in coppicing, has led to this butterfly having virtually no habitat left in which to survive. Open grassland of suitable type is a feature of a developing ecosystem and is not a climax vegetative state, so without intervention a site loses the crucial environmental factors that the butterfly requires as scrub develops or the sward becomes rank. Consequently, these butterfly populations tend to move around within a small area over a period of years as different areas meet its requirements. As pockets of semi-natural habitat have become more isolated within the farmed landscape so the ability of the butterfly to hop to other sites has been reduced and the result is local extinction. The population at Dolebury Warren though, occurs in sheltered pockets of limestone heathland and there cutting and treating bracken has enabled the Small Pearl-bordered Fritillary to thrive. Violets near the edge of the bracken paths are used by the larvae and the adults favour Marsh Thistles *Cirsium palustre* on which to nectar.

Away from Dolebury Warren and the Mendips there have been very occasional reports of the butterfly, for example in 1990 in the Gordano Valley. At the present time though the Dolebury Warren colony is the only confirmed extant site in the region.

It is perhaps ironic that the Pearl-bordered Fritillary that once was commoner than this species has been able to adapt even less and has become rarer even more quickly. Urgent action is required through the use of Biodiversity Action Plans or other means if we are not to lose the Small Pearl-bordered Fritillary from our region in the very near future.

## Pearl-bordered Fritillary    *Boloria euphrosyne* (Linn.)

**National status: Localised resident in the British Isles and declining.**
**Bristol region status: Extinct resident.**

Andrew Daw    20th May 2000

**Pearl-bordered Fritillary**

Concern over butterfly collecting is not necessarily a modern phenomenon. Alfred Hudd in 1884 was obviously dismayed by a decline in the Pearl-bordered Fritillary, '*Generally distributed throughout the district but not so common near Bristol as formerly. This is one of the victims of makers of "butterfly pictures," who used to capture them by hundreds at Leigh, and other localities where they are not now often seen in any numbers.*' Using the wings of butterflies to make up composite pictures was a particular Victorian fashion that thankfully did not survive long into the twentieth century. At that time exploitation of, what was a relatively common, woodland butterfly and a seemingly inexhaustible resource, led to the local naturalists (often with their own cabinet of specimens) to express regret over the impact of such commercialism.

Despite the predations of these 'business men' the Pearl-bordered Fritillary survived and was even described by E. Newman (1874) as '*One of the very commonest of wood butterflies in England.*' As has already been mentioned this species was commoner than the similar Small Pearl-bordered Fritillary and remained so despite gradual decline throughout the first half of the twentieth century. Turner (1955) considered it '*Generally distributed and fairly common in most parts*' and listed the following parishes within the Bristol region: '*Brockley, Abbots Leigh, Portishead (C.B.), Weston-s-Mare, Wrington (C.S.H.B.), Wraxall, Long Ashton (R.F.B.).*' J. Bird in his unpublished list from the 1950s gave the following localities: '*Walton-in-Gordano, Tickenham, Clevedon, near Shipham.*' C.S.H. Blathwayt's notebooks report the butterfly

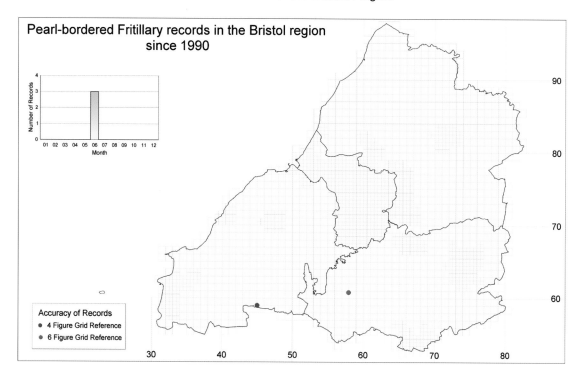

Pearl-bordered Fritillary records in the Bristol region since 1990

from Weston Woods, Leigh Woods and Wetmoor, for example, in the 1940s and 1950s.

It was in the second half of the century that it became obvious just how this butterfly was continuing to disappear from woodland strongholds. The larvae, as with the Small Pearl-bordered Fritillary, feed mainly on Common Dog-violet *Viola riviniana* but this butterfly is much more restricted to clearings within woodlands. It has not been the collectors of the butterfly that have done for it (although they may have contributed); it is the dramatic loss of suitable habitat as woodland management, in particular coppicing, has all but ceased across the country. By the beginning of the 1970s, although the Small Pearl-bordered had been able to cling on in more open sites the woodland-dependant Pearl-bordered had declined even more rapidly, Brown (1971) wrote: *'far scarcer in the West of England than the one previously described* [Small Pearl-bordered Fritillary]. *The apparent widespread distribution in Somerset is rather misleading; sightings were recorded from these localities during the early 1960s by members of the British* [Bristol *sic*] *Naturalists'*

*Society, but only in very small numbers, and there is doubt as to their authenticity. None have been recorded in more recent years, and it is possible that they could have been confused with its cousin the Small Pearl-bordered Fritillary* (Argynnis selene *Schiff.) which is on the wing at the same time of year and which, itself, occurs in most of these places. However, there is one definite exception, and that is a predominant colony of this butterfly existing alongside its relatives in the area around Goblin Combe. As with* selene, *it is seen here every year, although the first specimens are on the wing about a fortnight earlier. An unusual asymmetrical aberration was taken here in 1966 by the author, where some of the black markings on the forewing (right) are united by an extra black bar, whereas the left-hand side is completely normal. At Wetmoor, in Gloucestershire,...the butterfly is only occasionally met with and is frequently absent during some years.'* The last sighting of this butterfly in Leigh Woods was probably that of 4th June 1965, a single female (Cooper, 1966).

Meredith (1984) surprisingly does not mention the Wetmoor locality but does record

'*Common reduced to local.*' as the status in Gloucestershire. This omission may have been due to the fact that by 1983 the Pearl-bordered had already been lost from Wetmoor as part of the continuing disappearance from its former haunts across southern England. Sadly this state of affairs continued and if anything speeded up and by the advent of the Avon Butterfly Project only one small colony was left in the whole of the area, at Dolebury Warren. The final sighting of the Pearl-bordered Fritillary at this site was of an individual in 1995. Other single sightings of wandering individuals (reliably identified) include one at Chew in 1996. Other records have been submitted on occasion but have been considered to be erroneous. The similarity of the Small Pearl-bordered to the Pearl-bordered Fritillary has undoubtedly led to much confusion. This, coupled with the fact that they can both be on the wing at the same time and the similarity of the two English names has added again to the difficulty in sorting genuine sightings from errors.

The Pearl-bordered Fritillary has gone from being one of our commonest woodland butterflies to extinction in our region in a matter of 120 or so years. The only hope for the reappearance of this beautiful butterfly may lie with national biodiversity action plans which will attempt to stop the decline and to reintroduce it to former haunts. If this is to succeed and if we are to see the butterfly locally again then a means must be found to re-establish the type of woodland habitat that it absolutely requires, in other words, large scale coppicing programmes. This is a very big task, as it is unlikely that it will be a financially viable scheme without subsidy. Even if the habitat was recreated it is probably too late for the butterfly to re-colonise naturally and reintroduction would probably have to be considered. Despite these daunting obstacles an attempt must be made to enable the "pearl of the woods" to enrich the countryside that we live in.

# Queen of Spain Fritillary    *Issoria lathonia* (Linn.)

**National status: Rare immigrant.**
**Bristol region status: Very rare immigrant.**

There are only three records from the nineteenth century recorded in the literature from the Bristol region. Two were listed as follows by Hudd (1884): '*Glos. A specimen was taken many years ago in Garaway's Nursery Grounds, Clifton PHV. Bristol Stainton's "Manual" Vol. 1, p.43. Somerset. Mr Harding tells me a specimen was shown to Mr Arthur Naish, which was captured near Nailsea, about twenty years ago.*' The latter record is dated more precisely in the Victoria County History of Somerset as about 1858 (Hudd, 1906). The third record was noted by Bird as recorded in the Entomologist magazine '*On July 20th 1898 Alph Rylands of Clifton College, captured a specimen in Somerset, about 4 miles from Clifton.* (Ent. Vol. XXXI p.197).'

Nationally there were a number of influxes in the second half of the nineteenth century with 1868 and 1872 being notable and then hardly any were seen until the 1940s. This was followed by another dearth of immigration until the 1990s. The reasons for these fluctuations are unclear. The butterfly occurs throughout large areas of Europe and into southern Scandinavia, living in a variety of habitats. In some areas the species is apparently declining, in others increasing. The adult butterflies regularly undertake small scale movements within their breeding range obviously dispersing further afield when conditions favour it. On occasion individuals arriving in the British Isles are thought to have laid eggs and produced a home grown brood. In northern Europe Wild Pansy *Viola tricolor* and Field Pansy *Viola arvensis* are the usual foodplant of the larvae. (Asher *et al*, 2001).

In the twentieth century there are no records at all from the Bristol region, not even from the good year of 1945, until the record of

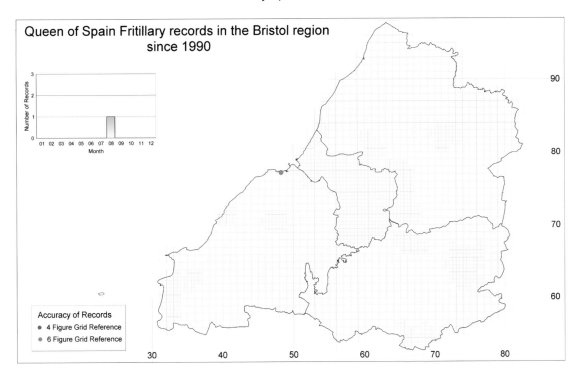

Queen of Spain Fritillary records in the Bristol region since 1990

22nd August 1994 by R. Higgins at Portbury Wharf. The latter coincided with one in a series of years in the 1990s when numbers of butterflies have been recorded over the country along with other unusual immigrant insects. In this particular instance the Portbury Wharf sighting occurred at the same time as Yellow-winged Darter dragonflies appeared at Chew Valley Lake. Furthermore there has been a suspicion that the Queen of Spain may have actually become established, at least temporarily, as a breeding species at Minsmere on the Suffolk coast. It is very tempting to jump to the conclusion that climate change is enhancing the potential for the Queen of Spain Fritillary to colonise the country and to become a fully fledged resident member of our butterfly fauna. This is far from proven yet, and the butterfly's populations on the continent appear to be increasing in some areas and decreasing in other others. If it should prove to be the case, this butterfly would be a splendid addition to the rather impoverished list of species that grace our shores.

# High Brown Fritillary    *Argynnis adippe* (D. & S.) ssp. *vulgoadippe* Verity

**National status: Rare declining resident of England.**
**Bristol region status: Extinct resident.**

The High Brown Fritillary is perhaps the butterfly species that is giving most cause for concern nationally as it has declined so much over the whole of its range in recent years. Today the only populations left are concentrated in Lancashire and Devon with a handful of sites in Wales and Herefordshire and the Malverns. This was not always the case and one hundred years or so ago, although not common, the High Brown Fritillary could be seen in July in woodlands across southern England including the Bristol region. Hudd (1884) regarded it as local and gave localities as '*Coombe Glen, Bristol    F.D.Wheeler.    Portishead    J.N.D. Brockley    J.W.C.    Clevedon    A.E.H.    Weston-super-Mare G.R.C.*' To this list Newman (1874) added '*Leigh*', presumably meaning Leigh Woods and presumably on the authority of Hudd. However by 1906, Hudd considered the

butterfly to be commoner in the south of Somerset than in the Bristol region and to be '*hardly ever found of late years in Leigh Woods or in other localities near Bristol.*' Despite this it seems populations did remain as Turner (1955) as well as giving the Victoria County History (VCH) localities includes a record from Abbots Leigh ascribed to R.F.Bretherton and a record from Bathford from J.E.T., both of which must have post-dated the VCH. Bird's unpublished list from the 1950s gives Tickenham.

By the 1970s the situation had got decidedly worse as Brown (1971) warned: '*The only locality known at present in either of the two vice-counties* [West Gloucestershire and North Somerset] *is Goblin Combe in North Somerset.... It is highly probable that many of our records of the Dark Green Fritillary* (Argynnis aglaia Linn.) *have been mistaken for this species, as this confusion commonly arises. In Goblin Combe itself, it is quite scarce and never more than three specimens have been recorded on any one occasion. This butterfly certainly needs all the protection it can get, and the problem is by no means a local one.'*

The issue of misidentification that Brown points out is a genuine problem. Positive identification is very difficult without a fortuitous view of the underside or by netting the butterfly to examine it closely. Until recent years butterfly identification guides often included distributional data that related to the nineteenth century, regurgitated time and time again, so that the significance of a High Brown record might have escaped many as the books stated that it was widely distributed across southern England. Consequently records may have been accepted without the rigour and verification that was necessary. Historic butterfly collections however do provide direct evidence of accurate identification. It was partly from these sources that Vickery (1993) was able to list the following sites in the Bristol region for the High Brown Fritillary: Goblin Combe, Dolebury Warren, Burrington Combe, Brockley Combe (Heslop specimens), Bourton Combe (erroneous records), Walton Common. At some of these sites undoubtedly this species flew alongside the so similar Dark Green Fritillary. Sadly today the latter butterfly flies alone at a number of those localities and at others there are no fritillaries at all.

The last sightings of the High Brown appear to have been in 1984 at Dolebury Warren and Walton Common (in the Gordano Valley) (Vickery, 1993). There is an isolated record from 1992 but, as a breeding species, the butterfly was lost about twenty years ago from the region. This concurs with the massive decline across the country that gathered pace after the Second World War. The reasons for this have been well studied. The violet-feeding woodland fritillaries (Common Dog-violet *Viola riviniana* and Hairy Violet *Viola hirta* are the oft quoted larval foodplants for this species) seem to share a temperature dependence as larvae. The larvae in all these species are dark in coloration, presumably to assist them in absorbing heat so that they can develop quickly in our relatively cool spring weather. As a group these butterflies form a series ranging from the least tolerant to low temperatures to the most tolerant. The least tolerant is the High Brown followed by the Pearl-bordered, Small Pearl-bor-

dered and then Silver-washed Fritillary. Crucial to achieving those high temperatures are clearings and glades in the woodland where the sun can warm the ground flora for long enough. As coppicing has ceased to be a common technique in woods (chopping down small areas in rotation to allow regeneration and so a supply of useful poles), a practice which has declined dramatically over the latter half of the twentieth century, so the dependant butterflies have disappeared. The first to be lost as the environment becomes too shady and too cool for the larvae is the High Brown Fritillary.

Interestingly though, the High Brown occurs in two different habitat types. The woodland populations are the ones that have virtually disappeared from the British Isles. The second habitat type is that of bracken dominated grassland (often on limestone) and often where again scrub or woodland clearance has taken place relatively recently. So in the Bristol region what type of habitat did our colonies exist in? Of the sites listed by Vickery, virtually all contain areas of grassland that were probably more akin to the latter habitat type rather than the woodland with coppicing. Although today visits to localities such as Goblin Combe will give the impression that they have been densely wooded for long periods this is false. The term Goblin Combe was often used to refer in fact to Wrington Warren which has now been coniferised. Meanwhile the remaining calcareous downland, very close to the Combe, is now in danger of being swallowed up by encroaching scrub and secondary woodland. Walton Common is another example where again woodland borders open downland. It may have been lack of management of the bordering woodland areas or coniferisation that led to the disappearance of the High Brown Fritillary in our region, but not necessarily a cessation in coppicing itself.

A national Biodiversity Action Plan and Species Recovery Plan are the straws that the conservation community now clutches to in attempting to stop this butterfly following others, such as the Large Blue, into obscurity in this country. Although old sites in the Bristol region could in theory be returned to a state that could favour the High Brown Fritillary, it is once again unlikely that natural re-population could ever take place given the extent of the fragmentation of the natural environment and the distance between remaining colonies.

# Dark Green Fritillary    *Argynnis aglaja aglaja* (Linn.)

**National status: Localised resident.**
**Bristol region status: localised resident, possibly declining.**

**Dark Green Fritillary** (worn individual)    Dolebury Warren, North Somerset

Although the Dark Green Fritillary is a violet-feeding fritillary, larvae usually on Common Dog-violet *Viola riviniana*, it is not so much of a woodland butterfly but a species of more open grassland. Indeed on calcareous grassland it may feed on Hairy Violet *Viola hirta*, a relatively widespread species in the region (Myles *et al*, 2000). Consequently, the Dark Green Fritillary has not suffered quite as much as the fritillaries of woodland have in the twentieth century. That said it faces its own particular problems.

Sadly the sight of this impressive butterfly in flight can no longer be glimpsed on Durdham Down in Bristol as it was in the middle of the nineteenth century (Hudd, 1884). In 1906 Hudd said about the Dark Green, High Brown and Silver-washed Fritillaries: '*Generally distributed throughout the county* [Somerset], *and may be found most years in suitable localities. Like the other Fritillaries they are all more plentiful in the central and southern parts of the county than in the north. They are hardly ever found of late years in Leigh Woods or in other localities near Bristol.*' However in 1884 he had mentioned the Dark Green as rather common at Brockley and included Clevedon, Portishead and Weston-super-Mare as other localities.

By the 1950s, Bird knew it from '*Clevedon, Tickenham and Walton Moor*'. In 1971 Brown recounted '*more widely distributed than the previous one* [Silver-washed] *owing to the larger areas of its habitat...We know of many localities in North Somerset, especially in the Mendip Hills...Goblin Combe provides another ideal habitat for the Dark Green Fritillary, and this butterfly is seen here in strength every*

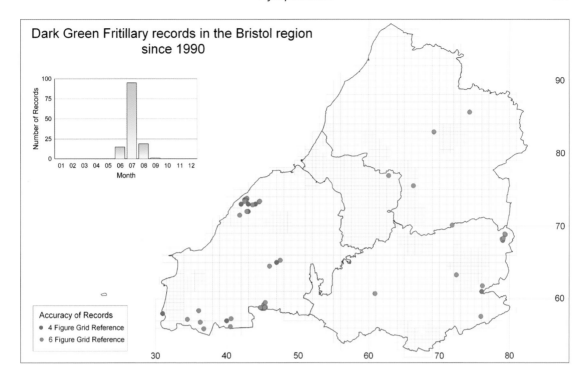

Dark Green Fritillary records in the Bristol region since 1990

year. *During 1970 some superb dark females were observed, not unlike sub-species* scotica *from northern Scotland. Reports are frequently received of observations from the coastal stretches near Brean* [just south of the Bristol region]*, as well as from the hills behind Clevedon. We rarely find records or discoveries of new localities, since most of our material is repetitive from one season to the next. As far as can be made out the status of this species is somewhat static at this time in the West of England.*' The latter statement was perhaps optimistic and Meredith's comment (1984) regarding Gloucestershire more apt '*Common then becomes local*'.

It is surprising that Brown makes no mention of any South Gloucestershire localities as the first edition of the Wetmoor Guide lists it as present. However, the second edition reports that it was lost at that site between 1983 and 1993, with a record from 1988.

The Avon Butterfly Survey results show that there are several strong colonies on the Mendips but although new sites have been discovered in the region this species survives in much smaller numbers than previously. Away from the main sites ephemeral colonies become established in good years at other places. Walton Common, Dolebury Warren,

Bannerdown and Goblin Combe are all reasonably secure colonies with a few turning up at other sites such as Folly Farm, Cleaves Wood and Ashton Court Meadow nature reserves in certain years. The first week or two of July usually sees most individuals on the wing.

The continued survival of this butterfly leaves no room for complacency as although it is still found widely across the region the density is not great and it could easily disappear from established sites. The greatest threat to the Dark Green Fritillary is probably the loss of suitable grassland habitat. Although the larvae of this species are much

Martin Evans 4th June 1989

**Dark Green Fritillary** (larva) Mendip Hills

more tolerant of cooler temperatures and higher sward than its cousins that live in woods, as grassland is improved or becomes shaded out due to scrub encroachment and woodland growth so the butterfly colonies become in danger of vanishing. It can also be lost if the sward is too short. Protection and appropriate management of the main sites is necessary to prevent the Dark Green Fritillary declining any more in the Bristol region.

# Silver-washed Fritillary    *Argynnis paphia* (Linn.)

**National status: Localised resident over England, Wales and Ireland.**
**Bristol region status: Localised resident.**

**Silver-washed Fritillary**    Leigh Woods, North Somerset

The Silver-washed Fritillary is the woodland fritillary whose larvae, which usually feed on Common Dog-violet *Viola riviniana*, can tolerate a greater degree of shade than its close relatives the High Brown, Pearl-bordered and Small Pearl-bordered Fritillaries. Consequently this, also the largest of the fritillaries, has remained a commoner species than those others mentioned. That is not to say that it has not declined in the British Isles in the last one hundred and fifty years.

In Bristol, it was in 1867 that a specimen was caught at Redland Green by Mr I.W.Clarke (Hudd, 1884) as was one at Cook's Folly in the Avon Gorge, recorded by Charles Bartlett. These sightings were of note as Hudd considered the butterfly to be '*Local and not very common in the district.*' However he also said '*Tolerably common in woods at Brockley*

*and Weston-super-Mare; scarce in Leigh Woods* [July 1894 R.M.P. at this site is given as a later annotation] *and near Brislington.*' In the Victoria County History of Somerset he went further with '*Hardly ever found of late years in Leigh Woods or in other localities near Bristol. In fact only a single specimen has ever been recorded from Leigh Woods so far as I am aware, a specimen caught by Mr Prideaux in July 1894.*' As with many reports about the county of Somerset he remarked that the species was commoner in the south than in the vicinity of Bristol.

Despite this, Peach (1939) included it in a list from Leigh Woods and Bird in the 1950s was still able to quote '*Tickenham, Clevedon, Walton-in-Gordano, Leigh Woods, Goblin Combe*' as localities. It was at this time that the population across the country was accel-

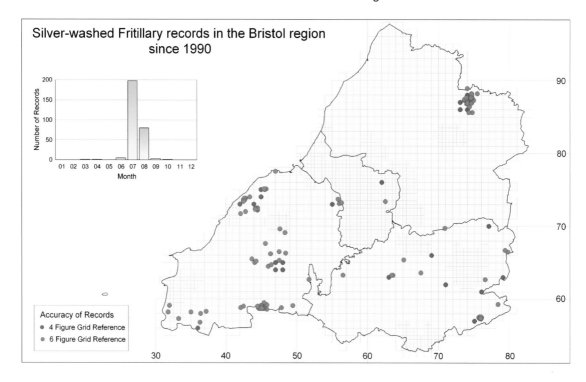

Silver-washed Fritillary records in the Bristol region since 1990

Accuracy of Records
● 4 Figure Grid Reference
● 6 Figure Grid Reference

erating in its decline (Asher *et al*, 2001), contracting into the southwest. Consequently major reductions were not really witnessed in the Bristol district with the situation remaining much as it was in Hudd's day i.e. able to continue to survive at the major woodland sites, despite the lack of management, longer than other more sensitive fritillaries.

Brown's paper (1971) showed concern over these populations in north Somerset: "*Individual specimens have been seen from time to time at several places in North Somerset, but its future prospects do not look so good. It is probable that many of these*

Silver-washed Fritillary (ab. *valesina*)

Kurt Vickery

*isolated specimens have originated from the deciduous woodlands near Tickenham, but the M5 development has recently devastated this region. Once again, Goblin Combe is another well known locality for this species, but its numbers vary from one year to the next.*" He also mentions Wetmoor in South Gloucestershire where he reported: '*In the Nature Reserve at Wetmoor, it is seen in most years but is not common.*' Surprisingly Meredith (1984) does not give Wetmoor as a locality, in fact he lists no sites from this part of the region. Both Wetmoor and Lower Woods' guides have always included it as a resident of the site.

There is some evidence to suggest that the Silver-washed Fritillary can also travel some distances and so colonise or re-colonise woodlands, perhaps more easily than some of the other fritillaries. The species was recorded on Steepholm, for example in 1902 and an unidentified *Argynnis* species reported in 1994, on the island, is thought to have been this butterfly (Parsons, 1996).

Today the major mixed woodlands in the region still support populations of this large butterfly which can best be observed nectaring at bramble flowers at the height of summer, mid July in particular. The complex of woodlands to the south west of Bristol (including Goblin and Brockley Combes) the woods surrounding Bath and on the Mendips, along with sites near Portishead and, in the north, at Wetmoor, contain reasonable numbers. However, following a peak in numbers in 1996 at the latter site the population crashed to their lowest ever level in 2000. Open habitat within woods is still a requirement for the butterfly to survive and so there is no room for complacency, as with so many of our restricted species. Careful monitoring of existing sites would help alert to the possibility that the butterfly could be in trouble. In these instances appropriate management of the environment can really make an impact. The introduction of coppicing to Leigh Woods in the 1990s in a series of trial plots is a case in point. From the above records we can see that the Silver-washed Fritillary has always been considered unusual in the woods, but following the coppicing the butterfly apparently re-colonised it naturally after an absence of many years. The previous record to this from the locality seems to be from 1977 (Harper, 1979). This example of successful management shows that it is possible to reverse the trends in the fortune of our butterflies given the right commitment and resources.

# Marsh Fritillary   *Euphydryas aurinia aurinia* (Rott.)

**National status: Declining localised resident throughout the British Isles.**
**Bristol region status: Extinct resident.**

Kurt Vickery   26th May 1991

**Marsh Fritillary**   Folly Farm, Bath & NE Somerset

As its name suggests the Marsh Fritillary is at home in open damp grasslands where the larvae feed gregariously on Devil's-bit Scabious *Succisa pratensis* and, on occasion, Field Scabious *Knautia arvensis* and Small Scabious *Scabiosa columbaria*. Unfortunately it seems to have been declining since the late seventeenth century, more severely during the twentieth century and is also disappearing in much of its European range (Asher *et al*, 2001).

However in the mid-nineteenth century it was still common enough, or at least its habitat was so common, that it could be seen in Old Market Street in the centre of Bristol as well as on the Bristol Downs (Hudd, 1884). At that time the River Avon in the city centre was not as controlled, contained and urbanised as it is today, the possibility of seeing this butter-

fly in such a locality being a real flight of fancy at the start of the 21st century.

Elsewhere Hudd considered the Marsh Fritillary to be '*Local, but not scarce in marshy meadows.*' and listed the following additional sites '*Boiling Wells, Bristol G.H. Almondsbury J.A.H. Alderley lower Woods, V.R.P. Portishead J.N.D. Hallatrow R.V. Sherring. Weston-super-Mare G.R.C.*' and added the following hand written notes later: '*Clevedon/Bath/Terry. Two at Clevedon 1885 Mr Jefferies J.M. (in litt. J.Mason)*'. In the Victoria County History (1903) Hudd added the comments '*Fairly common in marshy meadows near Bath, ... Clevedon, ... Portishead, ... Winscombe, ... Weston-super-Mare, etc. Very local, and much less common in most localities than formerly.*' The latter note hints at the national reduction that was taking

31st March 1991

Chris Wiltshire

**Marsh Fritillary** Lower Woods, Wetmoor, South Glouc. (last larvae seen at this site)

place and the probability that colonies were getting fewer in number in the Bristol region.

In February 1949, C.S.H. Blathwayt and C. Bell visited Leigh Woods and collected a very large number of Marsh Fritillary larvae which were bred through that year. They also recorded adults both in Leigh Woods and at Wetmoor that May and June. The following year they repeated this process at Wetmoor. However in the 1950s Bird only knew of it from Walton Moor and Turner (1955) considered it '*Very local but often very common in a few places*' i.e. individual colonies could contain large numbers of individuals.

Meredith (1984) stated '*Sporadically distributed; for a short period prior to 1919 occurred on the old rifle range now municipal tennis courts* [now disused] *on the Gloucestershire side of the Avon Gorge, one or two taken in the Gully also, Kingsweston Down one about 1920 (Heslop), Wickwar larvae and imagines 1949–1952 (Watkins, C.L.B., C.H.S.B., Proc BNS XXVIII pp 42, 194,263).*'

The Wickwar reference is undoubtedly to the Wetmoor site. Brown (1971) stated '*At present, only one remaining locality is known to the author in Gloucestershire*' and then '*it appears in strength about every four years at its haunt at Wetmoor...Mild damp winters, typical of the West of England, seem to be detrimental to the hibernating larvae, and this could be the cause of the continual fluctuation in numbers from one year to the next. There is very little in the way of variation within this colony, although quite dark specimens appear from time to time.*' This supposition about the climate of the west being detrimental is not

supported by the national situation. Currently the butterfly has disappeared from virtually the whole of the north, east and south east of England. It only remains in the west of Scotland, Wales and the south west of England. Asher *et al* (2001) suggest that the reasons for this are complex and involve the enormous loss of habitat (wet meadows), inappropriate management of the remaining sites (light grazing by cattle needed) coupled with the fragmentation of habitats that prevents re-colonisation and also possibly high rates of parasitism.

The Wetmoor locality has been the subject of some study in the past. For example, the butterflies were the subject of a short cine film made by C.L. Bell in the 1950s. It is very likely that this site, along with the nature reserve Hollow Marsh, at the other end of the region on the Mendips, formed large colonies from which in good years the butterflies would expand and form outlier colonies. At other times they would contract to just the core sites.

Saddlewood Roughs was another locality at this time but falls just outside the northern boundary of the current work.

Burrell (1995) listed the following sites for the region with the last date of any sighting of the Marsh Fritillary: Bathampton Wood/Down (1986), **Blagdon Lake** (1965), Coal Pit Heath (1982), Dundas Aqueduct (1982), **Folly Farm** (1993), Greyfield Wood (1990), **Hollow Marsh Meadows** (1987), Limeburn Hill (1990?), Old Sodbury (1984), Tucking Mill (1982), Wetmoor (Chase Lane and fields)(1984), Horwood Farm (1984), **Inglestone Common** (1984), **Lower Woods SSSI** (1991) and Woolard (1986). [Colonies in bold.]

Burrell fails to add that the situation may be more complex than at first glance as this butterfly is a favourite with enthusiasts for breeding in captivity from bought stock and often then the resultant imagines are released into the wild. Indeed at Wetmoor the last sighting was of larvae on 31st March 1991 when only eleven larvae were found compared to over 2000 the previous winter. It is known that larvae were released at the site in the mid 1980s and it is at least theoretically possible that this could have contributed to their decline, either through the introduction of disease or parasites or weakening of the genetic stock or even by over-stocking. The enormous number

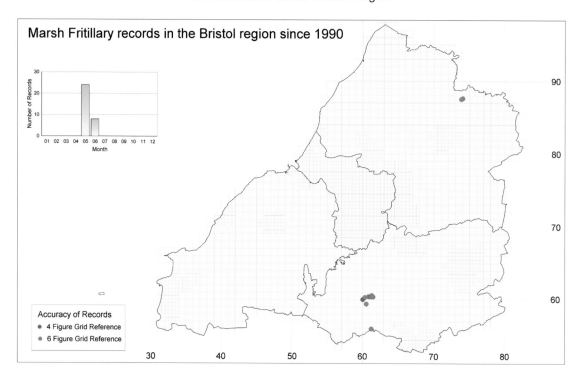

Marsh Fritillary records in the Bristol region since 1990

Accuracy of Records
● 4 Figure Grid Reference
● 6 Figure Grid Reference

of larvae present in 1990 ate **all** the available scabious in the meadow!

A further case of introduction of captive-bred stock is listed in the Bristol Naturalists' Society Proceedings for 1953. In it is stated: *'First imago seen at a new colony near Bristol on May 12. This colony was established in 1952 by C.L.B. and over 50 were counted in late May 1953.'* (Blathwayt, 1954).

As can be seen from Burrell's list above, at the time it was compiled there were no sites that were still known to hold the Marsh Fritillary. The last record was the Folly Farm sightings of 1993 and the Avon Butterfly Survey had identified the species as one of the fastest declining butterflies in the region as well as farther afield in Somerset on the Mendips and the Somerset Levels. The colonies were well known for fluctuating in numbers but post-1993 it seemed the butterfly had declined to a position where it disappeared and was unlikely to re-colonise.

At Folly Farm SSSI and nature reserve, the Marsh Fritillary had been first recorded by Rupert Higgins, in 1987. The site contains unimproved neutral grassland with abundant Devil's-bit Scabious and small numbers of the butterfly, up to 7, were seen most years from

1987 until 1993. Despite regular butterfly transects after that year, none were seen. In 1997 Avon Wildlife Trust decided to undertake a re-introduction programme (with the support of the local office of English Nature). The site was still considered to be in suitable condition for the insect, in terms of what was known about the required sward structure and the abundance of its food plant, although no reason for its extinction had been established. The guidelines for re-introductions adopted by the Joint Committee for the Conservation of British Insects (JCCBI) were not followed to the letter as five complete seasons with no sightings are usually recommended before introducing new stock. A local member of Butterfly Conservation provided advice and also stock from the south west of England for the re-introduction. As a consequence, 20 batches of larvae, each of several dozen, (to mimic the larval colonies of natural populations where larvae clump together for warmth in early spring sunshine) were released on the SSSI at the end of February 1997. A further 45 pupae were put out later that spring.

In the summer of 1997, adults were seen from 14 May to 6 June with up to 16 on any one day. Ten larval webs were found that

August and in the following spring up to 12 adults were seen from 14–21 May. Two years after the re-introduction, however, the only report was by Adrian Sharp who saw up to three imagines in mid-May 1999 and by 2000 the only sighting was of one female on May 31 by John Martin.

This attempt therefore to re-introduce the butterfly failed even though the habitat and management regime, light autumn grazing with beef cattle, appeared to offer suitable conditions. The exercise demonstrated that the reasons for local extinction maybe complex and not easily overcome. Whatever led to the extinction in 1993 may also have doomed this attempt to failure from the start, although a series of wet springs may have also contributed. It has re-emphasised the need to focus on conservation strategies to save species from dying out at existing sites as this last ditch strategy has little guarantees of success. The ethical and practical considerations of using captive bred stock require further debate at the local level as does the investment in time and resources needed to effectively monitor the success or failure of such experiments and to learn from them.

It may be that the British future of the Marsh Fritillary will depend upon suitable Biodiversity Action Plans and Species Recovery Plans being implemented effectively. This can be very successful as witnessed by attempts to stop the decline of the Heath Fritillary in Kent resulting in the number of colonies increasing from 14 to 18 in the last five years of the twentieth century. Any further attempts to reintroduce and protect the Marsh Fritillary should be approached as part of a national plan, not in isolation and not in response to local pressures.

## Glanville Fritillary  *Melitaea cinxia* (Linn.)

**National status: Resident restricted to the Isle of Wight and adjacent mainland coast.**
**Bristol region status: One introduced colony on the coast.**

Kurt Vickery  May 1990

**Glanville Fritillary**   Sand Point, North Somerset

The Glanville Fritillary is a European species at the extreme limit of its northern range in the British Isles. There are historic records from a scattering of sites in the south east of England dating mainly from the late 17th century to the mid 19th century but its stronghold has been and remains the south coast of the Isle of Wight. The reasons for this are thought to be that high temperatures are required for the larval development in the spring at sites where the foodplant, Ribwort Plantain *Plantago lanceolata*, grows in profusion. The regular slumping of the undercliffs on the Isle of Wight retain the early successional stage where the plant can flourish. (Asher *et al*, 2001.)

There is an early report of the Glanville Fritillary as an inhabitant of the Bristol region, as it is listed in the Bath Handbook (Morris, 1888), but as Hudd pointed out in his annota-

tions to his 1884 list, it was recorded '*probably in error*'. The accepted British inland sites amounted to a handful (four or five) and all from the east of the country.

In the 1980s in particular, the Bristol region saw a high incidence of a number of different lepidopteran species being 'put down' by local enthusiasts intent on bolstering or improving the local fauna. Livestock of many species was, and often still is, available through dealers, the stock regularly being derived from continental sources where many of our British species are more plentiful. It was in 1983 that a colony of the Glanville Fritillary was first reported from Sand Point above Weston-super-Mare. Also in the 1980s the Glanville Fritillary was seen at much more unsuitable sites, namely Brandon Hill in the centre of the city as well as Leigh Woods and other places in the region. Obviously a

Martin Evans  29ᵗʰ April 1986

Andrew Daw  May 1998

**Glanville Fritillary** (larvae)
Sand Point, North Somerset

**Glanville Fritillary**
Sand Point, North Somerset

considerable amount of captive bred stock was freely available and being released.

Sand Point was the site where the butterfly apparently found conditions to its liking as the colony survived and has persisted for nearly twenty years and in certain years it has flourished. In 1991, for example, over 20 individuals were counted on 27th May. Although it was still possible to see over ten on a visit in 1999 by that time there was concern that numbers were falling.

It is not surprising that it is the south facing slopes at the site that have supported the butterfly. Erosional rates at the promontory are not as great as on the Undercliff of the Isle of Wight but the exposed nature of the site tends to restrict the vegetation developing, coupled with some management that has been introduced. However, at the present time there is concern in some quarters that the levels of grazing may have been too high (irregular over-grazing by cattle) and the large scale flailing of scrub may explain the dramatic drop

in numbers of this butterfly in recent years. In fact the butterfly may now be extinct at the site as the last confirmed sighting was on 7 June 2000 by John Webber and Matthew Oates. The alternative view is that the butterfly has declined naturally due to a combination of poor years when the adult was on the wing, rampant bramble invasion, a collapse in the rabbit population and strong seasons for grass growth. The result being a drastic reduction in the amount of available plantain foodplant. (M. Oates, 2001 & pers. comm.)

It has been suggested that climate warming may enable the Glanville Fritillary to expand its natural range. Perhaps, if numbers recover at Sand Point, it could expand from this artificially established colony too. A warming climate however may not necessarily lead to ideal conditions for this butterfly. The experience of the mid 1990s to early 2000s is one of more extremes of particular weather types; witness the very high rainfall over the winter of 2000/2001. If inappropriate extremes coincide

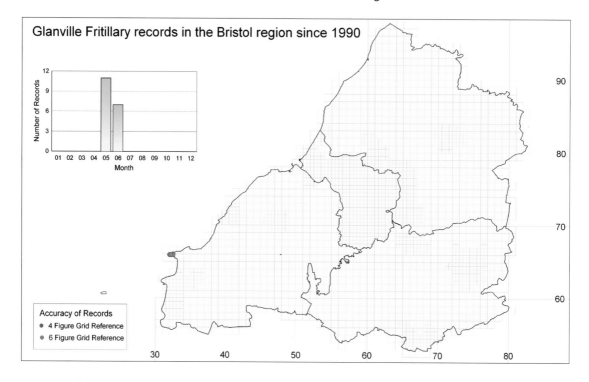

Glanville Fritillary records in the Bristol region since 1990

with crucial times in its lifecycle, such as the need for mild spring weather, then success will not be guaranteed.

The management of the Bristol region site for the Glanville Fritillary has been in itself a controversial subject. Should a site be maintained for a species which has never occurred there naturally, management which could perhaps affect endemic species adversely? If the butterfly has now died out there, should we be concerned? How much effort should we make to conserve a colony when its gene pool may have originated from who knows where and when the species still occurs naturally elsewhere in the British Isles?

There are other examples of similarly introduced colonies of this butterfly; Meredith (1984) records '*The species was introduced in 1976 to a Cotswold site. A colony survived for a few years, but it has apparently died out.*' On at least one occasion exception has been taken to artificially introduced colonies of butterflies; the non-native Map butterfly colony established in the Wye Valley around 1912 was reportedly exterminated by an entomologist who did not approve (Emmet & Heath, 1989). If the Sand Point colony is still extant, perhaps the best strategy is one of limited intervention. Management of the site in a way that should encourage the greatest diversity of plants and animals native to the site is likely to be relatively advantageous to the Glanville Fritillary. If under these conditions it cannot survive then so be it.

# Speckled Wood    *Parage aegeria* (Linn.) ssp. *tircis* (Godart)

**National status: Widespread resident across the British Isles, currently increasing its range.**
**Bristol region status: Common resident.**

**Speckled Wood**

Andrew Daw

A butterfly whose name sums up the habitat in which it is most familiar, woods where it delights in areas of dappled sunlight. It is a common species today and has probably always has been in the last two hundred years.

Despite this, its national populations have varied and have touched upon that of the Bristol region. At the beginning of the twentieth century, the Speckled Wood had retreated to strongholds of the south west of England, parts of Wales and Scotland. A reduction in the population locally although the butterfly never vanished, is hinted at by Hudd's comment (1884) '*Rather local, but abundant in many woods and lanes throughout the district, especially near Weston-s-M.*' His hand written additions state: '*Clevedon, rarer than formerly J.M. 88. Scarce at Leigh R.M.P.*'

If it had declined locally by the middle of that century Turner (1955) considered it '*Very common in the southern part* [of Somerset], *less so in the north*' and Bird listed it from '*Yatton, Clevedon, Walton-in-Gordano, Tickenham, Brockley Combe, Leigh Woods, Goblin Combe.*' By this time, the butterfly had also expanded again across most of southern England.

As with a number of species, in the main distributional range the Speckled Wood can utilise a greater variety of habitats than it can at the edge of its range where the population is presumably under greater pressure. In the Bristol region, part of its stronghold, Meredith (1984) reports '*Common and becoming more so even in suburban gardens, Clifton (J.W.N.). First appeared in our garden at*

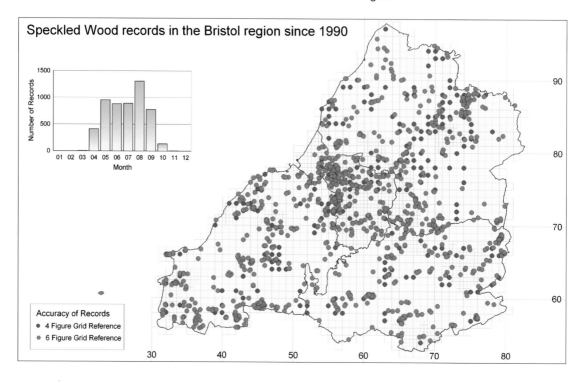

Speckled Wood records in the Bristol region since 1990

*Henleaze Bristol about 1923 and seen in subsequent years (Heslop).'* Furthermore Brown (1971) confirms '*In almost any suitable habitat in the Bristol area, but is never common...We usually see four broods every year, there being two parts to each generation. The first specimens appear on the wing in April and are of a particularly bright and even exotic character, with very prominent yellow markings. In the spring of 1967, the author captured two contrasting aberrations at one locality on the same day. They were both females and had emerged during a warm sunny spell following a period of heavy frosts and bitter cold. With the first specimen, the characteristic yellow patch surrounding the eye-spots on the forewings was absent, whereas on the second one most of the yellow markings on the forewings had been extended into broad streaks, and the eye-spots themselves were enlarged. It is thought that the prevailing weather could have been responsible for these variations. During the latter part of the year specimens are seen on the wing right up to the end of October.'*

Today the use of suburban and even urban gardens is common as a breeding locality. The heart of Bristol sees the butterfly inhabiting gardens and any green spaces such as allotments and surrounding lanes. This may have been a feature of the city at least since Heslop's observation of 1923. It remains common and widespread today with several broods per year. The larvae feed on a variety of grasses such as False Brome *Brachypodium sylvaticum*, Cock's-foot *Dactylis glomerata*, Yorkshire Fog *Holcus lanatus* and Common Couch *Elytrigia repens*, even as small weeds in gardens. Parsons (1996) records the first record for the island of Steepholm as 1975 but that it has been seen frequently in subsequent years and is probably breeding.

In the Avon Butterfly Project's survey, the Small Tortoiseshell is the species for which most reports have been received. The Speckled Wood is second in this list, just beating the Meadow Brown. However, each report may represent one individual or many and so is not necessarily a true reflection of abundance. The phenological data suggests there may be broods emerging in May, June, July/August and September. However, the situation maybe more akin to almost continual emergences with the greatest concentrations in spring and summer.

# Wall *Lasiommata megera* (Linn.)

**National status: Widespread resident of England, Wales and Ireland.**
**Bristol region status: Local but widespread resident.**

**Wall** Elmsley Lane, Kewstoke, North Somerset

Martin Evans   26ᵗʰ July 1992

The Wall is a slightly enigmatic butterfly, in some years fairly common, in others rare. It is a butterfly that loves dry spots in grassland where it can bask, occurring not only in natural habitats but also in quarries, disused railways and the like. The larvae utilise grasses of various different species such as Tor-grass *Brachypodium pinnatum*, False Brome *B. sylvaticum* and Cock's-foot *Dactylis glomerata* amongst others.

The localised occurrence is something that nearly all previous authors have commented upon in the Bristol region. Turner (1955) even went so far as to describe it as '*Generally distributed and very common in some parts*' of Somerset. Meredith (1984) also considered it '*Common*'. Whereas Brown (1971) summarised it more eloquently as '*Seen at some time or another, but only in very small num-*

*bers. Its strength varies from one season to the next, and occasionally it may be absent from certain popular haunts for quite a number of years. Unfortunately, it is extremely difficult to give any indication of the trends of this species, but in one or two localities its status never dwindles. These places are mainly in the open areas along the Cotswold escarpment in Gloucestershire, and Sand Point near Weston-super-Mare in Somerset also appears to be a stronghold of the Wall Brown. Despite extensive searches little in the way of variation has occurred.*'

Other localities have been Wetmoor in the north and, since 1975, Steepholm in the Bristol Channel (Parsons, 1996).

The Avon Butterfly Project results suggest it to be widely distributed although not particularly common. It lives in small colonies that

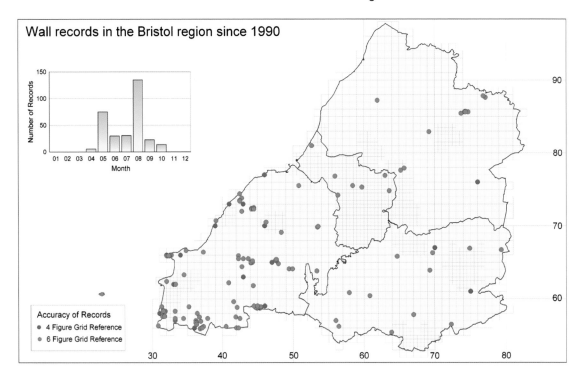

Wall records in the Bristol region since 1990

seem to be more prevalent in the south west of the region and as such is still relatively strong in the Sand Point area. One particular habitat where the butterfly seems to occur regularly is on the grasslands of Iron Age hill forts such as at Cadbury Hill near Yatton.

The distribution map though, may give a false impression of abundance as it appears to be only usually seen in quite small numbers. In the last few years, there is also a suggestion that there may have been a rapid and sharp decline. Adult butterflies can be seen in two broods each year, firstly in May and June and again in July and August, lasting into September sometimes. Numbers are usually smaller in the spring than for the second brood. Asher *et al* (2001) suggest that the Wall has declined in recent times in inland areas but the Avon Project results imply that this effect has also been felt locally in our coastal environment. Although grassland sites have declined the butterfly is thought to be quite temperature sensitive requiring hot dry localities. If so it is surprising that there has been a recent decline rather than the increase that milder weather in the last ten or more years should have perhaps assisted. Further research is needed on the precise habitat requirements of this species in all its life stages.

# Marbled White    *Melanargia galathea* (Linn.) ssp. *serena* Verity

**National status: Resident of southern England and South Wales.**
**Bristol region status: Widespread and fairly common resident.**

**Marbled White**    Barrow Gurney, North Somerset

John Aldridge    June 1984

The Marbled White seems to have had somewhat fluctuating fortunes in the Bristol region. Hudd (1884) reports the following '*Stapleton and Purdown, scarce. G.H. This pretty species used to be common in fields near Bedminster, but is now seldom met with in the neighbourhood of Bristol. Portishead and Clevedon, F.D.Wheeler. Weston-s-m G.R.C.*' Hudd's hand written notes to one copy of the publication add: '*Almondsbury, Sometimes abundant. See Knapp's Journal of a Naturalist (1829) p.291*' and '*Found in Somerset at Weston-s-m,...Clevedon & Portishead, but it has disappeared in the immediate neighbourhood of Bristol CGB. I p.209 .*'

Therefore, the butterfly seems to have been declining at the end of the nineteenth century. In the twentieth century Turner (1955) considered it (like so many butterflies) '*Generally common locally, particularly in the south*'. Bird gives the following sites, '*Tickenham, Leigh Woods, Clevedon, Goblin Combe, Walton Moor.*' Meredith (1984) has more illuminating information namely, '*Used to occur in one small corner of Kingsweston Down: it just lingered over a number of years but the last specimen was taken in my presence, in 1918 apparently reappeared there as reported in Proc BNS 1947 (Heslop). Exceptionally abundant 1950 (C.S.H.B.), Kingsweston Down common7.vii.71 (A.N.Grose), Wick few 25.vii.71 (D.R.Humblett).*' This evidence then suggests that there had been a recovery in numbers locally by the middle of the twentieth century. Blathwayt remarked in 1964: '*it seems to be spreading to a number of places in N. Somerset where it did not previously occur.*' (Burton, 1964). The fortunes of the

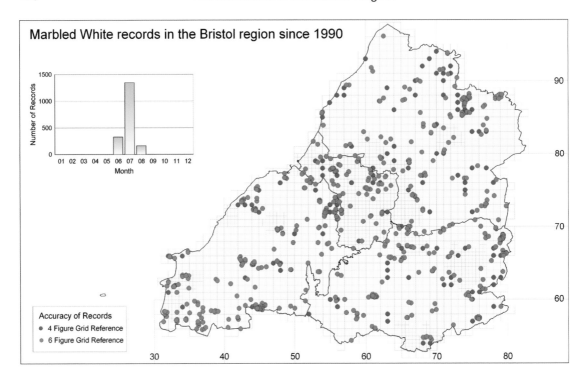

Marbled White records in the Bristol region since 1990

Accuracy of Records
• 4 Figure Grid Reference
• 6 Figure Grid Reference

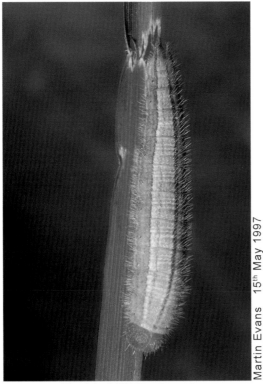

Martin Evans    15th May 1997

**Marbled White** (larva)
Wick Rocks, South Gloucestershire

Marbled White are partly dependant upon its breeding sites. Eggs are dropped in flight over the rough grassland it inhabits where Red Fescue *Festuca rubra*, the principal foodplant grows. Sheep's-fescue *F. ovina* is also commonly used along with several other grasses. Tall tussocky unimproved grassland is preferred.

In 1971 Brown's summary was '*This species, fortunately, does not appear to be in any danger, as indicated from the records. Although it is dying out in some of its former localities, we receive reports of new discoveries every year...It is not only plentiful on the limestone hillsides but also in many of the country lanes and rough fields extending between Gloucester and Bristol. At Kingsweston Down in northern Bristol...the Marbled White is common each year. In 1967, a superb aberration was taken here, in which the normal black markings were replaced by those of a pinkish-buff colour. In North Somerset, it occurs in nearly every type of habitat, ranging from the bleak open areas in the Mendip Hills, through to the coastal regions near Weston-super-Mare, including the inevitable Goblin Combe, and down across the Somerset lowlands...1970 appears to be a peak year for the*

Martin Evans 15th May 1997

**Marbled White** (pupa)
from larva found at
Wick Rocks, South Gloucestershire

*Marbled White, in Goblin Combe at any rate, where numbers of the butterfly were fighting for nectar on each flower head. A male specimen with normal forewings and near-transparent hindwings was caught at this time.'* (The aberration captured in 1967 is now in the possession of C.W.Wiltshire.)

In the last twenty years there has been an impression that the Marbled White appears to have done even better, increasing in abundance as well as colonising new sites. Even in the centre of Bristol on allotments and other green spaces the butterfly has been recorded and indeed may be breeding. The network of green corridors in big cities such as Bristol has probably played an important role in allowing this colonisation. These often linear parcels of land require protection to enable further improvements to the biodiversity of the urban environment to be maintained and increased. Elsewhere again, there is the feeling amongst many recorders that the Marbled White is currently thriving in our region, just as it is across the country. Unfortunately, the survey does not provide enough quantitative data to test these suggestions. Milder winters and warmer summers seem to be to its liking and at the moment the limitation to it seem to be the availability or otherwise of grassland sites. Early July sees peak emergence of the single brood.

# Grayling *Hipparchia semele semele* (Linn.)

**National status: A resident found around the coasts of the British Isles.**
**Bristol region status: Resident primarily on the coastal strip and the western end of the Mendips.**

1st August 1991

Martin Evans

**Grayling**   Barton Hill, North Somerset

This large powerful-flying butterfly was listed in the Victoria County History of Somerset as being so abundant that it '*swarms on limestone hills near Bristol...the Mendips.*' (Hudd, 1906). By Turner's time though (1955) this had become modified to '*Sometimes abundant on limestone hills, and on the moors, scarce and local elsewhere. Wrington, c. (A.H.T.), Tickenham (J.E.H.B.) 1919.*' Bird listed '*Uphill, Tickenham, Walton-in-Gordano, Clevedon, Mendips, Goblin Combe*' at around this time.

It was Brown (1971) who drew attention to the different habitats the Grayling occurs on when he stated '*renowned for its characteristic of inhabiting two quite different haunts. On the one hand it normally flourishes on limestone hills, whereas on the other it can be found in low-lying heathland areas. Although*

*we have no records from West Gloucestershire, the above statement can be applied to North Somerset. In the Mendip Hills, which are primarily limestone, the Grayling butterfly has been noted in less than five localities. On the rocky outcrops and open areas in Goblin and Brockley Combes it can also be found. In contrast, it is especially common along the coastal reaches either side of Weston-super-Mare, from Sand Point to Brean Down.*'

However Meredith (1984) did draw attention to one record from the West Gloucestershire vice-county with '*Used to occur at the Gully, Durdham Downs, Bristol (J.W.N.). Very local.*'

So, it would seem at a glance that the Grayling populations have declined substantially over one hundred years. Even where

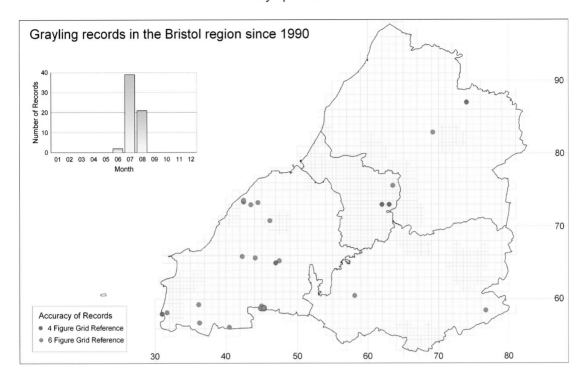

Grayling records in the Bristol region since 1990

they still occur they are usually in much smaller numbers than previously and certainly are not seen in 'swarms'. The localities where the butterfly lives in the region are characterised by dry grassland with bare patches where the adults in July and August can perch and perform their characteristic behaviour of thermoregulation. When alighting the Grayling always closes its wings immediately and orientates into a position where it will increase its temperature (side onto the sun) or reduce it (head on into the sun). The ova are also laid onto patches of grass amongst the bare areas, the usual species used being Sheep's-fescue *Festuca ovina*, Red Fescue *F. rubra* and Early Hair-grass *Aira praecox*, although the latter is scarce and unusual in the region as it favours acidic grassland. There are one or two sightings to the east of our region but it could be said that the coastal influence to the climate may extend as far as these places.

Although it is such a coastal species, the Grayling is not recorded from Steepholm Island where the necessary short turf is largely absent. It still remains as a localised butterfly on the coastal strip around Weston-super-Mare and on sites on the Mendips such as Dolebury Warren. As such, it is limestone downland, quarries and coastal cliffs that the butterfly lives on rather than low-lying heath in our region. The appropriate habitat is declining in the area, for example the reduction of grassland at Wrington Warren. However this does not explain totally the reduction in sites for the butterfly and the apparent reduction in population densities where it still occurs. There is considerable concern over the rate at which the Grayling has been disappearing recently in the region. One particular example concerns the colony that occurred at Troopers Hill within the conurbation of Bristol, above the River Avon. This post-industrial site is a typical one in that it has dry grassland with extensive areas of open ground and heather and gorse. Sadly though, the colony appears to have died out, last recorded there in 1994, even though the habitat has apparently remained entirely suitable. It is this sort of track record that highlights the concern over the possible decline that the species may be going through. The Grayling is a priority species for the region in terms of its current status. In particular it is a species that should be subject to local Biodiversity Action Planning initiatives.

# Gatekeeper or Hedge Brown   *Pyronia tithonus*
## (Linn.) ssp. *britanniae* (Verity)

**National status: Resident increasing in places over England, Wales and southern Ireland.**
**Bristol region status: Common and widespread resident.**

**Gatekeeper**

Kurt Vickery

As a generalist that feeds on a variety of grasses such as *Agrostis*, *Festuca* and *Poa* species as a larva, the Hedge Brown or Gatekeeper has long been a common species in the region. Hudd's summary of it was '*Abundant everywhere*' in 1884 and with the Meadow Brown, '*perhaps the two most abundant butterflies in the district, being found in thousands in most years*' in 1906.

The only change to this situation is the suggestion that the numbers of the butterfly under went some decline during the twentieth century as Meredith (1984) stated '*Bristol district common locally less so than formerly (J.W.N.)*'. However Brown's summary (1971) is probably accurate; '*found all over the two vice-counties but it is not usually observed in*

*very large numbers owing to its comparatively short season on the wing. However this is quite deceiving since if one approaches a suitable haunt at the right time when the weather is good, the species may often be found to be plentiful. We have much evidence of this each year from various localities and so this conclusion is well founded. 1968 was an outstanding year for it in the Bristol district, particularly in the City itself where it swarmed at Kingsweston Down. It may be safely said that nearly fifty percent were of the form ab.* multiocellata *Oberthur, some being quite extreme. Examples of "bleaches" or ab.* transformis *were also taken. Our latest record is of one butterfly at Yatton on 12th Sept 1965.*'

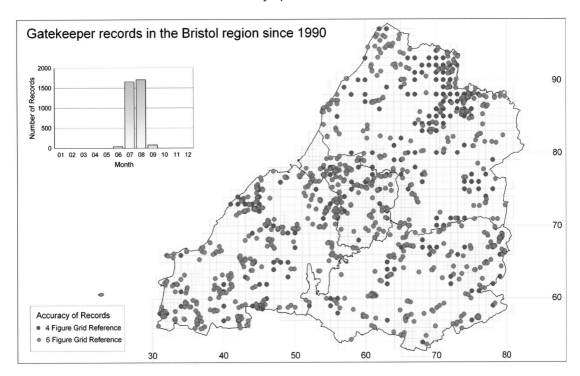

Gatekeeper records in the Bristol region since 1990

As well as 1968 being an outstanding year, Meredith also reports 1983 as a very good year for numbers. The Gatekeeper has been recorded on Steepholm since 1978 as an occasional visitor. This may reflect it is more mobile in years with higher summer temperatures (Asher *et al.* 2001).

The butterfly is a very common species at present in any wayside haunts, particularly associated with bramble banks. Our current climate seems to suit it. Hudd's comments are still just about appropriate for the Gatekeeper today, although overall numbers must be less. The butterflies can be seen on the wing from the beginning of July, lasting throughout August, with a few stragglers lingering into September.

## Meadow Brown    *Maniola jurtina* (Linn.) ssp. *insularis* Thompson

**National status: Common and widespread across the British Isles.**
**Bristol region status: Common and widespread.**

Tony Moulin  1998

**Meadow Brown**    Yatton, North Somerset

To many it comes as a surprise to hear that the Meadow Brown is regarded as the commonest British butterfly, as we are more familiar with Small Tortoiseshells, Peacocks and White butterflies in our gardens. However, the Meadow Brown is able to breed on relatively small pockets of grassland. As with the Gatekeeper, many species of grass will be used by the larvae as food including *Festuca*, *Agrostis* and *Poa* species amongst others. Consequently as well as undisturbed grasslands, waste ground, road verges and even urban parks, gardens and allotments can support the butterfly.

One hundred years ago, the Meadow Brown was undoubtedly even more abundant than today when there was even more available habitat and before the introduction of modern pesticides and herbicides. Newman

(1874) stated '*This is perhaps the most generally abundant of all our butterflies, frequenting every meadow where the grass is ready for cutting.*' Hudd (1906) regarded it as with the Gatekeeper one of '*the two most abundant butterflies in the district, being in thousands in most years.*'

This situation changed little during the twentieth century, Brown (1971) had '*little to say about this butterfly except that it is common nearly every year, and can be found on almost any suitable piece of land. Those specimens with white blotches known as "bleaches" are met with in most seasons, but are not nearly so frequent as in South-East England. It might be of interest to note that the butterfly usually appears on the wing in mid-June and seen up to the end of October, if mild weather prevails.*' The bleaches he

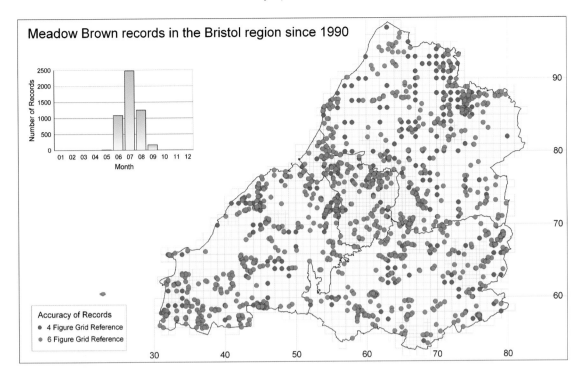

Meadow Brown records in the Bristol region since 1990

refers to are the odd specimens that are thrown up with areas on the wings as white or very pale brown in coloration giving the appearance of worn out individuals. These are in fact genetically inherited aberrations. Brown's comments upon the flight span are also still largely true today.

The Avon Butterfly project results confirm that the Meadow Brown remains very common but the current worries over the sudden reduction in some of our common birds is a salutary lesson that such situations can change very quickly. Indeed in certain parts of Europe the butterfly is declining (Asher *et al*, 2001) so continued monitoring of the numbers of the Meadow Brown is fully justified. The

phenological data indicates that in certain years the Meadow Brown is able to appear on the wing from late May. Numbers build steadily in June leading to a maximum population density in July and then tail off through August into September. Although considered to be the commonest butterfly nationally the Meadow Brown scores third in terms of the numbers of records received during the duration of the current survey, close behind the Speckled Wood and some way behind the Small Tortoiseshell. However, this may be a reflection of many records being from gardens rather than more rural habitats and does not necessarily reflect numbers of individuals, one record could represent many individuals.

## Small Heath   *Coenonympha pamphilus pamphilus* (Linn.)

**National status: Common and widespread resident across the British Isles.**
**Bristol region status: Common and widespread resident.**

Martin Evans   3rd September 1989

**Small Heath**   Mendip Hills

In these days of a greater interest in the wildlife within cities, so-called urban ecology, it is perhaps surprising to see a reference to the Small Heath from 1906 as follows '*one of the most plentiful and most generally distributed of our butterflies, and is found sometimes even in gardens in Bristol.*' (Hudd, 1906.) The disappointing aspect of this is that the Small Heath is no longer a resident of Bristol gardens, except perhaps in exceptional circumstances. In fact, it is not as common anywhere as it was in the nineteenth century when Hudd (1884) wrote '*Abundant everywhere, on heaths and downs.*' As with the Meadow Brown, which it often accompanies, the Small Heath larvae feed on grasses such as *Festuca*, *Agrostis* and *Poa* species. However, unlike the Meadow Brown it is rather more restricted to downs and unim-

proved grassland, particularly in well-drained sites. Furthermore, the Small Heath does not have just one brood per year but two or occasionally three in our region, appearing on the wing from May to September. A characteristic shared with the Grayling is the fact that the wings are never opened when the butterfly perches, but unlike the Grayling which alights on bare earth, the Small Heath alights on grasses and flowers. A comparison of the distribution map to that of the Meadow Brown will show how much more restricted this butterfly is today, compared to that species.

Turner in 1955 considered the Small Heath to be '*Very common in most parts of the county* [Somerset] *but in a few places it is quite uncommon or even scarce*' and Meredith thought it '*Common*' in Gloucestershire

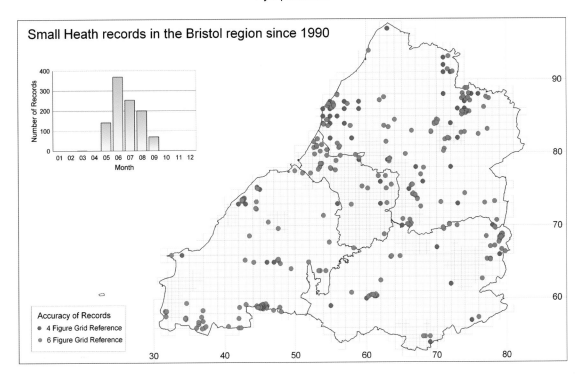

Small Heath records in the Bristol region since 1990

(1984). Yet again Brown (1971) has given more of an insight into the fluctuations of this butterfly 'Over the past eight years, the numbers of this little butterfly have increased noticeably, especially in the Bristol district, and reached a peak in 1969. In the early 1960's, only two or three specimens would ever be seen on a particular day, generally being more plentiful in the first generation...quite scarce on Filton Golf Course but in 1965 there was a marked increase in its strength. In other places such as Wetmoor, Tockington and Kingsweston Down the situation has been exactly the same, the last named colony being quite variable owing to its growing status...During 1970, we received a bulk of reports from the somewhat built-up areas east of Bristol, such as Purdown, where no fewer than fifty specimens were counted on a day in August. In North Somerset we have further evidence that this species is on the increase.' A.H.Weeks was able to beat the latter sighting, in 1987, when he counted over 100 on a visit to Dolebury Warren on 2 July that year.

According to Parsons (1996) the Small Heath has only been seen on Steepholm in 1902 and 1914 reflecting the poor dispersal mechanisms of the species. The Avon survey has shown that the Small Heath is still widely distributed and locally common but there are suggestions that it has been declining particularly in the final years of the millennium. It is certainly not as common as Brown implied it was in the 1960s. It is likely that this is due to the general continued degradation of the natural environment. Even episodes of reduced agricultural intensity, for example through the 'set aside' scheme, do not seem to have assisted it much. The amount of unimproved grassland left in the region continues to fall and populations of species that inhabit it become constantly more isolated. The preference of the larvae for the finer-leaved grasses could possibly be involved in this reduction, as with the requirement for a fairly close cropped sward.

As mentioned, three broods are possible here in the south of England particularly at the warmest and sheltered sites. The phenological graph however does not show three distinct peaks of emergence. Instead, as Asher *et al* (2001) explains, butterflies on the wing in May and June are the progeny from eggs laid the previous May and June which have taken twelve months over their development. Butterflies seen in July result from eggs laid the previous August and finally adult butterflies seen in August and September originate from eggs laid in the spring of the same year. In very many years over the period of the current survey, the Small Heath has been recorded into September confirming this third emergence during those years.

# Ringlet   *Aphantopus hyperantus* (Linn.)

**National status: Common and widespread resident across the British Isles.**
**Bristol region status: Common and widespread resident.**

**Ringlet**

The Ringlet is usually associated in particular with woodland rides and edges, hence Hudd's 1884 comment '*Rather local, in woods, but common where it occurs. Ringless varieties are not uncommon at Brockley Combe.*' His annotations to the list include: '*Abundant near Weston 1879 R.M.P.*' In Newman's book on the butterflies and moths of the country (1874) he mentions '*Mr Naish found it flying in incredible numbers in the woods adjoining Weston-super-Mare, and I have seen it in like profusion in many places.*'

The situation has not changed greatly upto the present day. Brown (1971) mentions again local abundance as well as aberrations that could be met with '*widely distributed...and can be found in a variety of different habitats...In other areas, such as Wetmoor near Wickwar...can be seen in far greater numbers,* where there is thick deciduous forest with overgrown rides...In Goblin Combe, the Ringlet is perhaps more abundant than in any of the surrounding areas. As can be expected, there is considerable variation with such numbers, and abs.* parvipuncta *and* caeca *are occasionally met with. These two forms are being bred experimentally with the hope of increasing the strength of their populations. Ab.* magnipuncta, *a much rarer variation, has also been found here, and in July of this year (1970) a superb asymmetrical "bleach" was captured.*'

In fact, Brown did not release aberrations into the population at Goblin Combe from his breeding experiments (C. Wiltshire, pers. comm.). The author is not aware of any other records of aberrations in recent years.

Unlike most other common brown butterflies, it is the coarser grasses that the Ringlet

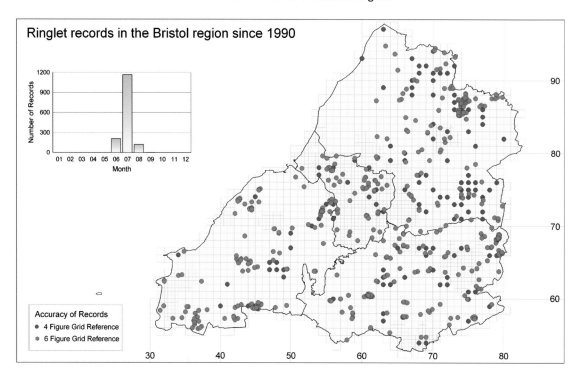

larvae feed on, such as Cock's-foot *Dactylis glomerata*, False Brome *Brachypodium sylvaticum*, Tufted Hair-grass *Deschampia cespitosa* and Common Couch *Elytriga repens*. Tall lush grasses on rich soils are a favourite but there is an impression of late that the Ringlet has been increasing within our region and so utilising patches of grass further away from the woodland edge, along roads and other green ways and corridors. As such, it does occur within the urban environment as well as in the surrounding countryside. Perhaps crucially, this butterfly appears to favour the damper grassland areas, avoiding the hotter, drier sites. It also appears to do well in the damper summers and can be seen flying in light drizzle.

Probably often over-looked as it so resembles the Meadow Brown at a glance when in flight, there is no immediate cause for concern over this butterfly except for the familiar observation that suitable breeding sites can so easily be lost. The distribution map helps to show that the butterfly is widespread in the region but absent from the low-lying, coastal areas. Butterflies appear first in June and the single brood lasts through to the middle of August. It is noted that years with poor summer weather, and therefore often with low numbers of butterflies, are usually good for the Ringlet.

# Monarch *Danaus plexippus* (Linn.)

**National status: Rare immigrant.**
**Bristol region status: Very rare immigrant.**

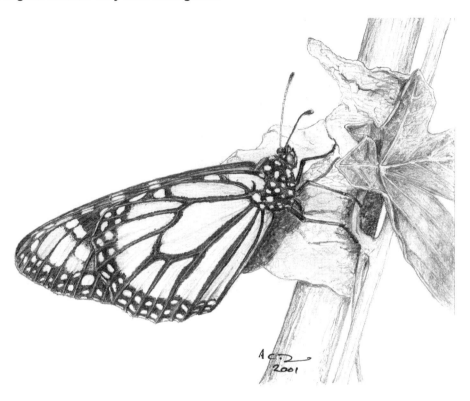

The Monarch is famous for the enormous roosts of hibernating butterflies that occur in Mexico and California. This very large and impressive species has been able to colonise other parts of the world including the Canary Islands and Spain where the larval foodplant, Milkweeds *Asclepias* species have become naturalized. There is some debate as to from where the occasional specimens that reach our shores originate, is it the well established colonies on the Canaries or the more recent ones in Spain and Gibraltar, or is it from the United States themselves with a direct (or ship assisted) flight across three thousand miles of the Atlantic Ocean? Burton & French (1969) suggested the latter source as the most likely given that some immigrations can be correlated with large scale movements on the North American continent, with land falls of North American bird species and with weather sys-

tems across the North Atlantic. There is always the possibility that some of the more recent sightings represent accidental escapes from the butterfly houses in this country that have become regular tourist attractions in the last twenty or so years.

The first record we know of for the Bristol region was reported by Turner (1955) '*A very rare immigrant, or importation, which is recorded in the county from time to time. Blagdon (Ent) 1933.*' This was followed by an unpublished record listed by J. Bird in the 1950s of his father's: '*Observed one specimen flying slowly along the road below Horton's Wood (above Walton Moor) (south) while on Home Guard duty in September 1940, H.W.B.*'

In the autumn of 1965, the naturalist and broadcaster John Burton participated in an experiment concerning the Monarch, with the leading authority on the butterfly, Professor

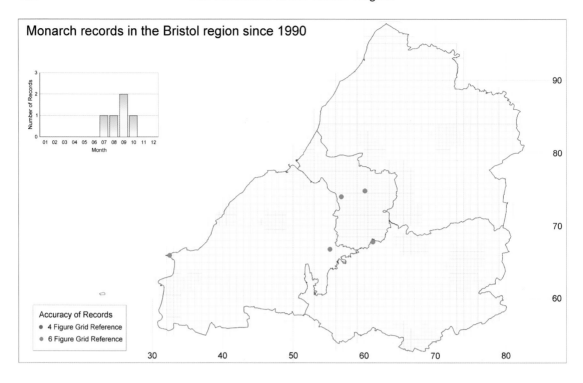

Monarch records in the Bristol region since 1990

Accuracy of Records
● 4 Figure Grid Reference
● 6 Figure Grid Reference

F.A. Urquhart of Toronto University, Canada. Burton was sent 50 live Monarch butterflies, tagged with an adhesive, numbered label on the wing. These were released from Cadbury Camp, near Clevedon on 6th September 1965 with the hope of recording information on their behaviour and movement when transposed from their native continent. Resultant sightings occurred as far afield as Kettering, Northamptonshire (110 miles away) and up to two weeks after the release. The fact that only eleven of the butterflies were ever reported is an interesting fact in itself. Only one was seen in the Bristol region following the release. This type of experiment was apparently not repeated. The national entomological community was alerted to the release of the butterflies by articles placed in most of the leading specialist journals and then followed by a summary of the results in 1966 (e.g. Burton, 1966). Television and radio also reported the event.

1968 was a special year when over sixty Monarchs (presumably genuine migrants) were seen in the British Isles and of these, two were just outside the Bristol region at Brent Knoll and Churchdown, (Brown, 1971). A single Monarch was reported from an Abbots Leigh garden in September 1981 (Sorrell, Way

& Weeks, 1983). In September 1983 a female was found dead in a field at Hinton Hill, Dyrham, north of Bath and is now in the Bristol Museum Collections (Accession Number: Ac2159) (Sorrell & Weeks, 1984). The latter record did not coincide with other reports from across the country and so may have been due to the release of a captive bred individual. A single individual was also seen at Middle Hope near Weston-super-Mare on 20 September 1992 by Matthew Oates (pers. comm.), again not a year when many were seen nationally. 1995 was however, a notable year with probably approaching two hundred individual butterflies reported across the country. Here in the Bristol region there were sightings within Bristol in August and October of that year. Two records were also reported to the Butterfly Project during 1996, one on Dundry Hill in July and one at Bristol Zoo in September but these may have been escapes from captive bred livestock as there were no reported sightings elsewhere. Even more recently there has been a further good year for immigration, over three hundred are thought to have been present in the country in the autumn of 1999 but there were no records from the Bristol region.

Whatever the natural origin of the butterflies, either North America or closer to home, the Bristol region is in a geographic position that means it has a high chance of being visited by these long distance travellers. As the larval foodplant does not grow here, colonisation is not possible but the sight of these occasional visitors is a very special one indeed and at present at least the chances of seeing one seem to be increasing.

# REFERENCES

Allan, P.B.M. (1966) *Copper butterflies in the West Country* Entomologist's. Rec. J. Var. Vol. 78 pp.161–166.

Anon (1986). *Research and survey in nature conservation: No 2, Monitoring the abundance of butterflies 1976–1985.* NCC, Peterborough.

Anon (1994) *Wetmoor Nature Reserve Lower Woods SSSI, a guide.* Gloucestershire Wildlife Trust.

Asher, J., Warren, M., Fox, R., Harding, P., Jeffcoate, G. & Jeffcoate, S. (2001) *The Millennium Atlas of Butterflies in Britain and Ireland.* Oxford University Press.

Avon Butterfly Project (1995) *1995 Provisional Butterfly Distribution Atlas.* BRERC, Publication No, 184. Bristol.

Bainbrigge Fletcher, T. (1937) Papilio machaon, *Linn. 1758 in Gloucestershire.* Proceedings of the Cotteswold Naturalists' Field Club for 1936 XXVI pt.1 91–94.

Baker, R.R. (1972) *Territorial behaviour of the nymphalid butterflies,* Aglais urticae *(L.) and* Inachis io *(L.).* J. Animal. Ecol. 41 pp 453–469.

Barrett, C.G. (1893) *The lepidoptera of the British Isles. Volume I Rhopalocera.* Reeve & Co., London.

Bird, J.F. (undated) *Macro-lepidoptera of Somerset* Unpublished list in the archive of the Bristol Naturalists' Society.

Blathwayt, C.S.H. (1954) *Lepidoptera notes Bristol district, 1953.* Proceedings of the Bristol Naturalists' Society for 1953 Vol. XXVIII pt. V pp.403–406.

Board, J. (1995). *A Study of the Small Blue* (Cupido minimus) *and its food plant at Dolebury Warren, Avon.* Unpublished. Bath College of Higher Education.

Bright, P.M. & Leeds, H.A. (1938) *A monograph of the British aberrations of the Chalk-hill Blue butterfly* Lysandra coridon *(Poda, 1761).* Richmond Hill, Bournemouth.

Bristowe, W.S. (1967) *The life of a distinguished woman naturalist, Eleanor Glanville (circa 1654–1709).* Entomologist's Gaz 67 pp.202–211.

Brown, A.D.R. (1971) *A review of the butterflies in the Bristol area.* Entomologist's. Rec. J. Var. Vol. 83. pp.101–108, 210–216, 236–240 & 316–322.

Burrell, P. (1995) *The current status of the Marsh Fritillary butterfly in Avon. A report prepared for English Nature.* (Unpublished) Bristol Regional Environmental Records Centre.

Burton, J.F. (1964) *Butterflies in Lepidoptera Notes Bristol District, 1963.* Proceedings of the Bristol Naturalists' Society for 1963 Vol. XXX pt. V pp.415–421.

Burton, J.F. (1965) *Butterflies in Lepidoptera Notes Bristol District, 1964.* Proceedings of the Bristol Naturalists' Society for 1964 Vol. XXXI pt I pp.59–66.

Burton, J.F. (1966) *Report on Monarch butterfly migration experiment, 1965.* Bulletin of the Amateur Entomologists' Society Vol. 25 (August, 1966) pp.90–91.

Burton, J.F. & French, R.A. (1969) *Monarch butterflies coinciding with American passerines in Britain & Ireland in 1968.* British Birds 62 pp.493–494.

Cater, W.F. (Editor) (1980) *Love among the butterflies* Collins, London.

Cooper, H.J. (1952) Lampides boeticus *in Bristol.* Entomologist Vol. 85 p.204.

Cooper, J.E. (1966) *Butterflies in Lepidoptera Notes Bristol District, 1965.* Proceedings of the Bristol Naturalists' Society for 1965 Vol. XXXI pt. II pp.165–171.

Donovan, C. (1942) *A catalogue of the macrolepidoptera of Gloucestershire.* Proc. Cotteswold Nat. Fld Club 27 pp.151–186

Duck, J.N. (1852) *The natural history of Portishead* Evans & Abbot, Bristol.

Emmet, A.M. & Heath, J. (Eds.) (1989) *The moths & butterflies of Great Britain & Ireland Volume 7, part 1 Hesperiidae – Nymphalidae The butterflies* Harley Books, Colchester.

Frohawk, F.W. (1938) *Varieties of British butterflies.* Ward Lock & Co., London.

Greene, J. (Rev.) (1870) (2nd edn.) *The insect hunter's companion being instructions for collecting and pre-serving butterflies and moths and companying an essay on pupa digging.* Van Voorst, London.

Grose, A.N. (1972) *Butterflies in Lepidoptera Notes Bristol District, 1971.* Proceedings of the Bristol Naturalists' Society for 1971 Vol. 32 pt. 2 pp.133–136.

Harding, G. (1899) *Additions and corrections to local list of lepidoptera.* Proceedings of the Bristol Naturalists' Society for 1895–1897 Vol. VIII pp.55–59

Harper, B.S. (1979) *Butterflies (Lepidoptera) in Entomological notes, Bristol District, 1977.* Proceedings of the Bristol Naturalists' Society for 1977 Vol. 37 pp.74–76.

Harper, B.S. (1981) *Butterflies (Lepidoptera) in Avon & District Entomological Report, 1979.* Proceedings of the Bristol Naturalists' Society for 1979 Vol. 39 pp.74–77.

Hawes, F.W. (1890) Hesperia lineola *Ochsenheimer: an addition to the list of British butterflies.* Entomologist: Vol. 23 pp. 3–4

Heslop, I.R.P., Hyde, G.E. & Stockley, R.E. (1964) *Notes and Views of the Purple Emperor* Southern Publishing, Brighton.

Heslop, I.R.P. (1945) Maculinea arion *in Somerset.* Entomologist: Vol. 78 p. 125.

Heslop, I.R.P. (1947) Nymphalis polychloros *in Somerset and the Bristol District.* Entomologist: Vol. 80 p. 218

Heslop, I.R.P. (1950) Maculinea arion *and* Apatura iris *in Somerset.* Entomologist: Vol. 83 pp. 20–21

Heslop, I.R.P. (1955) *The Mazarine Blue* Entomologist's Rec. J. Var. Vol. 67. pp. 178–179.

Hill, J.A. (1850) *Capture of lepidoptera at Almondsbury, Gloucestershire.* Zoologist pp. 2882–2884.

Hudd, A.E. (1884) *Catalogue of the Lepidoptera of the Bristol District. Reprinted from the 'Proceedings of the Bristol Naturalists' Society.' Vol. II to Vol. IV.* Bristol Naturalists' Society (Author's annotated copy.)

Hudd, A.E. (1906) *Insects Rhopalocera* in *The Victoria History of the Counties of England Somerset.* Archibald Constable & Co. Ltd., London pp. 89–92.

Lewin, W. (1795) *The Papilios of Great Britain.* London.

Martin. M.H. (1998) *Lower Woods Nature Reserve A Guide.* Gloucestershire Wildlife Trust.

Martin, M. & Rowlatt, S. (2001) *The Natural History of Lower Woods in 2000 AD.* Gloucestershire Wildlife Trust.

Meredith, G.H.J. (Dr) (1984) *Rhopalocera* in: Newton, J. & Meredith, G.H.J. (1984) *The macrolepidoptera of Gloucestershire* The Cotteswold Naturalists' Field Club. Alan Sutton, Gloucester.

Moore, B.W. (1975) Thymelicus lineola *Ochsenheimer (Essex Skipper) in the County of Avon.* Entomologist's Rec. J. Var. Vol. 87 p. 26

Morris, J.W. (1888) *Handbook to Bath. Prepared on the occasion of the visit of the British Association, 1888.* Pitman & Sons, Bath.

Muggleton, J. (1973) *Some aspects of the history and ecology of blue butterflies in the Cotswolds.* Proc. Trans. Br. Ent. Nat. Hist. Soc. 6 pp. 77–84

Myles, S. (Ed.), Green, I., Higgins, R.H., Kitchen, C. & Kitchen, M.A.R. (2000) *The flora of the Bristol region. Wildlife of the Bristol region: 1.* Pisces Publications, Newbury.

Newman, E. (1874) *An illustrated natural history of British butterflies and moths* Allen & Co., London.

Oates, M. (2001) *Butterfly introductions-wisdom or folly?* Atropos No. 14 pp. 22–27.

Parsons, A. (1996) *The invertebrates of the island of Steepholm in the Bristol Channel.* Wincanton Press.

Peach, A.H. (1939) *A list of lepidoptera from Leigh Woods* Proceedings of the Bristol Naturalists' Society for 1938 Vol. VIII pt IV pp. 435–437.

Peach, A.H. (1948) *Some records and observations of lepidoptera, 1947.* Proceedings of the Bristol Naturalists' Society for 1947 Vol. XXVII pt. IV pp. 221–222.

Pollard, E. (1977). *A method for assessing changes in the abundance of butterflies.* Biological Conservation. 12, 115–134.

Pollard, E. (1982). *Monitoring butterfly abundance in relation to the management of a nature reserve.* Biological Conservation. 24, 317–328.

Pollard, E., Elias, D.O., Skelton, M.J. & Thomas, J.A. (1975) *A method of assessing the abundance of butterflies in Monks Wood National Nature Reserve in 1973.* Entomologist's Gaz 26 pp. 79–88.

Pratt, C.R. (1983) *A modern review of the demise of* Aporia crataegi *L.: the black-veined white.* Entomologist's Rec. J. Var. Vol. 95 pp. 45–52, 161–166, 232–237.

Richardson, A. (1945) *Supplement to the catalogue of the macrolepidoptera of Gloucestershire.* Proc. Cotteswold Nat. Fld Club 28 pp. 76–107

Salmon, M.A. (2000) *The aurelian legacy. British butterflies and their collectors.* Harley Books, Colchester.

Samouelle, G. (1819) *The entomologist's useful compendium.* London.

Sorrell, G.W., Way, L.S. & Weeks, A.H. (1984) *Butterflies (Lepidoptera)* in *Avon & District Entomological Report, 1982.* Proceedings of the Bristol Naturalists' Society for 1982 Vol. 42 pp. 84–87

Sorrell, G.W. & Weeks, A.H. (1982) *Butterflies (Lepidoptera)* in *Avon & District Entomological Report, 1981.* Proceedings of the Bristol Naturalists' Society for 1981 Vol. 41 pp. 68–71.

Sorrell, G.W. & Weeks, A.H. (1984) *Butterflies (Lepidoptera)* in *Avon & District Entomological Report, 1983.* Proceedings of the Bristol Naturalists' Society for 1983 Vol. 43 pp. 49–53.

Stainton, H.T. (1857) *A manual of British butterflies and moths (Vol. 1)* Van Voorst, London.

Sutherland, J.P. (2001) *Orange-tip* Anthocharis cardamines *(L.) (Lep.: Pieridae) recorded from* Brassica rapa. Entomologist's Rec. J. Var. Vol. 113 p. 201.

Thomas, J.A. (1983) *The ecology and conservation of* Lysandra bellargus *(Lepidoptera: Lycaenidae) in Britain.* J. appl. Ecol. 20: 59–83.

Turner, A.H. (1955) *Lepidoptera of Somerset* Somersetshire Archaeological and Natural History Society, Taunton.
Vickery, K. (1993) *High Brown Fritillary Survey, Mendips, Somerset, 1993. Contract report for Butterfly Conservation.* (Unpublished)
White, J.W. (1912) *The flora of Bristol* Wright & Sons, Bristol.


## Other Sources not Mentioned in the Text

Anon (1984) *Common butterfly survey 1983.* Bristol Regional Environmental Records Centre Publication No. 31.
Anon (1987) *The natural history of the Chew Valley* Pensford.
Anon (undated) *Avon butterfly project 1995 provisional distribution atlas.* Bristol Regional Environmental Records Centre Publication No. 184.
Bath Natural History Society Magazine.
Bristol Naturalists' Society Proceedings.
Burton, J.F. (1971) *Somerset butterflies and their conservation.* The Somerset Trust for Nature Conservation 7th Annual Report.
Corlett, R. (1999) *Has the re-establishment of traditional woodland management practices at Avon Gorge NNR been successful in increasing butterfly abundance?* Unpublished dissertation for the degree of environmental quality and resource management. University of West of England.
Evans, M. (undated) *Avon Butterfly Project 1997 Provisional butterfly distribution atlas.* Bristol Regional Environmental Records Centre Publication No. 222.
Hall, W.G. (Ed.) (1971) *Man and the Mendips* Mendip Society.
Hawkins, A. (undated) *The common butterfly survey 1985.* Bristol Regional Environmental Records Centre Publication No. 81.
Manning, S. (undated) *The common butterfly survey 1986.* Bristol Regional Environmental Records Centre Publication No. 112.
Mellersh, N. & Hawkins, A. (undated) *The common butterfly survey 1984.* Bristol Regional Environmental Records Centre Publication No. 66.
Muggleton, J. (1974) *Dates of appearance of* Maculinea arion *(Linnaeus) (Lep., Lycaenidae) adults in Gloucestershire 1858–1960* Entomologist's Gaz 25 pp.239–244.
Muggleton, J. (1974) *A survey of the breeding sites of blue butterflies in Gloucestershire.* M.Sc. Thesis University of Bristol.
Pym, A. (undated) *The common butterfly survey 1987–1988* Bristol Regional Environmental Records Centre Publication No. 149.
Steven, J. (1999) *An investigation of current and potential Marsh Fritillary habitats in the former county of Avon.* Unpublished student thesis, produced in collaboration with the Avon Wildlife Trust.
Wiltshire, C.W. (undated, ?1989) *A survey to assess the breeding status of the Marsh Fritillary (*Eurodryas aurinia *(Rott.)) in Gloucestershire.* NCC, West Midlands.
Witchell, C.A. & Strugnell, W.B. (1892) *The fauna and flora of Gloucestershire.* James, London.

# CONTRIBUTORS

Contributors of records used in compiling the distribution maps and text relevant to 1990 onwards:

Adshead, Ms H.
Aldridge, Mr J.
Aldridge, Mrs M.E.
Andrews, Mr R.M.
Angles, Mr R.
Aston, Mr A.J.
Aston, Mr R.C.
Avon Wildlife Trust.
Bailey, Mr M.
Baker, Mr M.
Baker, Mrs J.
Baker, Mrs Y.M.
Baldwin, Dr.
Barnett, Mr R.J.
Barrett, Mr A.
Barrett, Mrs. G.
Bath Natural History Society.
Bernhard, Mr T.
Best, Ms L.
Betts Consultants.
Bickley Mrs D.
Bland, Mr R.L.
Blyth Dr.W.
Board, Mr J.
Bodley Mrs A.
Bolt, Mr A.
Bond, Mr J.
Boulton, Mrs A.
Bowen, Mr F.
Bowers, J.
Bowring, Mr D.
Boyd, Mr J.
Boyd, Mr J.R.
Boyd, Mrs J.M.
Brading, Ms A.
Brice, R.A.
Bristol Ecological Consultants.
Buckthorpe, Ms S.
Burberry, Mr R.A.
Burkey, Miss S.
Burrell, Ms P.J.S.
Burton, Mr J.F.
Butterfly Conservation
  (Gloucestershire Branch)
Cadwallader, Mr A.
Cameron, Mrs A.
Cape, Mr D.
Carey, Mr T.
Carter, M.J.
Castle Ms.T.
Chadwick, Mr P.J.
Cheesman, Mr.
Clarke, Mr L.
Clarke, Mr S.
Clarke, Mr. D.
Codrington, Mr and Mrs.

Collett, Ms C.
Conybeare, Mr D.G.
Conybeare, Ms B.
Conybeare, Ms.B.
Cooper, Mrs E.
Cooper, Ms F.
Cope, Mr R.
Corlett, R.
Corner, Mr T.
Corser, Ms E.
Coutanche, M.-J.
Coutanche, Mr A.
Cox, Mrs M.A.
Cresswell Associates.
Cropper, R.S.
Curry, A.M.
Davies, J.M.
Davis, Mr J.
Davis, Mr P.
Daw, Mr A.
Edmondson, Mr R.
Ellis, Mr M.
Evans, B.
Evans, Mr M.
Fawcett, Mr T.
Fletcher, Mr P.
Ford, Mr J.
Ford, Mrs M.
Foster, Miss P.
Foster, Mr D.
Foster, Mrs P.
Fournier Mr A. R.
Fowler, Mr S.
Fowler, Mrs M.
Foxwell, Mr D.
Fursman, Ms P.
Garraway, Mr T.E.
Geary, Mrs.
Gibb, Mrs N.J.
Gibbs, Mr D.
Giles, Mr K.F.
Goff, Mr N.
Grant A.
Grant, Ms S.
Gravestock, Miss I.F.
Green, Mr D.
Green, Mr I.
Gregory, Mrs H.F.
Gregory, Ms L.
Grimwood, Ms N.
Guest, Mr J.
Hackman, Mr P.
Hackman, Mrs J.
Haggett, Mr R.
Hall, Miss H.
Hallett, Ms S.

Harding, Mrs J.
Hardy, Mr T.
Harse, Mr P.
Hawkes, Mr D.
Hayman, Ms M.
Haynes, Mr R.
Heaton, Mr B.G.
Hedley, Mr S.M.
Heslop, Ms J.
Hewins, Ms E.
Hewitt, Dr K.
Higgins, Mr R.
Hill, Mrs M.
Hine, T.W.
Hiscocks, Mr G.K.
Holbourne Environmental
  Consultants
Holliday, Mr S.
Horlick, Mr D.
Humm, Ms N.
Hunt, Mr M.
Ingle, Ms R.
Jackson, Mr D.S.
James, Mr P.
James, Ms J.,
Jennings, Ms.E.
Jones, Mr D.
Kalfayan, Dr P.Y.
Kilburn, T.
Knight, Mr A.
Knight, Mr J.
Lamb, Ms C.
Land Use Consultants.
Landmark Environmental
  Consultants.
Langdon, S.V.
Lawrence, Ms D.
Laycock, Mr M.
Levy, D.A.
Levy. E.T.
Lewis, Mr R.
Lord, Mrs A.
Luff, G.A.
Luscombe, Dr M.
Mackenzie, J.
Marshall Mr D.T.
Martin, Mr J.
Martin, Mr J.P.
Martin, Mr P.
Martin, Mr R.
Mastrangelo, Mr J.D.
Mastrangelo, Mr P.
Mastrangelo, Ms N.
Matthews, Miss J.
May, Mrs C.
McDouall, Ms E.

McFarling, Mr C.
McGrath, Mr T.
McLaren, Mr R.
Meredith, Dr G.H.J.
Mielcarek, R.
Milbourne, L.
Milbourne, Mr N.R.
Millett, M.
Millman, Mr J.S.
Millman, Mrs P.
Moulin, Mr A.J.
Moulin, Mrs F.
Mulcock, C.&.P.
Munson, Ms E.
Murdoch, Mr D.
Musgrove, Mr A.J.
Myles, Ms S.
Nash, Mr K.
Newman, Mr D.
Nicholas Pearson Associates ltd.
Norman, Mr K.H.
Norman, Ms G.
Oates, Mr M.
O'Brien, Mrs S.
O'Connell, R.J.
Oliver Mrs P.
Oliver, Mr M.
Oliver, Mr R.L.
Oliver, Ms J.
Osborne, F.
Palmer, Mr R.
Parker, Mr P.
Parker, Mr S.
Parker, Ms C.A.
Parnell, Mr J.
Patch Ms.M.
Payne, Mr
Payne, Mrs
Pedlow, Ms A.
Peters, Mrs B.
Poole, Mr K.H.
Pooley, Mr R.
Pope, Ms.U.
Potts, Mrs M.
Powley, C.
Price, Ms B.
Pritchard, D.
Pritchard, Mr P.
Pym, Mr A.
Quinn, Mr. P.
Quinney, Mr F.G.T.
Radcliffe, Dr S.

Randall, Mrs.D.
Rawlings, Mr C.
Rees, Dr J.
Regini, Ms I.M.
Renshaw, Ms K.
Rich, Mr G.
Ridge, Mr.M.A.
Robbins, Mr R.
Robertson, Mr R.
Rodgers, Mrs P.
Rooney, Mr P.
Rouke, Ms S.
Rumble, Ms C.
Saddington, Mrs. J.
Saunders, Ms E.
Sciver, Mr J.
Scott, Mr T.
Shields, Ms L.
Silby, Mr P.A.
Silcocks, Mr T.B.
Simms, Dr M.J.
Simonds, Ms B.H.
Slade, Mr M.
Smith, Mr A.G.
Smith, Mr G.
Smith, Mr G.R.
Smith, Mr J.
Smith, Mr R.
Smith, Ms S.
Somerset Environmental Records
Centre.
Spice, Ms R.
Spiller, Mr.
Stabb, Mr R.D.
Stenson, Mr C.
Stevens, Ms E.
Stevenson, Mr P.
Stone, Mr G.
Stone, Mr P.
Stonebridge, Dr E.
Summers, Mrs J.
Sun Life Centre Group.
Sutton, Mr R.
Symes, R.E.
Tanner, Ms C.
Targett, Mrs K.
Taylor, Dr M.
Tizard, Mr B.A.
Tolerton, Mr P.
Toller, Mr J.
Townsend, Mr P.
Treharne, C.

Trump, Mr D.
Turvey, Ms K.
Twiggs, Mr T.N.
Tyler-Smith, Mr C.
Underhay, Mr N.
Valentine, Ms S.
Vickery, Mr K.
Walter, Mr D.
Walter, Mrs.
Walters, Ms J.
Wansdyke Woodland Survey Team.
Ward, Mr G.
Ward, Mr H.G.
Ward, Mr J.
Warden, D.
Wardill, J.
Wardill, J.C.
Warren, B.
Warriner, Mr R.E.
Waters, Mr D.
Watson, Mr G.
Watts, Mr D.I.
Webb, Ms J.B.
Webber, Mrs E.
Weedon, Mr C.
Weeks, Mr A.H.
Welford, Mr H.
Wells Central Junior School.
West Mendip Invertebrate Group.
West, Mrs H.
Weston, Ms V.
Wharton, Ms B.
White, C.
Williams, Mr P.
Williams, Ms J.
Willmott, H.
Wilson Mr R.
Wilson, Mr.
Wilson, Mrs.
Wilson, Mrs P.
Wilson, Ms C.F.
Wiltshire, Mr C.
Windsor, C. H.R.H. Prince of Wales.
Withers, Mr G.
Wood, Ms M.
Wood, Ms M.B.
Woodbridge, Mrs P.
Woodhall, A.
Woodyatt, Mrs C.
Wright, Mr T.
Wynn, Miss A.

# BUTTERFLY ORGANISATIONS

The following organisations may be of interest with regard to butterfly conservation in the Bristol region and nationally.

**Amateur Entomologists' Society**
P.O. Box 8774
LONDON SW7 5ZG

e-mail: aes@theaes.org
website: www.theaes.org

**Avon Wildlife Trust**
Bristol Wildlife Centre
32 Jacobs Wells Road
BRISTOL BS8 1DR

Telephone: 0117-917 7270
e-mail: mail@avonwildlifetrust.org.uk
website: www.avonwildlifetrust.org.uk

**Bath Natural History Society**
*The Membership Secretary*
Mrs Gillian Barrett
57 Lyncombe Hill
BATH BA2 2EB

**Bristol City Museum & Art Gallery**
Biology Section
Queen's Road
BRISTOL BS8 1RL

Telephone: 0117-922 3571
e-mail: general_museum@bristol-city.gov.uk
website: www.bristol-city.gov.uk/museums

**Bristol Naturalists' Society**
C/o Bristol City Museum & Art Gallery
Queen's Road
BRISTOL BS8 1RL

e-mail: info@bristolnats.org.uk
website: www.bristolnats.org.uk

**Bristol Regional Environmental Records Centre (BRERC)**
Ashton Court Visitors Centre
Ashton Court Estate
Long Ashton
Bristol BS41 9JN.

Telephone: 0117-953 2140
e-mail: brerc@btconnect.com
website: www.brerc.org.uk

**British Entomological & Natural History Society**
Dinton Pastures Country Park
Davis Street
Hurst
Reading
Berkshire RG10 0TH

Website: www.benhs.org.uk

**Butterfly Conservation (National Office)**
Manor Yard
East Lulworth
Wareham
Dorset BH20 5QP

Telephone: 0192-940 0209
e-mail: info@butterfly_conservation.org
website: www.butterfly-conservation.org

**Butterfly Conservation (West Country Branch)**
Membership Secretary
Mr Keith Gould
12 Alma Street
Taunton
Somerset TA1 3AH

e-mail: keith.gould@care4free.net

**Butterfly Conservation (Gloucestershire Branch)**
The Secretary
Chris Tracey
Bonnie Banks
Middle Spring
Ruscombe
Stroud
GL6 6DE

e-mail: chris@tracey94.fsnet.co.uk

**English Nature (Regional Office)**
Roughmoor
Bishop's Hull
Taunton
Somerset TA1 5AA

Telephone: 01823-283 211
e-mail: somerset@english-nature.org.uk
website: www.english-nature.org.uk

**English Nature (Regional Office)**
Bronsil House
Eastnor
Near Ledbury
Herefordshire HR8 1EP

Telephone: 01531-638 500
website: www.english-nature.org.uk

**Gloucestershire Wildlife Trust**
*Dulverton Building*
Robinswood Hill Country Park
Reservoir Road
Gloucester GL4 6SX

Telephone: 01452-383 333
e-mail: info@gloucswt.cix.co.uk
website: www.wildlifetrust.org.uk/gloucswt

**National Trust (Bath & Bristol Office)**
Stourhead Estate Office
Stourton
Warminster
Wiltshire BA12 6QD

Telephone: 0174-784 2011
Website: www.nationaltrust.org.uk

# INDEX

A37 road  8
*adippe vulgoadippe, Argynnis* see High Brown Fritillary
Adonis Blue  viii, 26, 37, 42, 106, 115, 117, **118–119**
*aegeria tircis, Parage* see Speckled Wood
*agestis, Aricia* see Brown Argus
*aglaja aglaja, Argynnis* see Dark Green Fritillary
Alderley Lower Woods  166
*alfacariensis, Colias* see Berger's Clouded Yellow
*antiopa, Aglais* see Camberwell Beauty
Apollo  **68**
*apollo, Parnassius* see Apollo
*argiolus britanna, Celastrina* see Holly Blue
*argus, Plebejus* see Silver-studded Blue
*arion arion, Maculinea* see Large Blue
Ashton Court Meadow  161
*atalanta, Vanessa* see Red Admiral
*aurinia aurinia, Euphydryas* see Marsh Fritillary
Avon Gorge  5, **21–27**, 28, 37, 64, 97, 100, 101, 116, 119, 129, 141, 167

B3114 road  8
Ball Wood  31
Bannerdown  **33**, 45, 117, 161
Barrow Gurney Woods  2
Barton Hill  181
Bathampton Meadows  60, 167
Bathford Hill  33
Bath White  **81–88**
*bellargus, Lysandra* see Adonis Blue
Berger's Clouded Yellow  72, **73**
Berwick Lodge Cutting (M5)  8
*betulae, Thecla* see Brown Hairstreak
Biddle Street SSSI  32, 46
Black-veined White  **80**
Blagdon Lake  6, 138, 167, 191
*boeticus, Lampides* see Long-tailed Blue
Boiling Wells  80, 166

Bourton Combe  142, 159
Brandon Hill  170
*brassicae, Pieris* see Large White
Brimstone  3, 4, 7, 8, 9, 17, 21, 27, 28, 29, 31, 33, 34, **71–79**
Brockley Combe  14, **31–32**, 31, 43, 61, 94, 99, 100, 106, 109, 111, 124, 128, 131, 132, 133, 147, 150, 153, 158, 159, 160, 163, 165, 173, 180, 189
Brown Argus  viii, 3, 5, 9, 18, 21, 27, 28, 29, 30, 31, 32, 33, 34, 36, 46, **111–112**
Brown Hairstreak  4, 20, 27, 29, **91–96**
Brown's Folly  3, 4, 5, **33**, 36
Burrington Combe  4, 5, 7, 133, 159

Cadbury Hill  **32**, 46, 119, 176
*c-album, Polygonia* see Coma
Camberwell Beauty  **141–144**
*camilla, Limenitis* see White Admiral
*cardamines britannica, Anthocharis* see Orange-tip
*cardui, Vanessa* see Painted Lady
Chalkhill Blue  viii, 5, 20, 27, 33, 34, 37, 45, 106, **111–117**, 118, 119, 124
Charmy Down Airfield  119
Cheddar Valley Railway  9, **32**, 46
Chequered Skipper  **55**
Chew Stoke (B3114)  8
Chew Valley Lake  5, 6, 139, 155, 157
*cinxia, Melitaea* see Glanville Fritillary
Cleaves Wood  **34**, 127, 161
Cleeve Toot  **31–32**
Clifton Downs  4, 141
Clouded Yellow  viii, 17, 22, 34, 72, 73, **71–76**, 134
Comma  3, 7, 8, 9, 10, 19, 21, 28, 31, 34, **141–149**
Common Blue  3, 5, 6, 7, 9, 18, 21, 27, 28, 29, 30, 31, 33, 34, 36, 111, **111–114**, 119
Cook's Folly Woods  128, 163
Coombe (Combe) Dingle  100, 109, 119, 147

Coombe Glen  158
*coridon, Lysandra* see Chalkhill Blue
Corporation Woods  31
*crataegi, Aporia* see Black-veined White
*croceus, Colias* see Clouded Yellow

*daplidice, Pontia* see Bath White
Dark Green Fritillary  6, 7, 22, 26, 27, 29, 30, 31, 33, 34, 36, 37, 158, 159, **160–162**
Dingy Skipper  viii, 4, 5, 6, 9, 16, 21, 27, 29, 30, 31, 33, 34, 37, **61–65**, 66, 67, 76
*dispar dispar, Lycaena* see Large Copper
Dolebury Bottom  22
Dolebury Warren  4, 5, 6, 7, **21–26**, 36, 37, 45, 46, 48, 63, 67, 93, 107, 108, 150, 151, 152, 155, 159, 160, 161, 181, 187
Dowlings Wood  33
Duke of Burgundy  viii, 4, 20, 32, 33, 34, 36, 37, **121–127**
Dundry Hill  70
Durdham Down  42, 70, 74, 100, 106, 109, 113, 116, 118, 119, 143, 160, 180

East Harptree Woods  113
Elmsley Lane  175
Essex Skipper  viii, 5, 6, 8, 19, 30, 33, 34, 36, 57, **58–60**, 61, 62
*euphrosyne, Boloria* see Pearl-bordered Fritillary

*faunus, Ochlodes* see Large Skipper
Filton Golf Course  119, 187
Folly Farm  6, 8, **31–33**, 37, 38, 45, 101, 103, 127, 161, 166, 167, 168

*galathea serena, Melanargia* see Marbled White
Gatekeeper  4, 7, 8, 10, 19, 22, 28, 29, 31, 34, **181–183**, 184
Glanville Fritillary  viii, 30, 36, 37, 41, 45, 142, **170–172**

Goblin Combe   2, 5, 6, 14,
   **31–32**, 36, 42, 66, 75, 97, 99,
   111, 112, 125, 131, 143, 148,
   151, 154, 158, 159, 160, 161,
   163, 164, 165, 173, 177, 178,
   179, 180, 189
Gordano Valley   2, 6, 29, 37,
   78, 99, 103, 104, 150, 152
Grayling   viii, 5, 6, 22, 30, 31,
   33, 36, 37, **180–181**, 186
Green Hairstreak   4, 5, 6, 20,
   22, 29, 31, 32, 33, 34, 37,
   **91–93**
Green-veined White   6, 7, 8,
   10, 17, 20, 29, 31, 34, 41, 71,
   83, **81–86**, 89
Greyfield Wood   168
Grizzled Skipper   viii, 4, 5, 9,
   16, 21, 29, 30, 31, 32, 33, 34,
   37, 64, **61–67**, 76
Grubbings   20

Haw Wood   106
Hawkesbury Upton   20
Hawkfield Meadows   6, 36
Hawkesbury Hill   20, 21, 116, 119
Hellenge Hill   5, **30**, 124
Henbury Golf Course   116, 119,
   141
High Brown Fritillary   viii, 7, 22,
   27, 34, 37, 41, **158–159**, 160,
   163
Highbury Hill   155
Hinton Charterhouse   58, 59
Hedge Brown   see Gatekeeper
Hollow Marsh   167
Holly Blue   viii, 3, 4, 8, 9, 10,
   18, 21, 22, 27, 28, 29, 30, 31,
   33, 34, 42, **121–122**
Horton Common   20, 110
Horton Great Trench   16, 20,
   21, 110, 116
Horwood Farm   16, 18, 112,
   167
Hursley Hill   8
*hyale, Colias*   see Pale Clouded
   Yellow
*hyperantus, Aphantopus*   see
   Ringlet

*icarus icarus, Polyommatus*
   see Common Blue
Inglestone Common   4, 8, 20,
   21, 95, 116, 119, 167
*io, Inachis*   see Peacock

Kewstoke Wood   141
Kingsweston Down   102, 111,
   112, 167, 177, 178, 182, 187

Kings Wood   3, **31–32**

Lamplighters Marsh   9
Large Blue   31, 43, 118, 120,
   **121–124**, 132, 159
Large Copper   **104**
Large Skipper   4, 5, 6, 8, 10,
   16, 21, 28, 29, 31, 34, 39, 57,
   61, **61–63**
Large Tortoiseshell   **141–142**
Large White   9, 10, 17, 31, 34,
   78, **81–82**, 83, 85, 86
Lawrence Weston Moor   6
*lathonia, Isoria*   see Queen of
   Spain Fritillary
Leigh Down   116, 120
Leigh Woods   2, 3, 27, **21–28**,
   42, 43, 46, 56, 66, 85, 87, 90,
   94, 98, 99, 100, 128, 147,
   154, 158, 160, 163, 165, 167,
   170, 173, 177
*lineola, Thymelicus*   see Essex
   Skipper
Little Avon, river   17
Long-tailed Blue   **105**
Lords Wood   2, 3, 130
Lower Woods   3, **11–21**, 21, 45,
   69, 71, 167
Loxton Estate   138
*lucina, Hamearis*   see Duke of
   Burgundy

M5 motorway   8
*machaon, Papilio*   see
   Swallowtail
*malvae, Pyrgus*   see Grizzled
   Skipper
Madam Lane   83, 138
Mapleridge Lane   7, 8
Marbled White   4, 5, 6, 8, 9, 19,
   21, 22, 27, 28, 29, 30, 31, 32,
   33, 34, 36, 37, **171–179**
Marsh Fritillary   viii, 21, 26, 27,
   32, 33, 34, 36, 37, 38, 43, 44,
   45, 46, 151, **161–169**
Mazarine Blue   **120**
Meadow Brown   3, 4, 5, 6, 7, 8,
   9, 19, 22, 28, 29, 31, 32, 34,
   174, **181–185**, 186, 190
*megera, Parage*   see Wall
Midger Wood   92, 125, 126
Middle Hope   5, **30**, 192
*minimus, Cupido*   see Small
   Blue
Monarch   **191–193**
Mount Skitham   107

Narrowways Junction   5, 7
*napi sabellicae, Pieris*   see

Green-veined White
Norton Radstock Coal Batches
   9

Orange-tip   3, 4, 6, 7, 8, 10, 17,
   21, 22, 28, 29, 31, 34, 85,
   **89–91**

Painted Lady   4, 18, 22, 29, 31,
   34, 134, **131–137**
*palaemon, Carterocephalus*
   see Chequered Skipper
Pale Clouded Yellow   **72**, 73
*pamphilus pamphilus,
   Coenonympha*   see Small
   Heath
*paphia, Argynnis*   see Silver-
   washed Fritillary
Paradise Bottom   27
Peacock   viii, 4, 8, 9, 10, 19,
   21, 28, 29, 31, 34, 79, 135,
   **141–146**, 148, 184
Pearl-bordered Fritillary   viii, 22,
   27, 31, 34, 36, 37, 44, 150,
   151, 152, **151–155**, 159, 163
Pensford Coal Tip   9, 67
*phlaeas eleus, Lycaena*   see
   Small Copper
*plexippus, Danaus*   see
   Monarch
*polychloros, Aglais*   see Large
   Tortoiseshell
Portishead Down   116
Priory Wood   125
Purple Emperor   20, 31, 43,
   124, **131–133**
Purple Hairstreak   3, 4, 7, 8,
   17,21, 22, 28, 29, 31, 32, 33,
   34, **91–99**

Queen of Spain Fritillary
   **151–157**
*quercus, Neozephryus*   see
   Purple Hairstreak

*rapae, Pieris*   see Small White
Radstock Railway   9, 67
Red Admiral   3, 4, 7, 9, 10, 18,
   22, 28, 29, 31, 34, **131–135**,
   136
Redland Green   72, 163
*rhamni rhamni, Gonepteryx*
   see Brimstone
Ringlet   3, 5, 6, 7, 9, 19, 22, 27,
   28, 29, 30, 31, 32, 33, 34,
   **189–190**
River Avon   7
*rubi, Callophrys*   see Green
   Hairstreak

Saddlewood Roughs   125, 167
Saint Catherine's Valley   6
Saint Philip's Marsh   9
Saint Thomas' Head   30
Sand Bay   30
Sandford Quarry   64
Sand Point   5, **30**, 36, 41, 45,
   75, 82, 117, 119, 142, 170,
   171, 172, 175, 180
*selene selene, Boloria*   see
   Small Pearl-bordered Fritillary
*semele semele, Hipparchia*
   see Grayling
*semiargus, Cyaniris*   see
   Mazarine Blue
Silver-spotted Skipper   **61**
Silver-studded Blue   viii, 20,
   **109–110**, 117
Silver-washed Fritillary   3, 19,
   22, 27, 28, 29, 31, 32, 33, 34,
   37, 46, 76, 159, 160,
   **161–165**
*sinapis sinapis, Leptidea*   see
   Wood White
Siston Common   6
Small Blue   viii, 4, 5, 8, 21, 22,
   **21–26**, 27, 37, 38, 46,
   **101–108**, 113, 115
Small Copper   5, 6, 7, 9, 18,
   21, 28, 29, 31, 34, **101–103**
Small Heath   viii, 3, 5, 6, 7, 8,
   9, 19, 21, 29, 30, 31, 34,
   **181–188**
Small Pearl-bordered Fritillary
   viii, 6, 7, 20, 22, 31, 37,

**150–152**, 153, 154, 155, 159,
   163
Small Skipper   3, 4, 5, 6, 8, 9,
   16, 21, 28, 29, 31, 32, 34, 44,
   **51–57**, 58, 59,60, 62
Small Tortoiseshell   viii, 4, 7, 9,
   10, 19, 21, 29, 31, 34, 79,
   135, **138–140**, 142, 145, 146,
   148, 174, 184, 185
Small White   8, 9, 10, 17, 31,
   34, 36, **81–84**, 85, 86
Speckled Wood   3, 4, 8, 9, 10,
   19, 21, 22, 28, 29, 31, 34,
   **171–174**, 185
Steepholm   5, 78, 81, 83, 85, 90,
   111, 113, 122, 135, 136, 149,
   164, 174, 175, 181, 183, 187
Swallowtail   20, **69–70**
*sylvestris, Thymelicus*   see
   Small Skipper

*tages tages, Erynnis*   see Dingy
   Skipper
Tickenham Court   41
*tithonus britanniae, Pyronia*
   see Gatekeeper
Troopers Hill   6, 36, 181
Tucking Mill   **34**, 117, 167

Uphill   5, **30**, 36, 115
Urchin Wood   31
*urticae, Aglais*   see Small
   Tortoiseshell

Wain's Hill   70

Walborough Hill   30, 36
Wall   5, 22, 27, 29, 30, 31, 32,
   33, 34, 46, **171–176**
*w-album, Satyrium*   see White-
   letter Hairstreak
Walton Common   4, 5, **29**, 36,
   46, 48, 59, 99, 129, 159, 161
Walton Moor   116, 147, 150,
   159, 160, 177, 191
Warleigh Wood   3, 125, 127
Wesley Drive   145
West Harptree (B3114 road)   8
Weston Big Wood   3, **29**
Weston Big Wood Quarry   9
Weston Golf Course   59, 119
Weston Moor   6, 7
Weston Woods   154
Wetmoor   3, 6, 14, **11–21**, 38,
   43, 44, 45, 48, 59, 65, 66, 75,
   92, 95, 99, 101, 110, 113,
   119, 125, 129, 130, 132, 133,
   148, 150, 154, 155, 161, 164,
   165, 167, 175, 187, 189
White Admiral   3, 18, 27, 31,
   32, **128–130**
White-letter Hairstreak   3, 4, 8,
   17, 18, 21, 22, 27, 28, 29, 31,
   32, 33, 34, 37, 46, 97,
   **100–101**
Wick Rocks   178, 179
Worlebury (Whorlebury) Hill   78,
   100, 106, 116
Wood White   20, 42, **71**
Wooscombe Bottom   134
Wrington Warren   31, 159, 181

# Bristol Regional Environmental Records Centre (BRERC)

BRERC has been collecting, collating, managing and making available data since 1974. Many hundreds, if not thousands, of people have contributed with records and record collecting as have many organisations, community groups, businesses, education establishments and authorities. Managing and making that data available has required much investment by BRERC in resources, research projects, development of database systems and validation and verification of the data. Most data provided to BRERC is in paper format, although increasingly we are receiving much data in digital formats. Most of the data required by enquirers is made available to them by BRERC in computer generated mapped formats.

Currently BRERC hold approximately 700,000+ species records on GIS. Each species record includes information added by BRERC about that species status. Digitised boundaries and information on the BRERC GIS includes all designated biological and geological sites, all known semi-natural habitats, Phase 1 habitat coverage for over a third of the BRERC area and various other sites and habitats drawn from projects such as Bristol Grasslands, Cotswold Grasslands and Ponds.

It has been estimated that there are several million species and habitat records in paper format held at BRERC. Records date back to the 19th century. These paper records include complete Phase 1 coverage for the BRERC area, survey reports using Phase 2, NVC, River Corridor and other survey methodologies, diaries from eminent ecologists, research papers, organisations' reports, community projects, consultant reports and ad hoc records.

BRERC is a 'not for profit' organisation and is administered through Bristol City Council on behalf of Bristol City, South Gloucestershire, North Somerset and Bath & North East Somerset Councils, English Nature and Avon Wildlife Trust. There is a Steering Committee that agrees and oversees the day to day running, policies and strategies of the Centre. This Steering Committee comprises of the Collections Manager of Bristol City Museum (Line Manager for BRERC personnel and administration), Ecologists of the Unitary Authorities, the Conservation Officers of English Nature and Environment Agency and the Director and Conservation Officers of Avon Wildlife Trust. This Steering Committee reports to a Joint Advisory Committee (JAC) consisting of the above officers and elected Councillors of the Unitary Authorities. The JAC sets the budget and work programme.

*Some other uses of BRERC's data holdings*

As well as the data search enquiries, BRERC provided data is routinely used to screen planning applications by various local authority departments and various organisations such as the Environment Agency, Avon Wildlife Trust and English Nature. Between 15000 and 25000 planning applications are made each year in our region. BRERC provided data is also used for determining the status and distribution of species and habitats locally, regionally and nationally. We also provide data that is used for contaminated land strategies, pollution control, emergency planning, habitat and species management and reporting to government on regional and national biodiversity targets.

In addition to the BRERC main database and Geographical Information System (GIS) we have a modern computer system which includes three dimensional mapping (Vertical Mapper), panoramic digital mapping, digital aerial photographs, digital soil mapping, many graphic programmes and several different types of databases and spreadsheets - and the skilled staff and volunteers to utilise and make sense of them. This is on top of our expertise in many different fields of ecology and wildlife conservation.